Sherry Balfour
220 Tampa
Park Forest
481-9731

INTERPRETATION OF MASS SPECTRA

SECOND EDITION
REVISED, ENLARGED, RESET

INTERPRETATION OF
MASS SPECTRA

SECOND EDITION
REVISED, ENLARGED, RESET

F. W. McLAFFERTY
Cornell University

1973
W. A. BENJAMIN, INC.
ADVANCED BOOK PROGRAM
Reading, Massachusetts

London · Amsterdam · Don Mills, Ontario · Sydney · Tokyo

INTERPRETATION OF MASS SPECTRA
FIRST EDITION, 1966
SECOND EDITION, REVISED, ENLARGED, RESET, 1973
  First printing, 1973
  Second printing, with corrections, 1974
  Third printing, with corrections, 1974
  Fourth printing, with additional corrections, 1977

Library of Congress Cataloging in Publication Data

McLafferty, Fred W
  Interpretation of mass spectra.

  Includes bibliographical references.
  1. Mass spectrometry.   I.   Title.
QC454.M22   1973   547'.35'33   73-1264

ISBN 0-8053-7048
ISBN 0-8053-7047 (paperbound)

Foreign-language editions of the first edition:

Spanish: Editorial Reverté, Barcelona
           1969

French: Ediscience, Paris
           1970

Italian: Tamburini-Masson, Milano
           (1973)

Foreign-language editions of the second edition:

Japanese: Kagaky Dojin
            (in preparation)

Printed in the United States of America

ISBN 0-8053-7047-1
ABCDEFGHIJ-MA-7987

To TIBBY

CONTENTS

PREFACE TO THE SECOND EDITION

The continuing growth in the field of organic mass spectrometry has been responsible in part for preparing a second edition of this book. Two specialized journals, *Organic Mass Spectrometry* and *International Journal of Mass Spectrometry and Ion Physics* each publish more than 100 pages per month. In 1972, the *Mass Spectrometry Bulletin* (*1.18*) listed approximately 3,500 articles in its section on organic chemistry; this appears to be comparable to the total number of articles in this field published before 1966! There has been a gratifying concomitant growth in the acceptance of mass spectrometry as an important method for structure determination of organic molecules. Interpretation of mass spectra is now included in higher level undergraduate courses or first-year graduate courses in most chemistry departments, and continuing education "short courses" in this field are popular for graduate chemists. My courses based on this book have been given more than twenty times to over one thousand students and practicing chemists; their suggestions and criticisms have been another major incentive for this revision.

The rapid development and acceptance of gas chromatography/mass spectrometry systems, especially those automated with dedicated on-line computers, has caused an exponential growth in the volume of mass spectral data which needs to be interpreted. Modern GC/MS systems can give interpretable mass spectra from 10^{-9} gram samples, a quantity much too small for other techniques for molecular information. Microgram amounts of complex mixtures of drug metabolites, environmental pollutants, flavor components, or insect pheromones can be separated by GC/MS to give as many as 100 component mass spectra in one or two hours. Although rapid progress is being made in computer systems for interpretation and reference file retrieval of mass spectra, there appears to be little chance that these will supplant the growing need for skilled interpreters.

In this second edition the basic steps recommended for interpretation of a mass spectrum (Table A-1) remain virtually unchanged. However, there are modifications in the presentation of the material to the students, as well as updating of that material. I remain convinced of the importance of utilizing natural isotopic abundances for the determination of elemental compositions (Chapter 2); following the suggestion of many who used the book as teachers and students, tables are now included which tabulate the isotopic abundances to be expected for combinations of a number of common elements (Tables 2-1, 2-2, and A-2). The growing availability and use of "multiple ion detectors" promises to increase the acceptance of this valuable technique.

Mechanisms of mass spectral reactions (Chapter 4) are now introduced at a much earlier stage, again following suggestions of many users of the first edition. Here I have attempted to generalize the tremendous advances in this field with a new overall organization of ion fragmentation mechanisms which hopefully will be of interest to experts in the field, as well as help to novices to assimilate the large amount of available material. To this end, it is recommended that the student skip the paragraphs in small type until he has mastered the fundamentals.

Another major change is the incorporation of a summary of the mass spectral behavior of common classes of compounds (Chapter 6). This is modeled after, although certainly does not replace, the classic text of Budzikiewicz, Djerassi, and Williams (*1.3*). It cannot be overemphasized that the only way to learn how to interpret mass spectra is actually to practice interpreting mass spectra. In this chapter the student applies the techniques and mechanisms presented in the first five chapters to unknown spectra of common types of compounds. Again, I must emphasize the importance of doing the unknowns; the student must attempt one or two unknowns for every 30–60 minutes of lecture or self-study. The solutions given in Chapter 9 are also a basic part of the book's instruction. A new section (Chapter 8) also has been added to cover the fundamental principles underlying the formation of mass spectra, reflecting our improved understanding of the quasi-equilibrium theory (*8.1*) and its applicability to the mass spectra of complex organic molecules.

Finally, you will find that my prejudice for the utility of mass spectrometry has not waned with the years. For those who conclude that the view presented here is overly optimistic, allow me to quote (with thanks to Dr. Willi Richter) an outside authority:

"The masses have boundless creative energy"—Mao Tse-tung.

F. W. McLafferty

Ithaca, New York
May 1973

ACKNOWLEDGMENTS

The contributions of many people have made this book possible. The following helped to plan and teach the courses in which this material was developed: Drs. J. W. Amy, A. L. Burlingame, M. M. Bursey, D. C. DeJongh, R. B. Fairweather, M. L. Gross, I. Howe, K. L. Rinehart, S. Ställberg–Stenhagen, E. Stenhagen, G. E. VanLear, and Mr. W. E. Baitinger. The following postdoctoral fellows and students read the manuscript critically and worked the problems: Drs. P. F. Bente, R. D. Board, E. M. Chait, L. R. Dusold, W. F. Haddon, H. Hauer, K.-S. Kwok, J. G. Lawless, S. P. Levine, R. M. Prinstein, T. W. Shannon, M. Senn, R. Venkataraghavan, T. Wachs, C. G. Warner; Ms. P. C. Wszolek, Ms. G. M. Pesyna, and Mr. B. Leong. Ms. Pesyna and Ms. S. L. McLafferty drew the bar graphs using a computer plotter program provided by Dr. Venkataraghavan, and L. MacCaskill drew the figures. I am especially indebted to Drs. Bursey, DeJongh, M. A. Baldwin, J. W. Serum, and N. Turro for checking the manuscript in detail. I should like to express my special appreciation to Mrs. Luba K. Blake for her outstanding services in typing the manuscript. Much of this edition was written during a sabbatic leave at the Laboratory for Organic Chemistry of the Eidgenössiche Technische Hochschule in Zurich, Switzerland; I am deeply indebted to Professors W. Simon, V. Prelog, and their colleagues for their warm hospitality and to the John Simon Guggenheim Memorial Foundation for Fellowship support.

F. W. M.

PREFACE TO THE FIRST EDITION

The field of organic mass spectrometry has undergone an explosive growth recently; the number of publications has more than doubled in the last two years. There are now numerous references citing the solution of difficult problems in specialized research fields by the use of mass spectrometry. Instrumental developments have made it much easier for the research man without special training to obtain good spectra on a routine basis, and such instruments are now becoming available in most major research laboratories. A mass spectrum from a submicrogram sample contains a wealth of specific analytical and structural information—much more information than the expert in the field now knows how to utilize; unfortunately this abundance can discourage the novice who turns for help to compendia of mass spectral information. Yet one of the major advantages of the basic information of a mass spectrum is its simplicity. The spectrum displays masses of the ionized molecule and its fragments, and these masses are simply the sums of the masses of the component atoms.

In contrast to the books that give detailed descriptions of the mass spectra of particular types of compounds, this book has been designed especially *to teach* the interpretation of mass spectra, with emphasis on the identification of unknown compounds. The book is intended as a supplementary text for courses such as qualitative organic analysis or spectroscopic methods, and as a self-study for scientists who are familiar with organic chemistry.

For the experienced mass spectrometrist many steps of the interpretation procedure are intuitive; this text attempts to enumerate the steps and illustrate them by application to common types of compounds. This book is not intended as a reference to spectra and fragmentation mechanisms of particular classes of compounds; such information is already available in the comprehensive volumes by Budzikiewicz, Djerassi, and Williams, and these are recommended as complementary material for this text. Similarly, other important aspects such as instruments, sample handling, and preparation of derivatives are well covered in other excellent reference volumes.

A sizable part of the book is devoted to the mechanisms of mass spectral decomposition reactions. Many mechanisms and rationalizations have been proposed previously; rather than catalog these, an attempt has been made to formulate basic rules governing these reactions, and to classify them in a few general categories. Although these generalizations may well involve some oversimplification, it is hoped that they will prove useful to the expert as well as to the novice in spectral interpretation.

This book is an outgrowth of a course that has been given six separate times to a total of over 600 scientists and students. They were required to solve unknown spectra as part of the instruction, and we feel that this is a major learning aid. The reader is urged to test his understanding of material by attempting to work the unknowns, checking his solutions with those in Chapter 10. The unknown spectra were chosen to illustrate principles of interpretation; for detailed characteristics of spectra from particular compound classes, the reader should consult the literature.

A prime objective of the book has been to show the "fun" of mass spectrometry—how the jigsaw-puzzle pieces of varying masses can be fitted together to construct an informative picture of the molecular structure. The field of interpretations and mechanisms of mass spectra is so new that it is not difficult to find fascinating areas which are virtually unexplored. In the author's opinion, the unimolecular reactions of gaseous organic ions represent an exciting new field of chemistry whose study should contribute substantially to our basic understanding of the behavior of molecules.

F. W. McLAFFERTY

Lafayette, Indiana
July 1966

GLOSSARY AND ABBREVIATIONS

$\overset{+}{\cdot}$	Radical cation, odd-electron ion (for example, CH_4^+)
$\curvearrowright$ (full arrow)	Transfer of an electron pair
$\curvearrowright$ (fishhook)	Transfer of single electron
[ ]	Relative abundance of the ion within the brackets
α, alpha cleavage	$R \dotplus C_\alpha \overset{\cdot+}{-Y}$; cleavage of a bond on an atom adjacent to the radical-bearing atom (but *not* the bond to the radical-bearing atom)
amu	Atomic mass units
A	Appearance potential
"A" element	Monoisotopic element
"A + 1" element	Element with an isotope whose mass is 1 amu above that of the most abundant isotope
base peak	Peak representing the most abundant ion in the spectrum
CA	Collisional activation
CI	Chemical ionization
cyclization, *rc*	Reaction in which a cyclized product (either the ion or neutral) is formed
daughter ion	Ionic reaction product
displacement, *rd*	Reaction in which cyclization to form a new bond at a carbon atom results in the loss of another group attached to that carbon atom
elimination, *re*	Reaction in which cyclization to form a new bond between two parts of an ion results in the loss of the actual group connecting these parts
$E_a(M^{+} \to D^{+})$	Activation energy for the reaction $M^{+} \to D^{+}$
$E_s(M^{+} \to D^{+})$	Ion internal energy required so that half of M^{+} ions will decompose to yield D^{+} before leaving the ion source

xvii

EE^+, even-electron ion	An ion in which the outer shell electrons are fully paired
EI	Electron ionization
FI	Field ionization
I	Ionization potential
i	Inductive initiation of a reaction through electron withdrawal by the charge site
isobaric	Ions of the same nominal mass but of different elemental compositions
$k(E)$	The function describing the change in the rate constant, *k*, with change in the internal energy of the ion, *E*, for a particular ion decomposition reaction
m/e	The mass of the ion divided by its charge (usually unity)
m*, metastable	The peak resulting from ion decompositions in a field-free drift region of the mass spectrometer
mmu, millimass units	0.001 atomic mass unit
M^+, molecular ion	The ionized molecule; the peak representing the ionized molecule which contains only the isotopes of greatest natural abundance
MI spectra	Metastable ion spectra
n-electrons	Nonbonding electrons
OE^+, odd-electron ion	An ion in which an outer shell electron is unpaired; a radical ion
Parent	The molecular ion
Precursor	The decomposing ion in any reaction
$P(E)$	The distribution function describing the probability for particular values of internal energy of an ion
r, rearrangement	A reaction in which the molecular arrangement of the atoms in either the ion or neutral product is not the same as in the precursor ion
r + db	Number of rings plus double bonds
*rc, rd, re, r*H	Rearrangements involving cyclization, displacement, elimination, and hydrogen transfer, respectively
relative abundance	The abundance (peak height) of an ion relative to the base peak in the spectrum (or, if so stated, relative to Σ_{ions})
σ, sigma electron ionization	A simple cleavage reaction visualized as taking place through initial ionization at the sigma bond cleaved in the reaction

Σ_{ions}	Total abundance of all ions in the spectrum
Σ_{40}	Total abundance of all ions in the spectrum of mass 40 and above
simple cleavage	An ion decomposition reaction which involves cleavage of only a single bond

INTERPRETATION OF MASS SPECTRA

SECOND EDITION
REVISED, ENLARGED, RESET

1

INTRODUCTION

1.1   Appearance of the Mass Spectrum

Learning how to identify a simple molecule from its mass spectrum is much easier than from other types of spectra. *The mass spectrum shows the mass of the molecule and the masses of pieces from it.* Thus the chemist does not have to learn anything new—the approach is similar to an arithmetic brain-teaser. Try one and see.

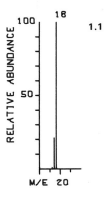

The abscissa indicates the mass (actually *m/e*, the ratio of mass to charge), and the ordinate indicates the relative abundance. If you need a hint, remember that the atomic weights of hydrogen and oxygen are 1 and 16, respectively. Check your answer (the solutions to the unknowns are given in Chapter 9).

Now try another simple spectrum, Unknown 1.2. Your structure will be correct if the molecule and its pieces have masses corresponding to those of the spectrum. (Make a serious attempt to solve each unknown before looking at the solution. This is a vital part of the book's instruction.)

1

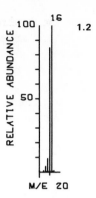

Unknown 1.3 contains carbon, hydrogen, and oxygen atoms. Obviously the possibilities for arranging these in a molecule of molecular weight 32 are limited. Compare any molecular structure possibilities with the major peaks of the spectrum.

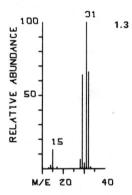

The actual recording from which the bar graph of Unknown 1.3 was made is shown in Figure 1-1. Note that for spectra from this particular spectrometer

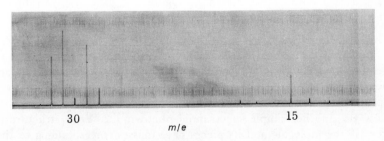

FIGURE 1-1. Mass spectrum of Unknown 1.3 recorded with a single galvanometer trace.

the mass scale is ascending in the opposite direction along the abscissa, and that a small amount of Unknown 1.1 appears as an impurity. Relative abundances are determined by measuring peak heights, as these are proportional to peak areas. Unknown spectra will be displayed in this book both as bar graphs and as tabulated data. The mass spectrometer has a dynamic range of greater than 4 orders of magnitude (that is, ion abundances of 0.01% are reproducible), so that linear bar graphs must omit the low abundance data. An accurate measurement of the small peaks is important in the determination of isotopic compositions. The tabular data for Unknowns 1.1, 1.2, and 1.3 are shown here.

Unknown 1.1		Unknown 1.2	
m/e	Relative abundance	m/e	Relative abundance
1	<0.1	1	3.1
16	1.0	2	0.17
17	21.	12	1.0
18	100.	13	3.9
19	0.08	14	9.2
20	0.22	15	85.
		16	100.
		17	1.11

Unknown 1.3			
m/e	Relative abundance	m/e	Relative abundance
12	0.33	28	6.3
13	0.72	29	64.
14	2.4	30	3.8
15	13.	31	100.
16	0.21	32	66.
17	1.0	33	0.98
		34	0.14

Some of the low-intensity ions tabulated in Unknown 1.3 appear only in a more sensitive recording, as shown in Figure 1-2. The five galvanometer

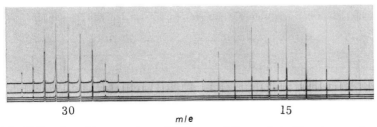

30   15

m/e

FIGURE 1-2.   Mass spectrum of Unknown 1.3 recorded with galvanometers of sensitivities x1, x3, x10, x30, and x100.

tracings have relative attenuations of x1, x3, x10, x30, and x100 (bottom trace, least sensitive). The "peak" height is generally determined by measuring the number of scale divisions from the base line (center of the noise) to the top of the peak, and then multiplying this by the galvanometer attenuation.

If you inspect Figure 1-2 closely you will find other peaks which are not shown in the spectra of either Unknown 1.1 or 1.3, and are not explainable in terms of its structure. This is largely due to the "background" in the instrument—compounds that are desorbing from the walls of the instrument or are leaking in from various sources. To avoid confusion, such a "background spectrum" is usually run before the sample is actually introduced into the instrument. Such a spectrum is shown in Figure 1-3. Can you identify any

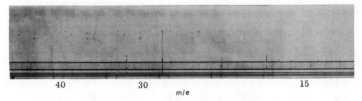

| 40 | 30 | 15 |

m/e

FIGURE 1-3.   Mass spectrum of a typical instrument "background."

of the components? The tabulated reference spectrum of air is shown in Unknown 1.4.

Unknown 1.4

m/e	Relative abundance	m/e	Relative abundance
14	4.0	32	23.
16	0.8	33	0.02
20	0.3	34	0.09
28	100.	40	2.0
29	0.76	44	0.10

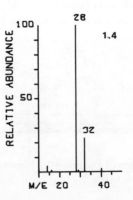

Can you assign the major peaks to the components of air? (For now, ignore the peaks of only a few percent relative abundance. Their significance will be discussed later.)

One of the atmospheric components in its pure state gives the spectrum of Unknown 1.5. Can you identify it?

Unknown 1.5	
m/e	Relative abundance
12	8.7
16	9.6
22	1.9
28	9.8
29	0.13
30	0.02
44	100.
45	1.2
46	0.42

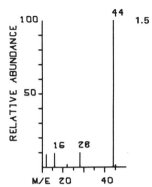

1.2 Formation of the Mass Spectrum

Of necessity this book gives little or no discussion of many important areas of mass spectrometry. Complete details of the method, techniques, and instrumentation are available in a number of excellent books (*1.1–1.10, 1.17*) and review collections (*1.11–1.16*). Compilations of references to the mass spectrometry literature are also available (*1.18–1.21*).

As in many chemical reactions used for analysis, the basic purpose of the mass spectrometer is to convert the sample into measurable products that are indicative of the original molecule. For this method the "reagent" initiating the conversion reaction is a beam of energetic (approximately 70 eV) electrons. The products formed are also rather unusual—gaseous positive ions, whose masses and relative abundances are displayed in the mass spectrum.

The heart of the mass spectrometer is the *ion source*, depicted schematically in Figure 1-4. The background pressure (pressure without any sample) in the source is usually below 10^{-7} torr—approximately 10^{-10} atm. The bombarding electrons are "boiled off" an incandescent filament and travel through the ion chamber to an anode on the opposite side. The stream of vaporized sample molecules (at a pressure of approximately 10^{-4} torr) entering the source interacts with the beam of electrons to form a variety of products, including positive ions. These are pushed out of the source by a relatively small "repeller" (or "draw-out") potential, and then are accelerated by a large potential difference (1 to 10 kV) between the ion accelerating plates. Small potentials can be applied to the "repeller" and "ion focus" plates to produce a defined beam of positive ions, analogous to the focusing

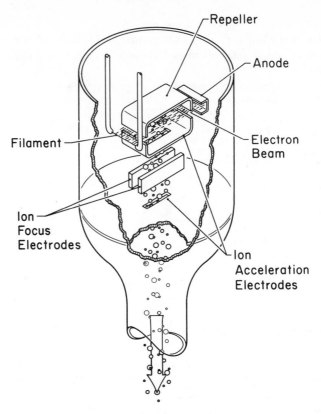

FIGURE 1-4.   Mass spectrometer ion source.

of the light beam in a spectrophotometer. The bulk of the sample molecules and any other electron impact products are removed continuously by vacuum pumps on the ion source housing.

The collimated ion beam from the source can be separated according to the respective masses (actually, mass-to-charge ratios, m/e) of the ions by a variety of techniques. Magnetic deflection, time-of-flight, quadrupole lens, radio frequency, cyclotron resonance, and cycloidal focusing are separating techniques employed in common types of mass spectrometers. Excellent detailed discussions of these methods are available in the literature (*1.1, 1.2, 1.5, 1.12, 1.16*) or from various commercial manufacturers of these instruments. Figure 1-5 illustrates separation of the ion beam by deflection in a magnetic field as employed in a single-focusing (focusing for direction) mass spectrometer. The mass which passes through the exit slit is dependent on the radius (r, cm) of the ion path in the magnetic field, the field strength (B, gauss), and the ion accelerating potential (V, volts) as defined by the fundamental equation

$$m/e = 4.82 \times 10^{-5} B^2 r^2 / V$$

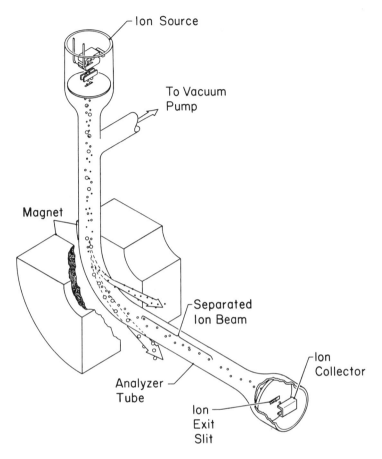

FIGURE 1-5. Single-focusing, magnetic sector mass spectrometer.

The positive ions striking the collector produce a flow of electrons proportional to the ion abundance, and this current can be measured accurately and with great sensitivity by modern electronic techniques. Amplification of the ion signal by an electron multiplier can make possible the detection of a *single ion* arriving at the collector. Thus, although the efficiency of ionization and transmission in the mass spectrometer may yield only one ion at the collector for 10^6 sample molecules introduced, excellent spectra can be obtained from *submicrogram* or even *nanogram* samples. Thus, the method can be used in a variety of research problems for which most of the usual structural tools do not have sufficient sensitivity.

Changing the magnetic field changes the amount of ion deflection, bringing a different m/e into focus on the collector slit. Continuously changing the magnetic field while recording the ion signals on a strip chart or similar recorder then produces a mass spectrum like those shown in Figures 1-1 to 1-3. A complete spectrum can be recorded in approximately one second with a modern oscillographic recorder, an even more rapidly on special instruments. Such rapid scanning is useful for very small samples or for the direct determination of separated components eluted from a gas chromatograph. However, rapid scanning can substantially decrease the accuracy of ion abundance measurement. This accuracy is important in the determination of elemental compositions from isotope ratios; check the performance of your instrument with known samples to be sure you have not sacrificed this accuracy unnecesarily.

THE SAMPLE INTRODUCTION SYSTEM. This must vaporize the sample so that the molecules will be separated from each other before ionization. Direct introduction into the ion source is preferred for the study of compounds of low volatility; samples are inserted with a probe through a vacuum lock into the ion source where they are vaporized by heating. This system has minimum requirements for both vapor pressure and quantity of the sample, making it possible to obtain spectra of nonpolar molecules in the 1000 to 2000 molecular-weight range in amounts of 10^{-6} to 10^{-9} g. *Warning*—it is very easy to use too much sample in the direct introduction system; one crystal which is large enough to see is usually sufficient. Care must be taken to avoid volatilizing the sample too rapidly; a controlled constant volatilization rate is much easier to achieve with a separate sample heater.

Samples with appreciable volatility at room temperature will be lost by vaporization during insertion of the direct probe through the vacuum lock; some probes can be cooled to as low as $-130°C$ to avoid this loss. More volatile samples can be introduced through a reservoir system (Figure 1-6). This requires vaporization of a large excess of sample (approximately 0.1 to 1 mg) into an evacuated, heated reservoir, from which the sample flows through a small orifice (molecular leak) into the ion source at a nearly constant rate. Because of the large pressure drop through the leak, the sample must exhibit a vapor pressure of at least 10^{-2} torr without being heated above its decomposition temperature. The reservoir system produces a more constant flow of sample into the ion source over a longer period (as much as an hour) in comparison to the direct introduction system, making possible the highly reproducible spectra required for quantitative analysis of multicomponent systems. However, the direct introduction system is much more desirable for qualitative studies because of lower sample requirements, higher molecular weight capabilities, speed, less thermal and catalytic decomposition, and faster pump-out.

The mass spectrometer can also be directly coupled to a gas chromatograph (GC/MS) so that the eluted components go directly to the ion source where their complete spectra are obtained "on the fly"; only nanograms of a component are required. The detection limits for a GC component using a single peak in the mass spectrum can be as low as 10^{-12} g; by monitoring two or three peaks sequentially, both high specificity and high sensitivity of detection can be achieved. Except for capillary columns it is necessary to reduce the sample pressure with a splitter or carrier gas separator before introduction into the ion source. A GC/MS system provides a convenient alternative for introduction of samples that are too volatile for direct ion source insertion. GC/MS is now being applied to a wide

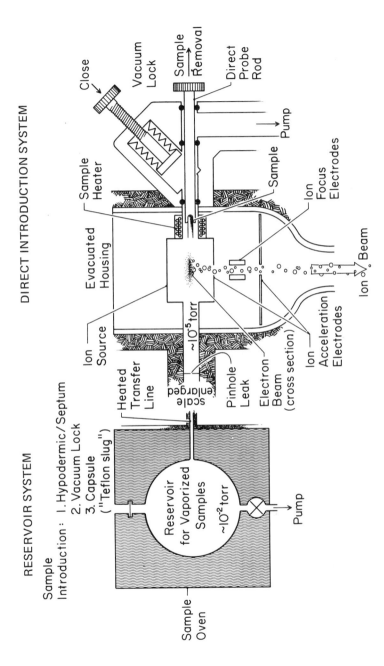

FIGURE 1-6.   Reservoir and direct-introduction sample systems.

variety of problems in which the sample quantities available are too small for study by other spectroscopic methods.

The main purpose of this book is to relate the positive ions formed by electron bombardment (indicated by the mass spectrum) to the molecular structure of the sample. The electron energies used are usually 50 to 100 eV, well above the 7 to 16 eV required for the ionization of molecules. Sample pressure in the ionization chamber is kept sufficiently low (below 10^{-4} torr) so that secondary collisions of the ions with molecules or electrons will be negligible. The initial result of the electron interaction with the molecule is formation of the molecular ion by ejection of another electron. Part (sometimes essentially all) of the molecular ions decompose further to the fragment ions of the spectrum. For example, the principal peaks in the spectrum of methanol (Unknown 1.3) are probably formed through the unimolecular processes below:

$$CH_3OH + e \rightarrow CH_3OH^+ \; (m/e \; 32) + 2e$$

$$CH_3OH^+ \rightarrow CH_2OH^+ \; (m/e \; 31) + H\cdot$$

$$\rightarrow CH_3^+ \; (m/e \; 15) + \cdot OH$$

$$CH_2OH^+ \rightarrow CHO^+ \; (m/e \; 29) + H_2$$

The *dot* will be used to indicate a radical, so that the symbol $^+$ signifies a radical ion. Note that conservation of charge demands that only one ion can be formed from the decomposition of a singly charged ion. It should be reemphasized that only *unimolecular* reactions are appreciable at the operating pressure of the ion source—reactions between ions or an ion and a molecule are rarely important.

In interpreting the mass spectrum, identification of the molecular ion determines the molecular weight and often the elemental composition of the molecule. The fragment ions indicate the pieces of which the molecule is composed, and the interpreter attempts to deduce how these pieces fit together in the original molecular structure. In recent years such correlations have been achieved for the spectra of a variety of complex molecules.

1.3 Standard Interpretation Procedure

You may have had difficulty with the solution of Unknown 1.5 because of apparently anomalous ions of low abundance (for example, m/e 22). Such ions can be helpful in elucidating structures, and, as molecules become more complex, such help is more and more necessary. To learn to utilize the variety of information that is available in the mass spectrum, it is strongly recommended that the outline of this book be followed *step by step* in interpreting an unknown spectrum. This procedure is set forth in Table A-1 (see Appendix) in a form designed to make it useful as a checklist when one is interpreting an unknown.

This is a general, simplified approach applicable to the "average" mass spectrum. With experience the first several steps will be largely automatic and can often be done at a glance. While you are learning, however, each of the steps should be done in this order, and your postulations, assignments, and conclusions from each step should be recorded, preferably on the spectrum. If more than one explanation appears possible for a particular spectral feature, be sure to note all possibilities.

1.4   Other Sample Information

It is important that all other available structural information (chemical, spectral, sample history) be incorporated into the interpretation wherever appropriate. When a sample is submitted by another research worker to the mass spectrometer laboratory for analysis, it is surprising how often other pertinent information is not transmitted. One of the strongest reasons to have the researcher interpret the mass spectra of his own samples is the importance of this information, for which the research man will have the broadest and most thorough understanding. The scientist who has interpreted infrared and nuclear magnetic resonance spectra of his own compounds should need no convincing on this point. This is also one of the main incentives for the preparation of this book—mass spectrometry should be for scientists, not just for mass spectrometrists.

1.5   Directions for Obtaining the Spectrum

Careful plans should be formulated for running the sample on the mass spectrometer. Such plans must be based on the available sample information discussed above and analytical information desired. This planning will be treated only briefly here, for much of it will be obvious after you have become familiar with the interpretation of spectra. Details are available in the general references (*1.1-1.10*).

The techniques of sample handling (see Section 1.3) utilized will depend on the vapor pressure, thermal stability, and amount of the sample available, as well as the quantitative accuracy of ion abundances desired. Direct ion source introduction is generally the most convenient method; samples of higher volatility may be lost during introduction by this method, however, and so should be run in the reservoir-leak system.

Other necessary directions (when differing from the standard operating procedure) include mass range of the scan, mass ranges in which a low background is imperative, sample and ion source temperatures, and factors affecting abundance-measurement accuracy and sensitivity (scan speed, amplification). A second scan with perfluorokerosene or some other internal mass standard may be in order if it is difficult to count the spectrum. It is sometimes desirable to run reference spectra under comparable operating conditions to differentiate between compounds of close structural similarities.

Special techniques are often necessary for transfer of the sample to the introduction system—for example, samples that are gaseous, volatile, hygroscopic, or unstable. If the presence of impurities is suspected, the sample can be fractionated into the inlet system and successive spectra compared.

Finally, proper precautions must be taken for the handling of toxic, noxious, corrosive, or otherwise dangerous samples. This is, of course, especially true if you must depend on others to run your spectra, and thus need their continuing cooperation.

1.6   Verification of Mass Assignments

It is very important that the masses assigned on the spectrum are *correct*—even an error of one mass unit can seriously confuse the interpretation. Such verification will not be necessary to solve the unknowns in this book, but it is of great practical importance in solving an actual unknown spectrum.

With most mass spectrometers you should be able to determine the *exact unit mass* of each ion for masses well above the "resolving power" quoted by the manufacturer for the instrument. Many modern analytical mass spectrometers have resolving powers above 1000, so for all peaks ordinarily encountered the unit mass should be exactly determinable. (Monoisotopic atomic weights are sufficiently close to whole numbers so that with single-focusing instruments almost all ions will appear nominally at whole number masses. Thus molecular and fragment ion weights are generally counted and recorded as whole numbers.)

If there is a mass indicator on your mass spectrometer, become familiar with its reliability by running the spectra of known compounds. With peaks for which an accurate mass measurement is critical, rerun the spectrum of the unknown compound simultaneously with a known compound whose spectrum gives a peak nearly adjacent in mass. Perfluorokerosene or perfluorotributylamine is convenient for this, as they give characteristic peaks throughout the spectrum and are quite volatile.

To verify the m/e of the ions, start at the low mass end of the spectrum. The approximate m/e can be estimated from the instrument settings, and should be marked on the spectrum when it is run. A further check can usually be made on background peaks, especially m/e 18, 28, and 32, as it is very difficult to get all traces of air and moisture out of an instrument (see Figure 1-3). For quadrupole and cyclotron resonance (omegatron) spectrometers, the scale is linear with m/e. For magnetic and time-of-flight instruments, the m/e scale is often proportional to $(m/e)^{1/2}$; that is, masses 16, 25, 36, 49, 64, and so on are regularly spaced. Keeping in mind the relationship of mass to distance along the abscissa, count up in mass for the peaks shown in the spectrum of pyridine (Figure 1.7). What is the m/e of the most abundant ion in the spectrum?

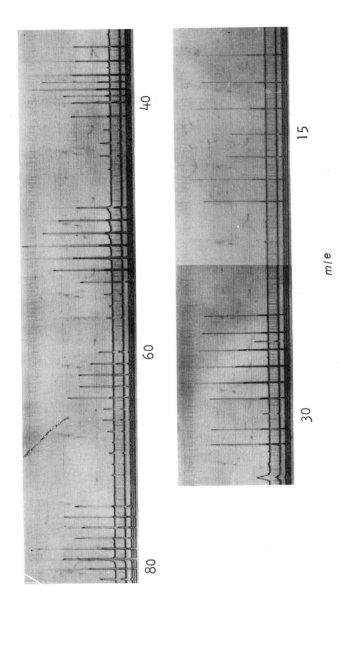

FIGURE 1-7.   Chart recording of the mass spectrum of pyridine.

For spectra with more sparsely spaced ions, a paper mass ruler can be constructed to carry the count across blank regions of the spectrum, but the mass ruler should be referenced to the actual peaks in the spectrum as often as possible during the counting. Temperature, hysteresis, and other magnet instabilities can cause hourly variations in the accuracy of such a mass ruler. The dynamic recording range of the mass spectrometer is so great, however, that there are usually sufficient peaks at the highest sensitivity to make such a counting technique quite accurate.

1.7 Multiply Charged and Metastable Ions

Watch for two types of peaks that often appear at nonintegral masses, and therefore may lead to an erroneous count. Multiply charged ions can appear at fractional masses; for example, the peak at m/e 39.5 in Figure 1-7 is actually a doubly charged ion of mass 79 and so appears at m/e 79/2. Can you identify other doubly charged ions in this spectrum?

So-called "metastable ions" can also appear as fractional masses, but these can be easily recognized by their characteristic width and diffuseness as compared to a regular peak. These arise in a magnetic instrument from the decomposition of ions after they are accelerated but before they are deflected in the magnetic field; for the decomposition $m_1 \rightarrow m_2$ the metastable decomposition product, m^*, will appear at m/e m_2^2/m_1. In Figure 1.7 the broad peak at approximately m/e 34.2 arises from the metastable decomposition m/e $79^+ \rightarrow m/e$ 52^+ in the field-free drift region between ion acceleration and magnetic deflection, and thus appears at m/e $(52)^2/79 = 34.2$. Multiply charged and metastable ions are discussed further in Sections 4.3 and 7.1.

Before continuing to Chapter 2, try Unknowns 1.6 to 1.9, again ignoring the small peaks adjacent to large ones.

Unknown 1.6	
m/e	Relative abundance
12	0.91
13	3.6
14	0.10
24	6.1
25	23.
26	100.
27	2.2
28	0.02

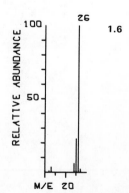

Unknown 1.7	
m/e	Relative abundance
12	4.2
13	1.7
13.5	0.88
14	1.6
15	0.12
26	17.
27	100.
28	1.6

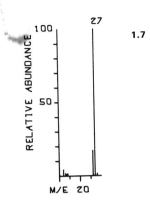

Unknown 1.8	
m/e	Relative abundance
14	17.
15	100.
16	1.0
19	2.0
20	0.34
31	10.
32	9.3
33	89.
34	95.
35	1.1

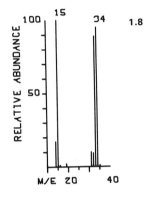

Unknown 1.9	
m/e	Relative abundance
12	3.3
13	4.3
14	4.4
15	0.07
16	1.7
28	31.
29	100.
30	89.
31	1.3
32	0.21

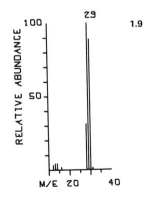

2

ELEMENTAL FORMULAS

The modern analytical mass spectrometer will determine the m/e of any peak in the spectrum *to the nearest mass unit*. In addition, it is possible to determine the *elemental composition* of peaks. The most powerful technique for this utilizes exact mass measurement with a high-resolution mass spectrometer; measurement of the mass of a peak with sufficient accuracy defines its elemental composition unequivocally (this technique is described in Section 7.5). As an alternative not requiring this sophisticated instrumentation, the presence of isotopes of known natural abundance offers a useful and simple method for determining elemental composition for many ions. Even if you have high-resolution information on elemental compositions available to you, it is important that you understand thoroughly the use of isotopic abundances, as this is basic to an understanding of mass spectra.

2.1   Stable Isotopes; Classification According to Natural Abundances

A *chemically pure* organic compound will give a *mixture* of mass spectra because the elements that compose it are not isotopically pure. The classic case of this is the element neon, which Sir J. J. Thomson showed gave not one peak at its chemical atomic weight of 20.2, but two peaks at masses 20.0 and 22.0, in relative abundances of 10:1. Table 2-1 shows that a number of common elements have more than one isotope of appreciable natural abundance.

The effect of isotopes on a mass spectrum is illustrated in Unknown 2.1, which contains molecular ions at m/e 36 and 38. Their characteristic isotopic ratio of 3:1 should make the element easily recognizable from the data of Table 2-1. (Ignore ions of low relative abundance. Their significance will be explained later in this chapter.)

TABLE 2-1   *Natural Isotopic Abundances of Common Elements (2.1)*

Element	A Mass	A %	A+1 Mass	A+1 %	A+2 Mass	A+2 %	Element type
H	1	100	2	0.016			"A"
C	12	100	13	1.08			"A + 1"
N	14	100	15	0.36			"A + 1"
O	16	100	17	0.04	18	0.20	"A + 2"
F	19	100					"A"
Si	28	100	29	5.1	30	3.4	"A + 2"
P	31	100					"A"
S	32	100	33	0.80	34	4.4	"A + 2"
Cl	35	100			37	32.5	"A + 2"
Br	79	100			81	98.0	"A + 2"
I	127	100					"A"

Unknown 2.1

m/e	Relative abundance
35	12.
36	100.
37	4.1
38	33.
39	0.01

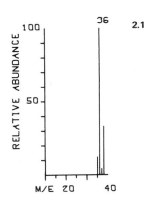

It is highly important that you become familiar with the data of Table 2-1. Note that the isotope of lowest mass is the most abundant for all these elements, quite fortunately. Note also that the isotopic abundances of the elements can be classified into three general categories: "A"—those elements with only one natural isotope; "A + 1"—those elements that have two isotopes, the second of which is one mass unit heavier than the most abundant isotope; and "A + 2"—those elements that have an isotope that is two mass units heavier than the most abundant isotope. The "A + 2" elements are the easiest to recognize, and therefore you should look for these first.

2.2   "A + 2" Elements: Oxygen, Silicon, Sulfur, Chlorine, and Bromine

A second isotope makes an especially prominent appearance in the spectrum if it is more than one unit higher in mass than the most abundant isotopic species. Bromine and chlorine, and to a lesser extent silicon and sulfur, are striking common examples. The presence of these elements in an ion is often easily recognized from the "isotopic clusters" produced in the spectrum. Thus an element of Unknown 2.2, like Unknown 2.1, can be recognized from the characteristic isotopic ratio of the ions separated by two mass units. Again ignore the small peaks next to the large ones. An initial inspection of the bar graph presentation is often an easy way to identify such isotopic clusters.

Unknown 2.2

m/e	Relative abundance	m/e	Relative abundance
12	1.2	48	0.95
13	1.4	79	10.
14	3.8	81	10.
15	59.	91	4.2
16	0.62	92	2.4
39.5	0.19	93	6.8
40.5	0.20	94	100.
46	1.3	95	3.6
46.5	0.30	96	96.
47	2.3	97	1.1
47.5	0.28		

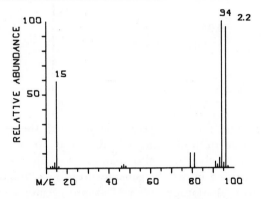

If there is more than one atom of these elements present in the molecule, the result is even more striking. For hydrogen bromide the isotopic molecular ions at m/e 80 and 82 ($H^{79}Br$ and $H^{81}Br$) are in the relative proportions of roughly 1:1. The mass spectrum of Br_2 shows prominent molecular ions at masses 158, 160, and 162 of relative abundances 1:2:1 due to the ions $^{79}Br_2$, $^{79}Br^{81}Br$ and $^{81}Br^{79}Br$, and $^{81}Br_2$, respectively. In a similar fashion, any ion structure containing three bromine atoms will exhibit four peaks at intervals of two mass units in the ratio 1:3:3:1. The characteristic patterns resulting from combinations of the chlorine and bromine isotopes are illustrated by the bar graphs of Figure 2-1; a number of values for combinations of "A + 2" elements are given in Table A-2 in the Appendix.

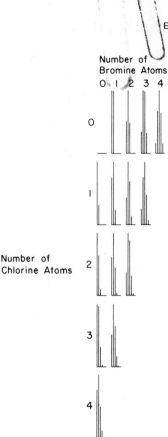

Number of
Bromine Atoms
0 1 2 3 4

0

1

Number of
Chlorine Atoms 2

3

4

FIGURE 2-1   "Isotopic clusters" resulting from combinations of up to four chlorine and four bromine atoms. Numerical data for these and additional combinations (including sulfur and silicon) are given in Table A-2.

The abundances resulting from combinations of several atoms of the same element can be calculated from the binomial expansion $(a + b)^n = a^n + na^{n-1}b + n(n - 1)a^{n-2}b^2/2! + n(n - 1)(n - 2)a^{n-3}b^3/(3!) + \cdots$. Thus for a peak containing four chlorine atoms, the abundance of the $(A + 4)^+$ relative to A^+ should be $4 \cdot 3 \cdot 1^2 \cdot 0.325^2/2 = 0.635$. Details of the calculations of these ratios are given in the comprehensive text by Beynon (1.1).

It should be recognized that a pair of peaks separated by two mass units could be due to formulas differing by two hydrogen atoms, instead of the presence of an "A + 2" element. Fortunately, there is little possibility of such confusion for the molecular ion; as will be discussed later, it is highly unlikely that an ion formed by the loss of two hydrogen atoms from the molecular ion, $(M - H_2)^+$, will have an abundance greater than that of the molecular ion.

For oxygen the $(A + 2)^+$ abundance is very low (0.20%). Thus it is often necessary to determine the number of oxygen atoms after the "A + 1" elements as well as the other "A + 2" elements have been identified.

2.3   "A + 1" Elements: Carbon and Nitrogen

The three "A + 1" elements in Table 2-1 are hydrogen, carbon, and nitrogen, but the $^2H/^1H$ ratio is so low that we shall consider hydrogen to be an "A" element. Each element exhibits its isotopic abundances independently; thus the carbon atom in the CH_3Br molecule of Unknown 2.2 contributes 1.1% of the abundance of the m/e 96 peak ($^{12}C^1H_3{}^{81}Br^+$) to the 97 peak ($^{13}C^1H_3{}^{81}Br^+$). Note that the 95 peak is composed of $^{12}C^1H_2{}^{81}Br^+$ as well as $^{13}C^1H_3{}^{79}Br^+$; this emphasizes the desirability of identifying first the "A + 2" elements.

Increasing the number of carbon atoms in an ion increases the probability that one of these atoms will be a ^{13}C isotope; $[(A + 1)^+]/[A^+]$ for a C_{10} ion will thus exhibit ten times the probability of C_1, or 10 x 1.08% = 10.8%. This provides a means of determining the number of carbon atoms, which is obviously of key importance in interpreting the spectra of organic compounds.

Table 2-2 tabulates the probability that an ion of a particular number of ^{12}C atoms will contain one ^{13}C atom, although obviously this value can easily be obtained by multiplying the number of ^{12}C atoms by 1.1%. The factor of 1.1% per carbon atom is used for convenience and to correct for the small contribution of deuterium from the usual hydrogen content of the ion. (For the unknowns in this book assume a possible relative error of ±10% or absolute error of ±0.02, whichever is the greater, in the determination of relative abundance.)

In Unknown 2.3 determine the maximum number of carbon atoms in the ions of m/e 43 and 58. The results indicate that the m/e 43 peak is formed from the m/e 58 by the loss of what group?

Notice that this method of calculation gives (except as noted in Section 2.4) the *maximum* number of atoms of each type in the elemental composition. The presence of interfering ions from any source, such as other fragment ions, impurities, or background, will cause the indicated number of atoms to be erroneously high. In Unknown 2.3, calculating the number of carbon atoms of m/e 41 from the relative abundance of ions in m/e 42 gives a ridiculously high number of carbon atoms. This technique, then, can be usefully applied only to "clean" portions of the spectrum. Try assigning elemental compositions to other major ions in Unknown 2.3 where this technique is applicable.

This spectrum also contains minor, but meaningful, peaks at masses 45 and 60. These are too small to be due to contributions of "A + 2" elements of Table 2-1; m/e 43 cannot have the composition $C_2H_3O^+$ because the "A + 2"

TABLE 2-2   *Isotopic Contributions for Carbon and Hydrogen*

If the abundance of the ion A^+ is 100 (after correction for ^{13}C isotopic contributions to it), then its isotopic contributions will be:

	$(A + 1)^+$	$(A + 2)^+$		$(A + 1)^+$	$(A + 2)^+$
C_1	1.1	0.000	C_{21}	23	2.5
C_2	2.2	0.012	C_{22}	24	2.8
C_3	3.3	0.036	C_{23}	25	3.0
C_4	4.4	0.073	C_{24}	26	3.3
C_5	5.5	0.12	C_{25}	28	3.6
C_6	6.6	0.18	C_{26}	29	3.9
C_7	7.7	0.25	C_{27}	30	4.2
C_8	8.8	0.34	C_{28}	31	4.5
C_9	9.9	0.44	C_{29}	32	4.9
C_{10}	11.0	0.54	C_{30}	33	5.2
C_{11}	12.1	0.67	C_{31}	34	5.6
C_{12}	13.2	0.80	C_{32}	35	6.0
C_{13}	14.3	0.94	C_{33}	36	6.4
C_{14}	15.4	1.10	C_{34}	37	6.8
C_{15}	16.5	1.27	C_{35}	39	7.2
C_{16}	17.6	1.46	C_{36}	40	7.6
C_{17}	18.7	1.65	C_{37}	41	8.0
C_{18}	19.8	1.86	C_{38}	42	8.5
C_{19}	20.9	2.07	C_{39}	43	8.9
C_{20}	22.0	2.30	C_{40}	44	9.4

For each additional element present, add *per atom:*

$(A + 1)^+$: N, 0.37; O, 0.04; Si, 5.1; S, 0.80.
$(A + 2)^+$:   O, 0.20; Si, 3.4; S, 4.4; Cl, 32.5; Br, 98.0.

Typical values for $(A + 3)^+$: C_{10}, 0.016; C_{15}, 0.06; C_{20}, 0.15; C_{25}, 0.31; C_{30}, 0.54; C_{35}, 0.87; C_{40}, 1.3. $(A + 4)^+$: C_{25}, 0.018; C_{40}, 0.13.

Calculated assuming $^{13}C/^{12}C = 1.08\%$ with 1.5 H atoms per C atom; ±0.5 H/C changes the intensity of $(A + 1)^+$ by only ±0.7% of its value, $(A + 2)^+$ by ± 1.5% of its value.

contribution of oxygen would be 0.2%. The peak at m/e 45 arises from $C_3H_7^+$ ions containing *two* ^{13}C atoms and one ^{12}C atom. The abundance of such $(A + 2)^+$ ions relative to the A ion depends on the number of carbon atoms, just as $[(A + 1)^+]/[A^+]$ does: these abundances are also tabulated in Table 2-2.

Of course $(A + 2)^+$ isotopic contributions can also arise from the "A + 2" elements. After assignment of the number of carbon and nitrogen atoms from the $(A + 1)^+$ abundance value, the $(A + 2)^+$ value must be rechecked. This is especially necessary for the detection of oxygen; although the $^{18}O/^{16}O$ value of 0.20% is small, the large dynamic recording range of the mass spectrometer can make the accuracy of the $(A + 2)^+$ value sufficient for this purpose. For

Unknown 2.3

m/e	Relative abundance	m/e	Relative abundance
1	1.1	36	0.08
2	0.10	37	1.0
12	0.13	37.1 m	0.06
13	0.26	38	1.8
14	0.96	39	12.
15	5.3	39.2 m	0.4
16	0.06	40	1.6
19 d	0.04	41	27.
19.5 d	0.01	42	12.
20 d	0.02	43	100.
24	0.03	44	3.3
24.1 m	0.01	45	0.05
25	0.46	48	0.06
25.1 m	0.11	49	0.40
25.5 d	0.36	50	1.2
26	6.1	51	1.0
26.5 d	0.08	52	0.26
27	37.	53	0.74
27.5 d	0.05	54	0.19
28	32.	55	0.93
29	44.	56	0.72
30	0.98	57	2.4
30.4 m	0.14	58	12.
31.9 m	0.20	59	0.54
35.1 m	0.02	60	0.01

(m) "metastable" peak.
(d) doubly charged ions.

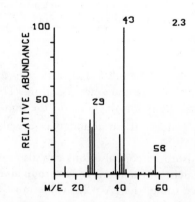

example, the molecular ion region of benzoic acid, $C_7H_6O_2$, shows these abundances:

m/e	Relative abundance
121	0.71
122	78.
123	6.0
124	0.52

Can you account for these abundances in terms of the formula? Note that the maximum number of oxygens indicated would be erroneously high if correction is not made for the $(A + 2)^+$ contribution of carbon. What would the [m/e 124] value be for the alternative formulas $C_8H_{10}O$ and $C_6H_2O_3$? (Answer: 0.42 and 0.61, respectively; note that moderate experimental accuracy easily distinguishes between these possibilities and the true composition.)

Try Unknown 2.4, making sure to assign elemental compositions to as many ions as possible before attempting to assign the molecular structure.

Unknown 2.4

m/e	Relative abundance	m/e	Relative abundance
25	5.2	45	32.
26	38.	46	2.5
26.5	0.15	47	0.14
27	74.	52	1.4
27.5	0.26	53	6.0
28	12.	54	2.3
29	4.3	55	74.
30	0.13	56	2.6
31	0.48	57	0.19
41	1.2	71	4.3
42	1.3	72	100.
43	5.8	73	3.5
44	14.	74	0.48

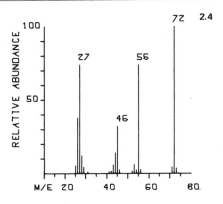

2.4   Overlap of "A + 1" and "A + 2" Elements

To use the $[(A + 1)^+]/[A^+]$ ratio in calculating the number of carbon (or nitrogen) atoms, the elemental composition of the A^+ and $(A + 1)^+$ peaks must be the same (except that the latter must contain a single ^{13}C atom and one less ^{12}C atom, or ^{15}N in place of ^{14}N). You should learn to recognize several situations in which the elemental compositions will differ, and to make appropriate corrections where possible. If ^{28}Si or ^{32}S is present in the A^+ ion, a correction of 5.1% or 0.80%, respectively, of $[A^+]$ must of course be made to $[(A + 1)^+]$.

If an ion A^+ contains an "A + 2" element, the corresponding peak with one less hydrogen atom, $(A - 1)^+$, will make an isotopic contribution to the $(A + 1)^+$ peak which must be subtracted before using $[(A + 1)^+]/[A^+]$ to determine the number of "A + 1" elements present. For example, in Unknown 2.2, multiple corrections must be made to utilize the $[m/e\ 95]/[m/e\ 94]$ ratio for calculation of the number of carbon atoms in m/e 94. The 4.2% abundance of $C^{79}Br^+$ $(m/e\ 91)$ indicates a 4.1% contribution of $C^{81}Br^+$ to m/e 93. Thus the abundance of $CH_2{}^{79}Br^+$ should be 2.7% by difference, so that $CH_2{}^{81}Br^+$ will contribute about 2.6% to m/e 95. This leaves about 1.0% for $^{13}CH_3{}^{79}Br$ at m/e 95, consistent with the presence of one carbon atom in the m/e 94 peak. However, here it is preferable to use the $[(A + 3)^+]/[(A + 2)^+]$ value, as these peaks contain no isotopic contribution from the $(A - 1)^+$ ion; the observed $[m/e\ 97]/[m/e\ 96]$ ratio agrees with the value expected for one carbon atom. Note that, if the A^+ ion contains n "A + 2" elements, only the $[(A + 2n + 1)^+]/[(A + 2n)^+]$ value will not be subject to an isotopic contribution from the $(A - H)^+$ ion.

It is also possible that the A^+ peak may contain a ^{13}C contribution from the $(A - 1)^+$ peak, but unless the latter is of greater abundance this correction can usually be ignored. For example, the spectrum of toluene has $(M - 1)^+$ as its base peak (see below); this $C_7H_7^+$

m/e	Composition	Relative abundance
91	C_7H_7	100.
92	$C_6{}^{13}CH_7$, C_7H_8	80.
93	$C_5{}^{13}C_2H_7$, $C_6{}^{13}CH_8$	5.8
94	$C_5{}^{13}C_2H_8$	0.18

ion should thus cause a ^{13}C contribution of 7.7% and 0.25% to the m/e 92 and 93 peaks, respectively; the remaining 72.3% at m/e 92 should in the same manner contribute 5.6% and 0.18% to the m/e 93 and 94 peaks, respectively, to give the values shown. If the uncorrected abundances had been used for $[m/e\ 93]/[m/e\ 92]$, 6.6 (instead of 7.0) carbon atoms would have been indicated. Note that this is the only case in which the calculated number of carbon atoms is *less* than the true value, and that it can be recognized in that $[(A - 1)^+]/[A^+] > 1$. Note also that, if the $(A - 1)^+$ ion contains oxygen, the ^{18}O contribution to $[(A + 1)^+]$ will partially or wholly offset this error.

It is also possible that elemental compositions containing only lowest mass isotopes will contribute to the $(A + 1)^+$ peak. Such contributions to the $(M + 1)^+$ peak (one mass unit above the molecular ion) can arise only from ion-molecule reactions or impurities (see Chapter 3), but at lower masses other fragment ions can contribute to $(A + 1)^+$. An example mentioned above is Unknown 2.3; the $[m/e\ 42]/[m/e\ 41]$ ratio is much higher than the 3.3% predicted by the $C_3H_5^+$ formula of m/e 41 because m/e 42 contains $^{12}C_3H_6$ as well as $^{12}C_2{}^{13}CH_5$. Unfortunately, an accurate correction cannot be made for this contribution from the low resolution data; thus, the $[(A + 1)^+]/[A^+]$ ratio can give only the *maximum* number of carbon atoms in the ion (except, possibly, when $[(A - 1)^+]/[A^+] > 1$; *vide supra*).

Unknowns 2.5 and 2.6 represent only the molecular ion regions of the spectra of two compounds. Determine their elemental compositions, assuming that there are no contributions from impurities or ion-molecule reactions.

Unknown 2.5		Unknown 2.6	
m/e	Relative abundance	*m/e*	Relative abundance
60	9.0	129	30.
61	19.0	130	100.
62	100.	131	31.
63	3.8	132	98.
64	4.4	133	12.
65	0.09	134	32.
		135	1.7
		136	3.5
		137	0.07

2.5   "A" Elements: Hydrogen, Fluorine, Phosphorus, and Iodine

After the number of each "A + 2" and "A + 1" element has been determined (or estimated, depending on the experimental accuracy), the balance of the mass of the peak must be due to the monoisotopic "A" elements. The assignment of the total elemental composition (or of the several possible compositions) is then completed by utilizing numbers of these elements consistent with rules of bonding.

Try an example:

m/e	Relative abundance
127	100.
128	0.00
129	0.00

No "A + 2" or "A + 1" elements are possible. All of the "A" elements but phosphorus are monovalent, so this grouping must be due to a single one of these (which?), or a combination of these with phosphorus (but H_3P_4 should give a relative abundance of 0.06 at *m/e* 128 as H is actually an "A + 1" element).

These two examples involve the same masses:

m/e	Relative abundance	
69	100.	100.
70	1.1	0.00
71	0.00	0.00

What is the maximum number of "A + 2" elements? Of "A + 1" elements? For the data in the first column, the presence of one carbon should be an obvious possibility; did you think of N_3? Compositions that satisfy the data are CF_3 and PF_2.

Try these procedures with Unknowns 2.7 and 2.8.

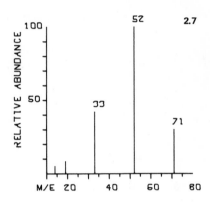

Unknown 2.7	
m/e	Relative abundance
14	5.2
15	0.02
19	8.4
33	42.
34	0.15
52	100.
53	0.39
71	30.
72	0.11

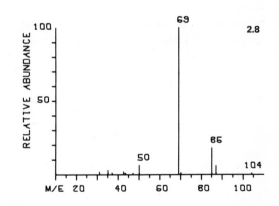

Unknown 2.8	
m/e	Relative abundance
12	0.31
19	0.19
31	1.80
32	0.02
35	3.0
37	1.0
42.5	1.7
43.5	0.57
47	0.51
49	0.18
50	6.3
51	0.07
66	0.28
68	0.10
69	100.
70	1.2
85	18.
86	0.23
87	5.9
88	0.07
104	0.75
105	0.01
106	0.24

2.6 Rings plus Double Bonds

Because of the valencies of the elements involved, the total number of rings and double bonds in a molecule of the formula $C_x H_y N_z O_n$ will be equal to $x - \frac{1}{2}y + \frac{1}{2}z + 1$. For ions, the calculated value may end in "$\frac{1}{2}$," and this fraction should be subtracted to obtain the true value. Use of this should be more obvious by inspection of the examples in Table 2-3. The value 4 found for

TABLE 2-3   *Rings plus Double Bonds* $(r + db)$

For the general formula $C_x H_y N_z O_n$
   (more general case $I_y II_n III_z IV_x$, where I = H, F, Cl, Br, I; II = O, S; III = N, P; and IV = C, Si, etc.)

Total rings plus double bonds = $x - \frac{1}{2}y + \frac{1}{2}z + 1$
For an even-electron ion (see Section 3.2), the true value will be followed by "$\frac{1}{2}$"

Examples:
  $C_5 H_5 N$: rings plus double bonds = $5 - 2.5 + 0.5 + 1 = 4$
        For example, pyridine$^+$ (odd-electron)
  $C_7 H_5 O$: rings plus double bonds = $7 - 2.5 + 1 = 5.5$
        For example, $C_6 H_5 CO^+$, benzoyl (even-electron)

---

pyridine represents the ring and three double bonds of this molecule, while the 5.5 calculated for the benzoyl ion represents the ring, the three double bonds of benzene, and the double bond of the carbonyl group. Calculate the number of rings and double bonds for the empirical formulas that you found for m/e 43 and 58 in Unknown 2.3.

If other elements are present, these are counted as additional atoms of the element C, H, N, or O to which they correspond in valency. Thus, the number of silicon atoms should be added to the number of carbon atoms, the number of halogen atoms to the number of hydrogen atoms, and the number of phosphorus atoms to the number of nitrogen atoms. Note also that this is based on the lowest valence state of the elements and does not count double bonds formed to elements in higher valence states. Thus, the formula indicates one double bond in $CH_3 NO_2$ (nitromethane), no double bonds in $CH_3 SO_2 CH_3$ (dimethyl sulfone), and a *negative* value in $H_3 O^+$.

2.7 Shortcuts for Assigning Elemental Compositions

To reiterate, you must extract all possible elemental composition information before attempting to assign a structure. However, this can usually be done quickly if a few logical rules are observed.

1. If possible, assign first the composition of the ion of highest mass; if this is the molecular ion, the correct elemental composition thus gives the maximum number of each element that can be found in any lower mass peak. The elemental composition of other high mass ions can greatly reduce the possible compositions that need to be considered for other ions.

2. Determine next the ion compositions for which the highest accuracy appears possible. For a group of peaks spaced at 1-amu intervals, a determination using the peaks of highest mass in the group usually has the best accuracy. Thus in Unknown 2.14,

$[m/e\ 65]/[m/e\ 64] = 2.3$, indicating C_2, while $[m/e\ 63]/[m/e\ 62] = 4.8$ (although m/e 62, 64, and 65 are composed almost entirely of isotopic molecular ions, approximately half of m/e 63 is due to a ^{37}Cl contribution from the m/e 61 ion).

3. If several elemental compositions are possible, a lower mass peak of more certain composition may narrow the choice. For example, if m/e 120 could be C_9H_{12} or C_8H_8O, the assignment of m/e 105 as C_7H_5O would make C_9H_{12} less probable as a possibility for m/e 120.

4. In the determination of the number of carbon (and/or nitrogen) atoms from $[(A+1)^+]/[A^+]$, note that the presence of an "A + 2" element will cause any $(A-H)^+$ ion to also contribute to the $(A+1)^+$ peak.

5. The $(A+2)^+$ peak arising from the presence of a sufficient number of carbon atoms can interfere with the recognition of the "A + 2" elements, especially oxygen. However, a rough estimate of the number of carbon atoms should provide a sufficiently accurate correction to identify the "A + 2" elements, which will then permit determination of the carbon number.

2.8 Exercises

Extensive experience has shown that *practice* is necessary to develop one's ability to determine elemental compositions from isotopic abundances. (Perhaps this is because the chemist must become accustomed to the fact that the mass spectrum shows that his carefully purified compound is a mixture of isotopically different molecules.) It is important that you understand this procedure, as it is the key primary step in interpreting an unknown spectrum. Can you assign compositions and rings-plus-double-bonds values to the fragmentary spectra shown in Unknowns 2.9 through 2.13? The peaks of Unknowns 2.9, 2.10, and 2.12 contain the molecular ion (M^+); peaks in Unknowns 2.11 and 2.13 arise from losses from M^+ as indicated.

Unknown 2.9		Unknown 2.10		Unknown 2.11	
m/e	Relative abundance	*m/e*	Relative abundance	*m/e*	Relative abundance
130	1.0	73	26.	84	0.00
131	2.0	74	19.	85	40. $(M-19)^+$
132	100.	75	41.	86	2.0
133	10.	76	80.	87	1.3
134	0.65	77	2.7	88	0.00
135	0.03	78	0.03		

Unknown 2.12		Unknown 2.13	
m/e	Relative abundance	*m/e*	Relative abundance
179	2.2	354	1.3
180	1.1	355	100. $(M-15)^+$
181	7.4	356	28.
182	55.	357	36.
183	8.3	358	9.2
184	0.61	359	1.2
185	0.02	360	0.10
		361	0.01

Unknown 2.14

m/e	Relative abundance	m/e	Relative abundance
24	1.3	37	0.8
25	5.7	38	0.34
26	22.	47	2.5
27	77.	48	1.2
28	1.5	49	0.92
29	0.02	50	0.37
30	0.12	59	1.5
30.5	0.24	60	5.8
31	0.16	61	8.7
31.5	0.09	62	100.
32	0.06	63	4.8
35	2.2	64	31.
36	1.0	65	0.71

Unknown 2.15

m/e	Relative abundance	m/e	Relative abundance
26	1.2	40	28.
27	2.5	41	1.2
28	1.5	50	1.8
31	4.9	51	2.5
31.5	1.3	52	0.11
32	2.2	61	4.3
32.5	0.9	62	6.8
33	2.1	63	10.
33.5	0.11	64	1.9
37	4.4	65	49.
38	8.2	66	100.
39	32.	67	5.6
		68	0.14

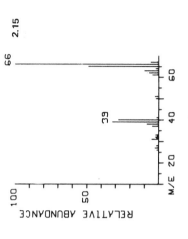

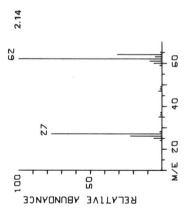

Unknown 2.16

m/e	Relative abundance	m/e	Relative abundance
15	3.7	43	2.7
27	3.3	44	0.29
28	4.1	55	2.0
29	3.6	56	2.7
30	6.2	57	5.6
31	0.10	58	100.
39	4.8	59	3.6
40	1.4	60	0.05
41	18.	73	0.41
42	11.	74	0.02

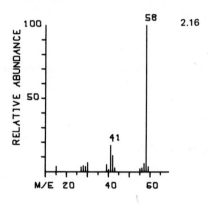

3

THE MOLECULAR ION

The molecular ion, M^+, provides the most valuable information in the mass spectrum; its mass and elemental composition show the molecular boundaries into which the structural fragments indicated in the mass spectrum must be fitted. Thus the next step in spectral interpretation is to identify M^+. In the mass spectrum of a pure compound the molecular ion, if present, must be found at the highest m/e in the spectrum. Unfortunately, for a number of types of compounds, the molecular ion is not sufficiently stable to be found in appreciable abundance. Thus, it is possible that the peak at highest m/e is not M^+. There are tests that can be applied to the peak at highest mass which can demonstrate that it is not the molecular ion, although these tests cannot demonstrate the converse.

Before discussing these tests, two possible sources of confusion should be pointed out. Firstly, the molecular ion species usually gives several isotopic peaks; the one that is literally of the highest mass in the spectrum is not the most abundant. By convention mass spectrometrists calculate the molecular weight (the m/e of "the" molecular ion peak) on the basis of the mass of the most abundant isotope of each of the elements present. For benzene (C_6H_6), which has a substantial m/e 79 and a m/e 80 peak, the molecular ion is considered to be at mass 78 (C = 12, H = 1). For compounds containing a number of chlorine and (or) bromine atoms, the situation can be even more confusing. The molecular weight of the molecule Br_2 is considered to be 158, twice the mass of the most abundant isotope, ^{79}Br. However, in the mass spectrum of Br_2, the most abundant ion is at m/e 160, as the relative abundance of the $^{79}Br^{81}Br$ is almost twice that of the $^{79}Br_2$ (see Section 2.2). Proper elucidation of the elemental composition of M^+ will avoid confusion because of this.

Secondly, the peak of highest mass may be an artifact caused by an impurity, spectrometer background, or an ion-molecule reaction. If the first is suspected, further purification can be carried out. It is often convenient to fractionate the sample in the mass spectrometer by partial vaporization; allowing only part of the sample to vaporize into the instrument will increase the contribution of the more volatile components to the spectrum. Background scans should always be run before each sample. Background peaks from adsorbed materials may increase substantially when a new sample is introduced because the new sample displaces the background material from the inlet system walls. If the sample pressure in the ion source becomes too high, secondary reactions of the ions with molecules can become appreciable. Such ion-molecule reactions give rise to peaks above the molecular weight, and some types of molecules have a high cross section for such reactions (see Section 3.6). Such ions can be identified by their relative increase with increased sample pressure or with lower ion repeller potentials.

3.1 Requirements for the Molecular Ion

The following are necessary, *but not sufficient*, requirements for the molecular ion in the mass spectrum of a pure sample.

1. It must be the ion of highest mass in the spectrum.
2. It must be an odd-electron ion (Section 3.2).
3. It must be capable of yielding the important ions in the high mass region of the spectrum through the loss of logical neutral species (Section 3.4).

If the ion in question fails any of these tests, it cannot be the molecular ion; if it passes all these tests, it is still possible that it is not the molecular ion. Other methods of molecular weight determination are discussed in Section 3.6.

3.2 Odd-Electron Ions

Ionization of the sample molecule occurs through the loss of an electron, and therefore the molecular ion is a *radical* species. Such an ion, either molecular or fragment, with an unpaired electron is called an "odd-electron" ion, and designated by the symbol $\dot{+}$. It is often useful and convenient in explaining and classifying ion decomposition reactions to distinguish between such radical ions and "even-electron" ions, those in which the outer shell electrons are fully paired; the symbol $+$ will be used only to refer to even-electron ions (*1.3, 3.1–3.4*).

This concept can be visualized in its simplest form with structures that include the outer shell electrons:

$$H_2C::CH_2 \xrightarrow{-e} H_2C\dot{:}CH_2 \text{ or } H_2C=CH_2\dot{+}$$

The structures showing localized charges are only approximations; usually a number of canonical resonance forms can be drawn to approximate the electron distribution in the ion. Note that the symbolism $\stackrel{+}{\cdot}$ is meant only to indicate an ion with an *unpaired* electron, *not* an electron *in addition* to those the formula represents; adding an electron to CH_4 would give the negative ion, CH_4^-.

If you were able to determine the elemental composition for the proposed molecular ion, the rings-plus-double-bonds formula will show immediately if the ion is an odd-electron species. For the general formula $C_x H_y N_z O_n$, the value of $x - \frac{1}{2}y + \frac{1}{2}z + 1$ will be a whole number for any odd-electron ion; examples are given in Table 2.3.

3.3   The Nitrogen Rule

For most elements encountered in organic compounds there is a fortunate correspondence between the mass of an element's most abundant isotope and its valence; either the values of both are even-numbered, or both are odd-numbered, with nitrogen as the major exception. This leads to the so-called "nitrogen rule," which can be stated as follows:

If a compound contains an even number of nitrogen atoms, its molecular ion will be at an even mass number. As examples, the following molecules yield even-mass molecular ions: H_2O, m/e 18; CH_4, m/e 16; C_2H_2, m/e 26; CH_3OH, m/e 32; $CClF_3$, m/e 104; C_6H_5OH, m/e 94; $C_{17}H_{35}COOH$, m/e 284; cholesterol, $C_{27}H_{46}O$, m/e 386; H_2NNH_2, m/e 32; and aminopyridine, $C_5H_6N_2$, m/e 94. An odd number of nitrogen atoms causes $M^{\stackrel{+}{\cdot}}$ to be at an odd mass number: NH_3, m/e 17; $C_2H_5NH_2$, m/e 45; and quinoline, C_9H_7N, m/e 129. Thus if the ion of highest m/e is at an odd mass number, to be the molecular ion it must contain an odd number of nitrogen atoms.

This relationship applies to all ions, not just $M^{\stackrel{+}{\cdot}}$; thus the nitrogen rule can also be stated as follows:

An odd-electron ion will be at an even mass number if it contains an even number of nitrogen atoms. Similarly, an even-electron ion containing an even number of nitrogen atoms will appear at an odd mass number. You may find this confusing at first; until you get used to working with this, it will probably be easier to derive this from the first statement, remembering that $M^{\stackrel{+}{\cdot}}$ is an odd-electron ion.

✓*Unknown 3.1.*   Indicate whether ions of the following formulas are odd-electron or even-electron: C_2H_4, C_3H_7O, C_4H_9N, C_4H_8NO, C_7H_5ClBr, C_6H_4OS, $C_{29}F_{59}$, H_3O, and C_3H_9SiO. Which of these ions will appear at even mass numbers?

3.4   Logical Neutral Losses

There are only a limited number of neutral fragments of low mass which are commonly lost in decompositions of molecular ions. The presence of another major ion separated from the highest mass ion by an anomalous mass or elemental formula will indicate that the latter ion is not the molecular ion. Presence of an abundant (as compared to its neighboring ions) ion 5 mass units below the ion of highest m/e would have to represent the loss of five hydrogen atoms—a highly unlikely decomposition. A common small neutral fragment lost from the molecular ion is the methyl radical. For example, $C_5H_{12}^{+}$ (m/e 72) can yield $C_4H_9^{+}$ (m/e 57) by loss of $CH_3 \cdot$. However, an abundant $(M - CH_2)^{+}$ is very rare. Thus, the presence of a major ion of m/e 58 would indicate that an m/e 72 ion could not be the molecular ion even if it were at the highest mass in the spectrum. Such a mass difference of CH_2 is commonly encountered when two such homologous ions are produced by decomposition of a larger ion; for example, $C_2H_5C(CH_3)_2NH_2^{+}$ (m/e 87) gives both $C_4H_{10}N^{+}$ (m/e 72) and $C_3H_8N^{+}$ (m/e 58).

Mass losses of 4 to 14, 21 to 25, 33, 37, and 38 are highly unlikely. Common neutral fragments lost are shown in Table A-5. If the elemental composition of the fragment lost can be deduced, this gives an even more powerful test. For example, the presence of a major $(M - 15)^{+}$ ion is common but a major $(M - NH)^{+}$ is probably an anomalous ion; the loss of 35 is logical only if chlorine is present.

Can the ion of highest mass be the molecular ion if the following are the major ions of high mass in the spectrum?

Unknown 3.2. $C_{10}H_{15}O$, $C_{10}H_{14}O$, $C_9H_{12}O$, $C_{10}H_{13}$, $C_8H_{10}O$

Unknown 3.3. C_9H_{12}, C_9H_{11}, C_9H_9, C_8H_9, C_8H_7, C_7H_7

Identifying and testing the molecular ion are important keys to Unknowns 3.4 and 3.5.

3.5   Molecular Ion Abundance versus Structure

The abundance of the molecular ion, $[M^{+}]$, depends mainly on its stability and the amount of energy needed to ionize the molecule (Table A-3). Particular structural features tend to show characteristic values of these properties, so that the magnitude of $[M^{+}]$ provides an indication of the structure of the molecule. Table A-4 in the Appendix gives typical $[M^{+}]$ values for a number of types of compounds, listed in order of decreasing abundance.

Unknown 3.4

m/e	Relative abundance	m/e	Relative abundance	m/e	Relative abundance
12	2.7	36	1.9	61	100.
13	3.0	37	2.3	62	9.9
14	0.63	38	0.68	63	32.
15	0.05	47	6.5	64	0.67
24	4.0	47.5	0.22	70	0.09
25	15.	48	5.9	72	0.07
26	34.	48.5	0.19	74	0.02
27	0.75	49	4.2	95	3.0
30	0.06	49.5	0.02	96	67.
30.5	0.19	50	1.5	97	3.3
31	0.32	51	0.31	98	43.
31.5	0.06	59	2.6	99	1.2
35	7.0	60	24.	100	7.0
				101	0.16

Unknown 3.5

m/e	Relative abundance	m/e	Relative abundance
31	42.	70	0.69
32	0.47	85	100.
35	2.5	86	1.1
36	0.06	87	33.
37	0.72	88	0.35
38	0.02	100	2.8
43	0.49	101	0.07
47	1.7	119	52.
49	0.57	120	1.2
50	11.	135	24.
51	0.13	136	0.52
62	0.19	137	7.7
69	57.	138	0.16

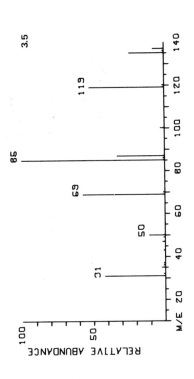

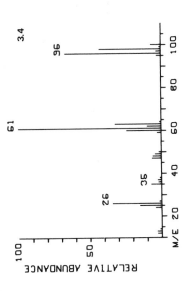

In general, the chemical stability of the molecule parallels the stability of $M^{\ddagger}$, and so is reflected in the abundance of $M^{\ddagger}$; $[M^{\ddagger}]$ usually increases with increased unsaturation and number of rings, as illustrated by the striking abundance of $M^{\ddagger}$ in strychnine (Figure 3-1). The effect of molecular weight is less clear-cut; increasing the chain length up to C_6 or C_8 generally decreases $[M^{\ddagger}]$ substantially (see Table A-4), but often $[M^{\ddagger}]$ increases again for longer straight chains. Chain-branching substantially decreases $M^{\ddagger}$ stability and thus its abundance.

If less energy is required to ionize the molecule (that is, if it has a lower ionization potential), more molecular ions of lower internal energy ("cool ions") will be formed, and $[M^{\ddagger}]$ will tend to be higher. As shown in Table A-3, the ease of ionization of the outer-shell nonbonding electrons on heteroatoms increases in going down a column or to the left in a row of the periodic table. This accounts for the dramatic increase in $[M^{\ddagger}]$ for mercaptans in comparison to the corresponding alcohols; primary amines show a smaller, though significant, increase in $[M^{\ddagger}]$ versus the corresponding alcohols. Williams (*3.5*) has utilized this effect in a technique for compounds whose mass spectra do not show a molecular ion; a recognizable $M^{\ddagger}$ peak can often be obtained by adding a functional group of low ionization potential through chemical derivatization.

3.6   Other Techniques for Molecular Weight Determination

When identification of the molecular ion is doubtful or negative, there are a number of auxiliary techniques that can be valuable.

THE $(M + 1)^+$ ION.   Raising the sample pressure in the ion source increases the probability of reactions of the ions with sample molecules before removal from the reaction chamber. Such "ion-molecule reactions" (*3.6, 3.7*) are bimolecular, so that the relative abundance of ions from such reactions increases with the sample pressure or with decreased repeller potential. (The latter is caused by the increased residence time of the ions in the ion source.)

A common ion-molecule reaction involves the abstraction of a hydrogen atom to form an ion of m/e that is one unit above the molecular weight, $(M + 1)^+$. It is fortunate that many types of compounds that give molecular ions of low abundance have a high cross section for such an ion-molecule reaction (*3.6*). Such compounds include aliphatic amines, alcohols, ethers, nitriles, sulfides, and similar compounds with heteroatom sites.

CHEMICAL IONIZATION.   Electron bombardment of methane or other gases at high pressures (1 torr) in a special ion source produces an abundance of "reagent" ions such as CH_5^+ which will react with added sample molecules through a variety of ion molecule reactions including charge exchange (*3.7*). Heteroatom-containing molecules such as those listed above can give abundant $(M + 1)^+$ ions; hydrocarbons often yield $(M - 1)^+$ ions which are also useful for molecular weight determination. Although fragmentation is greatly reduced in comparison to electron-ionization spectra, recent studies indicate that valuable structure information can be obtained for a variety of compounds (*3.8*). Of special interest is the use of the reagent gas as the carrier gas for gas chromatography (GC), so that the total GC column effluent can be introduced into the mass spectrometer without a splitter or carrier gas separator.

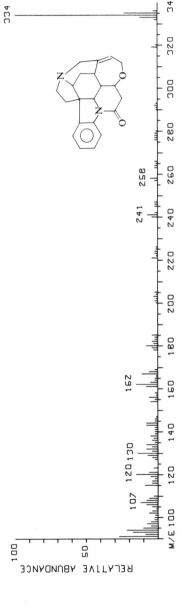

FIGURE 3-1 Mass spectrum of strychnine.

FIELD IONIZATION. The technique of "field ionization" can also produce molecular ions from compounds for which the electron impact spectra show no appreciable $M^{\ddagger}$ (*3.9*). In this technique, ionization is effected in a high field gradient between a sharp tip or edge and the entrance slit into the mass spectrometer. Apparently ionization does not take place through the usual Franck–Condon transition, but by a "tunneling" process so that the molecular ion can be formed in a lower energy state. "Field desorption" is an especially promising technique in which sample molecules adsorbed on the emitter can be ionized directly, so that spectra can be obtained from compounds of higher molecular weight and lower thermal stability (*3.9*).

LOW-ENERGY ELECTRON BOMBARDMENT. Because the molecular ion is the precursor of the other ions in the spectrum, it requires the least energy for its formation. Therefore, if the energy of the electron beam is lowered, the $M^{\ddagger}$ ion should be the last one to disappear. Note, however, that the *absolute abundance of* $M^{\ddagger}$ *is lowered by lowering the electron energy*; if $[M^{\ddagger}] = 0$ at 70 eV, reducing the electron energy will not produce a measurable $[M^{\ddagger}]$. This technique can show if a higher mass ion is due to an impurity, but if this peak is of low relative abundance at 70 eV, the test may be inconclusive. Of course the fact that a particular ion has the lowest appearance potential of any in the spectrum does not prove that this is a molecular ion—only the converse is true.

Unknown 3.6

m/e	Relative abundance	m/e	Relative abundance
12	1.9	42	1.5
13	3.4	43	3.1
14	8.3	44	4.7
15	51.	45	6.2
16	5.6	46	35.
26	1.6	47	0.17
27	6.9	48	0.15
28	6.3	59	0.06
29	8.0	60	4.0
30	100.	61	53.
31	1.4	62	0.82
32	0.53	63	0.22

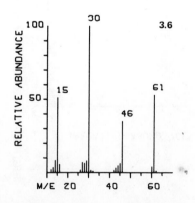

RATE OF EFFUSION. The sample flow rate out of the reservoir into the ion source is inversely proportional to the square root of the molecular weight of the compound. The measurement is most conveniently done by comparing the decay in the abundance of peaks from the unknown compound with time as compared to a reference compound measured simultaneously. The decay rate can be increased to a more convenient rate by using the small volume between the mass spectrometer isolation valve (if present) and the leak. The chief causes of error are association to give higher-molecular-weight telomers, and adsorption. For non-polar compounds, good accuracy can often be obtained (*1.1, 1.2*). This is also useful for the detection of impurities.

METASTABLE IONS. Shadoff has found metastable transitions (see Section 7.1) involving decomposition of the molecular ion in cases in which the $M^{\dagger}$ itself is not detectable in the spectrum (*3.10*). Examples cited are CCl_4, $CH_3C_6H_4NHCONH_2$, $(C_3H_7)_2C(CH_3)OH$, and $NC(CH_2)_5COOH$.

Unknown 3.7

m/e	Relative abundance	m/e	Relative abundance
35	41.	74	0.16
37	13.	82	29.
41	1.2	83	0.33
42	0.80	84	19.
43	0.15	85	0.20
47	40.	86	2.9
48	0.46	87	0.04
49	13.	117	100.
50	0.16	118	1.0
58.5	4.7	119	96.
59.5	4.5	120	1.0
60.5	1.4	121	30.
61.5	0.16	122	0.31
70	1.4	123	3.1
72	0.92	124	0.04

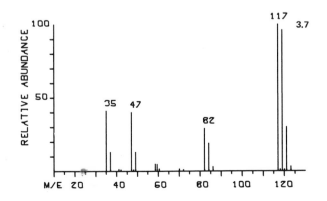

ION FRAGMENTATION MECHANISMS*

Our initial description (Chapter 1) that "the mass spectrum shows the mass of the molecule and the masses of pieces from it" is oversimplified in that it neglects the important second dimension of a mass spectrum: ion *abundance*. The use of isotopic abundances to indicate elemental compositions has already been discussed in Chapter 2; in addition, the abundance of a particular fragment ion relative to the abundances of the molecular ion and other fragment ions can be a very useful indication of the *structure of that fragment and its environment in the molecule*. However, to make use of this information it is necessary to understand the factors controlling fragment ion abundances. A preliminary, somewhat empirical, discussion of these factors will be given here; the basic processes involved in forming mass spectra will be examined in Chapter 8. It is important to emphasize, however, that there are serious limitations to our present knowledge of mass spectral reactions. To recognize for more complex molecules what alternative structural possibilities could give rise to the observed mass spectral features, it is necessary to study the spectra of closely related molecules.

The chemistry of such ion decomposition reactions can be viewed as another field of chemistry, but fortunately for most chemists studying this book, there are many close similarities to pyrolytic, photolytic, radiolytic, and other energetic reactions, and there are even many general similarities to condensed phase (solution) organic reactions. The largest points of difference are that ionic and usually radical species are involved in each reaction in the mass spectrometer, and their combined effects sometimes appear unusual to the organic chemist. Chemists may also question the reliability of structural information based on rearrangement reactions.

---

* *Important:* DO NOT bother with the details in fine print until you have mastered the main parts (larger type) of this chapter and worked the unknowns.

We shall attempt to show in this chapter that there is a strong tendency for these ion decomposition reactions to occur through chemically reasonable processes.

4.1   Types of Ion Reactions

Mass spectral reactions are *unimolecular*; the sample pressure in the ion source is kept sufficiently low that bimolecular ("ion–molecule") or other collision reactions are usually negligible. Molecular ions are formed with a wide range of internal energies. Those that are sufficiently "cool" will not decompose before collection and will appear as M^+ in the spectrum. If sufficiently excited, the M^+ ions can decompose by a variety of energy-dependent reactions, each of which results in the formation of a product ion and one or more neutral species; this primary product ion may have sufficient energy to decompose further. In the mass spectrum of ABCD the abundance of BCD^+ will depend on the average rates of its formation and decomposition, while $[BC^+]$ will depend on the relative rates of several competitive and consecutive reactions. In general, the most abundant fragment ion peaks in

$$ABCD \quad \xrightarrow{-e} \quad ABCD^+ \quad \longrightarrow \quad A^+ + BCD\cdot$$

$$\longrightarrow \quad A\cdot + BCD^+$$
$$\quad\quad \llcorner\!\!\rightarrow BC^+ + D$$

$$\longrightarrow \quad D\cdot + ABC^+$$
$$\quad\quad \llcorner\!\!\rightarrow A + BC^+$$

the mass spectrum correspond to the *most stable ion products of the most favorable reaction pathways.*

NUMBER OF BONDS CLEAVED.   Reactions involving only the cleavage of a single bond in the odd-electron (OE^+) molecular ion must produce an even-electron (EE^+) fragment ion and a neutral radical species. The two fragments compete for the charge and the unpaired electron; the

$$CH_3CH_2^+CH_3 \quad \longrightarrow \quad CH_3CH_2^+ + \cdot CH_3$$

$$\longrightarrow \quad CH_3CH_2\cdot + CH_3^+$$

abundances of the two ionic products from this type of reaction would be equal only by coincidence. We shall call these "simple cleavage reactions" to distinguish them from rearrangement and other more complex reactions.

In contrast, an OE^+ ion is formed from M^+ through reactions involving the cleavage of *two* bonds. Rearrangements and reactions involving fragmentation of a ring are two ways in which abundant $OE^{\ddag}$ ions can be produced.

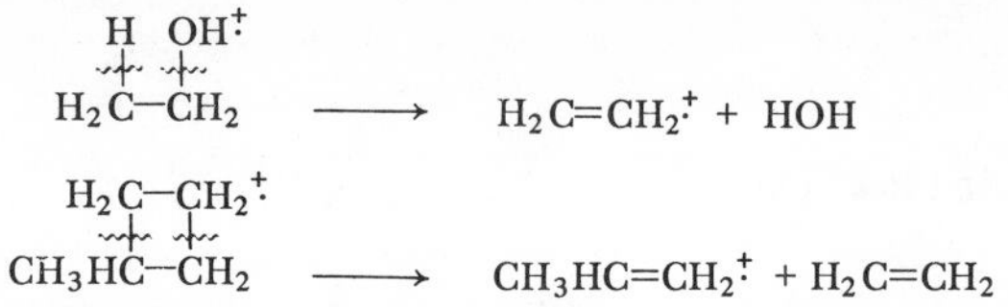

$$\underset{\substack{H \quad OH^{\ddag} \\ \cdot \cdot \cdot \cdot \\ H_2C-CH_2}}{} \longrightarrow H_2C=CH_2^{\ddag} + HOH$$

$$\underset{\substack{H_2C-CH_2^{\ddag} \\ \cdot \cdot \cdot \\ CH_3HC-CH_2}}{} \longrightarrow CH_3HC=CH_2^{\ddag} + H_2C=CH_2$$

Cleavage of three (or any odd number) of bonds of $M^{\ddag}$ produces an EE^+ ion. However,

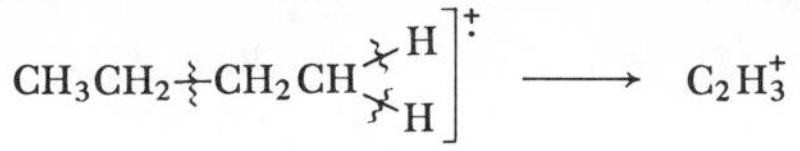

$$\left[CH_3CH_2 \overset{\cdot}{\div} CH_2 CH \overset{H}{\underset{H}{\diagdown}} \right]^{\ddag} \longrightarrow C_2H_3^+$$

cleavage of one bond of an $OE^{\ddag}$ fragment ion in which the sites of the unpaired electron and the charge are separated can yield a secondary $OE^{\ddag}$ product ion: $\cdot CH_2 CH_2 CH_2 CH_2^+ \rightarrow CH_2=CH_2 + CH_2 CH_2^{\ddag}$. In the above reactions giving $OE^{\ddag}$ ions, the first bond cleavage has the effect of separating the radical and charge sites.

The number of bonds cleaved in the decomposition of an even-electron ion does not affect the type of product ion ($OE^{\ddag}$ or EE^+) that is formed. However, formation of an $OE^{\ddag}$ ion must be accompanied by formation of a radical neutral species; this separation of an electron pair in the decomposing EE^+ ion is an energetically unfavorable process, so that in the decomposition of EE^+ ions the formation of EE^+ secondary product ions is favored.

$$
\begin{array}{llll}
CH_3CH_2CH_2^+ & \longrightarrow & CH_3^+ + CH_2=CH_2 & \text{(Favored)} \\
& \longrightarrow & CH_3\cdot + CH_2CH_2^{\ddag} & \text{(Unfavored)}
\end{array}
$$

4.2   Important Odd-Electron Fragment Ions

Because $OE^{\ddag}$ fragment ions are formed in significant abundance only through special types of decomposition, the next step in the interpretation procedure is to *indicate all important odd-electron ions* in the spectrum; it is best to mark these directly on the spectrum. In formulating possible structures for the unknown you will have to account for the presence (and absence) of these $OE^{\ddag}$ product ions; the rearrangement and ring decompositions involved in their formation are often especially characteristic of molecular structure. Odd-electron species are generally less stable than even-electron; this difference becomes less pronounced, however, as the ratio of the rings-plus-double-bonds value to the total number of bonds in the ion increases.

Important $OE^{\ddag}$ ions are even less probable in the lower mass end of the spectrum; thus abundant even-*mass* peaks in this region are usually due to ions containing an odd number of nitrogen atoms, such as CH_4N^+, m/e 30. Similar reasoning leads to a corollary of the nitrogen rule:

A scarcity of important even-mass ions, especially at lower m/e values, indicates an even-mass molecular weight. (However, the presence of abundant even-mass ions does not necessarily indicate an odd-mass $M^{\ddagger}$.) This can be seen in the mass spectrum of neopentane, molecular weight 72, which shows no molecular ion (Figure 4-1).

m/e	Relative abundance	m/e	Relative abundance
15	6.3	43	1.6
16	0.07	44	0.05
26	1.4	51	1.0
27	15.	52	0.27
28	2.4	53	1.2
29	38.	54	0.20
29.5	0.49	55	2.8
30	0.85	56	4.3
38	1.4	57	100.
39	13.	58	4.4
40	1.4	59	0.08
41	41.	71	0.04
42	2.3		

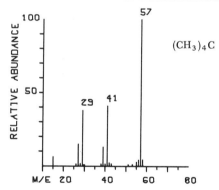

FIGURE 4-1   Mass spectrum of neopentane.

4.3   Relative Importance of Peaks in Spectral Interpretation   *- Read*

Before proceeding further it is imperative that we define the "importance" of a peak more carefully. Abundance is not the only criterion of the significance of a spectral peak; a measurable molecular ion, no matter how weak, is still the most important peak for interpretation of the spectrum. Additionally, as discussed above, odd-electron fragment ions are more important than even-electron ions which are similar in abundance and mass.

A third criterion of the significance of an ion is its relative mass position in the spectrum; its importance per unit abundance increases significantly with increasing mass. The smaller, more stable ions of low mass are mainly produced by further decompositions of the larger mass fragment ions, often through a variety of pathways. Thus, although the ions at the low mass end of the spectrum tend to be much more abundant, *the ions at higher masses are much more indicative of the molecule's arrangement of atoms.* This is particularly true of ions in the same homologous series. In the spectrum of a $C_{20}H_{42}$ saturated hydrocarbon, a $C_{16}H_{33}^+$ ion, $(M - C_4H_9)^+$, of 5% relative abundance would be much more indicative of a particular structural feature, such as a C_4H_9 group attached to a tertiary carbon atom, than a $C_4H_9^+$ ion of 100% abundance (the "base peak").

For groups of ions that differ only in their number of hydrogen atoms (*e.g.*, the group $C_4H_5^+$, $C_4H_6^+$, $C_4H_7^+$, $C_4H_8^+$ and $C_4H_9^+$, *m/e* 53–57), *the ion with the most hydrogen atoms is of by far the greatest importance* per unit of abundance. There is generally a substantial probability (dependent on ion structure) that the lower mass ions in such a group are decomposition products of the ion with the most hydrogen atoms or of its higher homologs; even-electron ion products should be expected in higher abundance from such decompositions. This rule can be illustrated by considering the importance of the following fragment ions found in three mass spectra which all exhibit $C_7H_{16}O^+$ molecular ions.

m/e	A	B	C
55	35.	40.	25.
56	15.	20.	50.
57	100.	100.	50.
58	10.	3.3	1.6
59	0.46	0.24	0.12

In *A*, the peak at *m/e* 58 is of special significance because it represents an odd-electron ion, despite its relatively low abundance in comparison to *m/e* 57. On the other hand, the odd-electron ion at *m/e* 56 is of clear significance only in *C*. The specific structural importance of *m/e* 57 (EE$^+$) in all three spectra is reduced by its relatively low mass position in the spectrum (57/116), despite this ion's high abundance.

The broad peaks from *metastable ion decompositions* can be of substantial importance, despite their very weak abundances; their significance is discussed in Section 7.1. However, *multiply charged ions* have found little application for structure determination. Probably the most useful generalization is that abundant (a few percent or more of the base peak) doubly charged ions are only found for highly stabilized molecules, such as fused-ring aromatics. Multiply charged ions are also abundant for some organometallic compounds and metals (such as mercury vapor). With an ionic charge (*e*) of 2, odd-numbered ion masses (*m*) will appear at fractional *m/e* (ending in .5); thus in most cases they are easily discernible in the spectrum. Note that the most abundant doubly charged ions do *not* necessarily correspond in formula to the major singly charged ions.

4.4   Basic Factors Influencing Ion Abundance

Detailed studies of favored fragmentation reactions have now been made for a wide variety of compounds (1.1–1.5; 4.1). These studies have led to generalizations concerning the common types of reaction which occur (1.10, 3.4, 4.2, 4.3). In the following outline an effort has been made to classify common mechanisms for a wide variety of structural types into fewer, more basic categories. Despite the danger of oversimplification, it is hoped that the student will find compensating efficiency in the learning process through postponing the consideration of exceptions until after simplified generalizations have been digested.

There appear to be three general driving forces for unimolecular ion decompositions:

STABILITY OF REACTION PRODUCTS.   Product ion abundance increases with an increase in the stability of either the ionic or the neutral reaction products, although the ion's stability is the more important influence; the fragment of lowest ionization potential (Table A-3) is favored as the ionic product. Ion stabilization through *electron sharing* of non-bonding electrons is a primary force in many reactions; for example, the stability of the even-electron oxonium ion $R-\overset{+}{C}=O \leftrightarrow R-C\equiv\overset{+}{O}$ is increased because ionization at the heteroatom creates a new bonding orbital (note that $RC\equiv\overset{+}{O}$ is isoelectronic with $RC\equiv N$). *Resonance stabilization* of the π-electrons, such as the aromaticity of the tropylium cation $C_7H_7^+$, and the *inductive effect* are also important.*

A notable exception to this rule is the widespread preference for the loss of the *largest* alkyl radical at a reactive site:

$$\underset{C_2H_5-\underset{\underset{\displaystyle +}{|}}{\overset{\overset{\displaystyle CH_3}{|}}{C}H}-C_4H_9^+}{} \to [C_2H_5\underset{+}{\overset{\overset{\displaystyle CH_3}{|}}{C}}H] > [^+CH\overset{\overset{\displaystyle CH_3}{|}}{}C_4H_9] > [C_2H_5\overset{+}{C}HC_4H_9] > [C_2H_5\overset{+}{\overset{\overset{\displaystyle CH_3}{|}}{C}}C_4H_9]$$

LABILITY OF THE BOND(S) CLEAVED AND THE STABILITY OF THE BONDS FORMED.   Bond labilities within the decomposing ion often parallel reactivities known from chemical processes in solution.* For example, the decreasing strength of the C—X bond for the halogens (X = F, Cl, Br, and I) is reflected in an increasing abundance of the cleavage product $(M - X)^+$ in haloalkane spectra. If formation of a new bond is possible, this helps to compensate for the energy required for the bond cleavage of the decomposition.

---

* Equation 8-8, Chapter 8, shows that the activation energy for the reaction $ABCD^{\ddagger} \to AB^+ + \cdot CD$ is equal to the ionization potential of $AB\cdot$ plus the dissociation energy of the $AB-CD$ bond minus the ionization potential of ABCD.

STERIC FACTORS. Kinetic effects are sometimes more important than thermodynamic effects in influencing reactions. Steric factors are of special importance in rearrangement reactions; for example, hydrogen atom rearrangements are much more prevalent than rearrangement of larger groups, and the elimination of molecules involving elements of groups ortho to each other on an aromatic ring is favored over the corresponding rearrangement in meta and para isomers.

Unknown 4.1. Predict which will be the most abundant product ion in the mass spectrum of 1-(*p*-aminophenyl)-2-phenylethane, $H_2NC_6H_4CH_2CH_2-C_6H_5$.

4.5 Reaction Initiation at Radical or Charge Sites

A system (*4.2*) of predicting preferred decomposition pathways in a wide variety of compounds is based on the simplistic assumption that the reactions are initiated at the favored sites for the unpaired electron and for the positive charge in the decomposing ion. Such a site is viewed as providing the driving force for particular types of reactions which are characteristic of the chemical nature of the site. Although it can be argued that this depiction only gives, at best, an approximation of the actual electronic displacements occurring in the reaction, it provides a convenient way to correlate (and for you to remember) a large number of the reactions of diverse structural moieties with relatively few rules. In the remainder of this chapter we shall try to establish the basic principles of this mechanistic approach; their application to the mass spectral behavior of specific functional groups will be treated in Chapter 6.

Loss of a σ-electron from a single bond should greatly weaken it, and could lead directly to fragmentation. However, if ionization arises from loss of a nonbonding or π-electron, fragmentation can occur only after some electron transfer has taken place. In inducing such transfer the radical and charge sites have basically opposite effects. There is a strong tendency for the unpaired electron to be *donated to form a new bond,* while the positive charge *attracts or polarizes adjacent electrons.* This behavior is similar to that in other chemical systems; the radical site's electron-donating ability is strongly dependent on the nature of the site, paralleling its strength as a Lewis base. It should be emphasized, however, that these are competitive effects; the relative importance of the possible mass spectral reactions will depend on the *relative* driving forces of the corresponding radical and charge sites in the precursor ion.

PROBABILITY OF IONIZATION AT A PARTICULAR SITE. The most favored radical and charge sites in the molecular ion are assumed to arise from loss of the molecule's electron of lowest ionization potential (*I*); typical *I* values are given in Table A-3. In general the *I* value of a π-bond is lower than

favored class of electron

nonbonding > conj. π > uncong. π > σ

that of a σ-bond; the I value of a conjugated π-bond system is lower than that of an unconjugated π-bond; and the I value of the non bonding (n-) electrons on a heteroatom is lower than that of a π-bond. The I values of n-electrons of heteroatoms generally decrease as the element is lower and farther left in the periodic table. The preference for radical and charge sites is comparable to the stability of the corresponding electronic state of the ion, for example:

$$H_3CCH \overset{+\cdot}{-} CH_2 > H_3C \overset{+}{C}H=CH_2 > H_3CCH=CH \overset{+}{\cdot} H$$

$$R \overset{+\cdot}{S}CH_2CH_2 \overset{..}{O}R > R \overset{..}{S}CH_2CH_2 \overset{+\cdot}{O}R > R \overset{+}{S} \overset{+}{\cdot} CH_2CH_2 \overset{..}{O}R.$$

(The symbol $\overset{+}{\cdot}$ at the end of the molecule signifies an odd-electron ion without designating the radical site. Use of either $\cdot$ or $^+$ within the molecule, as in $CH_3 \overset{+}{\cdot} CH_3$, implies localization of the radical or the charge.) These radical site preferences represent the degree of electron deficiency in the highest-occupied molecular orbital of $M^{\overset{+}{\cdot}}$. In certain cases it is also useful to visualize the sites as canonical forms of the overall resonance structure of the molecular ion in which the "preference" described above represents the relative contribution of the canonical form to the overall structure, such as:

$$R_2C=\overset{\cdot+}{\overset{..}{O}} \longleftrightarrow R_2 \overset{+}{C} - \overset{\cdot}{\overset{..}{O}}:$$

Note that this preference for a site implies that products predicted to arise from less favored sites will tend to be of lower, but not necessarily zero, abundance.

SIGMA ELECTRON IONIZATION (σ):

Alkanes: $R \overset{+}{\cdot} CR_3 \xrightarrow{\ \sigma\ } R\cdot + \overset{+}{C}R_3$

S, Si etc.: $R \overset{+}{\cdot} YR \xrightarrow{\ \sigma\ } R\cdot + \overset{+}{Y}R$

If the electron lost in ionization comes from a single bond, cleavage at this location will of course be favored. The more abundant ionized fragment will be the one better able to stabilize the positive charge. For saturated hydrocarbons such single bond ionization is the lowest energy process; this can then account for favored alkane fragmentation at carbon atoms which are more highly substituted, and which therefore should be more easily ionized. (The percentage values indicate the ion abundance relative to the base peak of the spectrum.)

$$(CH_3)_3C-CH_2CH_3 \xrightarrow{-e^-} (CH_3)_3C \overset{+}{\cdot} CH_2CH_3 \xrightarrow{\ \sigma\ } (CH_3)_3C^+ + \cdot CH_2CH_3 \quad (4\text{-}1)$$
$$100\%$$

For saturated C—Y bonds, where Y is a heteroatom, the difference between the ionization potentials of the bonding and nonbonding electrons on Y decreases going down in the periodic table; for third-row elements such as silicon, phosphorus, and sulfur, ionization of a bonding electron can be of competitive importance. Stabilization of the resulting heteroatom ion is aided by participation of the inner shell electrons.

$$C_2H_5SC_2H_5 \xrightarrow{-e^-} C_2H_5S^{\overset{+}{\cdot}}C_2H_5 \xrightarrow{\sigma} C_2H_5\cdot + \overset{+}{S}C_2H_5 \qquad (4\text{-}2)$$

$$55\% \, (C_3H_7S^+ = 100\%)$$

RADICAL SITE INITIATION (ALPHA CLEAVAGE, α):

Saturated group: $\quad R\frown CR_2\overset{\cdot +}{-}YR \xrightarrow{\alpha} R\cdot + CR_2{=}\overset{+}{Y}R$

$$\overset{+}{Y}R\frown CH_2\frown CH_2 \xrightarrow{\alpha} YR^{\overset{+}{\cdot}} + CH_2{=}CH_2$$

Unsaturated heteroatom: $\quad R\frown CR{=}\overset{\cdot +}{Y} \xrightarrow{\alpha} R\cdot + CR{\equiv}Y^+$

Alkene (allylic cleavage): $\quad R\frown CH_2\frown CH{-}\overset{\cdot +}{CH_2} \xrightarrow{\alpha} R\cdot + CH_2{=}CH{-}\overset{+}{CH_2}$

Retro-Diels-Alder (double α-cleavage):

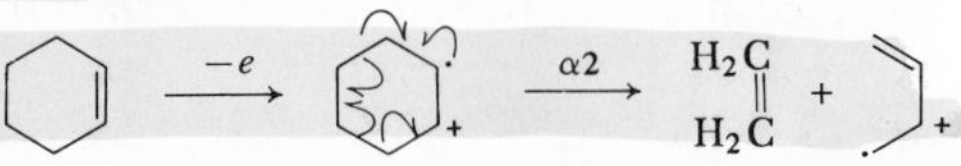

Reaction initiation at the radical site arises from its strong tendency for *electron pairing*; the odd electron is *donated to form a new bond* to an adjacent atom. This is accompanied by cleavage of another bond to that atom; thus this is commonly called the "α-cleavage reaction" (4-3). Following the

aliphatic ether

$$CH_3\frown CH_2\overset{\cdot +}{-}OC_2H_5 \xrightarrow{\alpha} CH_3\cdot + CH_2{=}\overset{+}{O}C_2H_5 \; (\leftrightarrow \overset{+}{C}H_2{-}OC_2H_5) \qquad (4\text{-}3)$$

$$50\% \, (CH_3O^+ = 100\%)$$

convention of Shannon (*3.3*) and Djerassi (*1.3*), the "fishhook" half-arrow will indicate transfer of a *single* electron; the conventional doubly barbed arrow indicates transfer of an electron pair.

The driving force is like that underlying the high reactivity of neutral radicals in reactions such as dimerization and hydrogen abstraction. The tendency for the radical site to initiate a reaction in competition with the charge site generally parallels the radical site's tendency to donate electrons: $N > S, O, \pi, R\cdot > Cl > Br > I$, where π signifies an unsaturated site and $R\cdot$ an alkyl radical. (This ordering does not mean, however, that a chlorine atom cannot initiate a radical site reaction in the absence of stronger driving forces.) The donating ability of a particular site is affected by its molecular environment; for predicting this, conventional resonance and inductive effects are generally applicable.

Ionization of an aliphatic ether (4-3) should occur preferentially by loss of an *n*-electron of the oxygen. Donation of the unpaired electron to the adjacent C—O bond is followed by transfer of an electron from another bond of this α-carbon atom. The resulting one-electron bond then cleaves to give the alkyl radical and the resonance-stabilized oxonium ion; the greater the double-bond character of the ion, the lower will be the activation energy of the reaction. Note that only the radical site moves; the charge site remains on the oxygen.

Unknown 4.2.   Predict which will be the most abundant product ion in the mass spectrum of 1-hydroxy-2-aminoethane.

α-Cleavage at the carbonyl group can be visualized similarly with formation of the stable acylium ion (4-4). A reaction initiated by an olefinic double

$$C_2H_5 \diagdown \overset{\cdot+}{\underset{C_2H_5 \diagup}{C}}=\overset{\cdot}{O} \xrightarrow{\ \alpha\ } C_2H_5\cdot + C_2H_5{-}C{\equiv}\overset{+}{O} \qquad (4\text{-}4)$$
$$100\%$$

a cylium ion (handwritten)

carbonyl group (handwritten)

bond yields an allyl ion (reaction 4-5); here the radical site can be on either atom of the double bond. (An allylic-type cleavage should be less favored at

$$CH_3{-}CH_2{\overset{\cdot+}{{-}CH{-}}}CH_2 \xrightarrow{\ \alpha\ } CH_3\cdot + CH_2{=}CH{-}\overset{+}{C}H_2\ (\leftrightarrow \overset{+}{C}H_2{-}CH{=}CH_2) \qquad (4\text{-}5)$$
$$100\%$$

allyl ion (handwritten)

olefin double bond (handwritten)

a carbonyl double bond because of poor resonance stabilization of the resulting ion, reaction 4.6.)

$$CH_3{-}CH_2{-}\overset{\cdot+}{C}(C_2H_5){-}\overset{\cdot}{O} \nrightarrow CH_3\cdot + CH_2{=}C(C_2H_5){-}\overset{+}{O} \longleftrightarrow \overset{+}{C}H_2{-}C(C_2H_5){=}O$$
$$0.5\%\ (C_3H_5O^+ = 100\%) \qquad\qquad\qquad (4\text{-}6)$$

A radical site effective for α-cleavage initiation can also be generated by ring opening or rearrangement. In cyclohexene this leads to olefin elimination in a reaction resembling a retro-Diels-Alder reaction to yield the butadiene ion (4-7). However, in this case, the reaction steps may well occur in a concerted fashion, not stepwise as shown.

ring opening (handwritten)

$$80\%\ (C_5H_7^+ = 100\%) \qquad (4\text{-}7)$$

The overwhelming driving force provided by the nitrogen atom's electron-donating ability makes the α-cleavage reaction dominant in the spectra of primary aliphatic amines: m/e 30 is the most abundant ion of RNH_2 for R = CH_3 to R = $n\text{-}C_{14}H_{29}$. The substitution of a terminal hydrogen atom in n-decane by an amine group causes the profound spectral change shown in Figure 4-2.

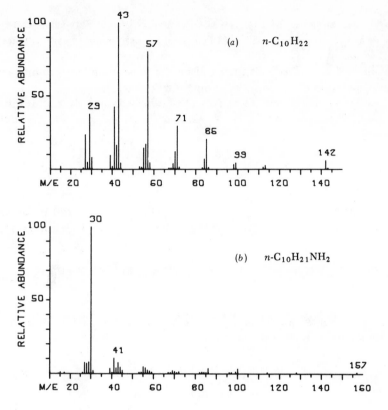

FIGURE 4-2. (a) Mass spectrum of n-decane. (b) Mass spectrum of 1-amino-n-decane.

An α-cleavage reaction can also be viewed as a consequence of the first two general reaction driving forces listed in Section 4.4. Cleavage of a bond to the adjacent carbon atom in the amine makes possible the formation of the stable immonium ion, $CH_2=\overset{+}{N}H_2$; this is favored over the carbonium ions formed in the alkane because $CH_2=\overset{+}{N}H_2$ production involves *formation of a new bond* to help compensate energetically for the one cleaved.

The importance of ion stability can be illustrated by the effect of competition of different functional groups in the same molecule. For the compounds $C_2H_5CH(OCH_3)$-$CH_2CH_2CH_2CH_2-CY-C_2H_5$, Spiteller (4.4) has reported the abundance of the $C_2H_5C=Y^+$ ion relative to that of the $C_2H_5CH=OCH_3^+$ ion in the same spectrum. He obtains the following values for various —CY— groups: —CHCl—, CHBr—, —CHI—, <1; —CHOH—, 5; —CHSH—, 5; —CO—, 50; —CH(SCH_3)—, 100; —CH(OCH_3)—, 100; —C(—OCH_2CH_2O—)— (ethylene ketal), 500; —CH(NH_2)—, 1000; and —CHN(CH_3)_2—, 2000.

In listing these driving forces it was also noted that *the loss of the largest alkyl group is favored.* A primary amine has three bonds to the α-carbon atom which can be cleaved by this reaction. In 1-amino-decane two of these bonds are to hydrogen atoms, and, following this rule, the $(M-H)^+$ is very small (0.6%). In an α-substituted primary amine such as 3-amino-3-methylhexane this mechanism (4-8) predicts characteristic peaks at m/e 72, 86, and 100

$$\underset{\underset{\overset{|}{C_2H_5}}{\overset{|}{\underset{|}{C}}}}{\overset{CH_3}{\underset{|}{C_3H_7-\overset{+\cdot}{C}-\overset{+\cdot}{N}H_2}}} \xrightarrow{\alpha}$$

$$[C_2H_5C(CH_3)=\overset{+}{N}H_2] > [C_3H_7C(CH_3)=\overset{+}{N}H_2] > [C_3H_7C(C_2H_5)=\overset{+}{N}H_2] \quad (4\text{-}8)$$

$$m/e\ 72 \qquad\qquad m/e\ 86 \qquad\qquad m/e\ 100$$

with abundances decreasing in this order. In secondary and tertiary amines obviously there is even a larger number of α-cleavage possibilities. Note that such ions fall in an homologous series $C_nH_{2n+2}N^+$ (m/e 30, 44, 58, 72, ...).

$$\underset{\underset{|}{}}{\overset{|}{-C-\overset{+\cdot}{N}H-C-}} \qquad\qquad \underset{\underset{\overset{|}{-C-}}{|}}{\overset{|}{-C-\overset{+\cdot}{N}-C-}}$$

Ions of this formula can also be formed by fragmentation of the bonds further removed from the functional group or by loss of C_nH_{2n} ($n > 1$) molecules from larger $C_nH_{2n+2}N^+$ ions.

Test your understanding of this concept with Unknowns 2.16, 4.3 through 4.7, and Figure 4-3, which are isomeric saturated amines. First write down all

Unknowns 4.1–4.7

	Relative abundance						
m/e	2.16	4-3[a]	4.3	4.4	4.5	4.6	4.7
15	3.7	3.3	0.71	0.52	3.1	1.3	1.9
27	3.3	11.	2.9	2.7	4.6	10.	0.75
28	4.1	14.	4.6	5.1	9.1	11.	4.2
29	3.6	13.9	2.2	2.2	3.6	8.1	9.1
30	6.2	73.	100.	100.	29.	13.	2.9
31	0.10	1.3	2.1	2.2	1.3	0.27	4.1
32	—	0.38	0.30	0.32	1.8	—	0.39
33	—	—	0.01	—	—	—	1.1
39	4.8	0.81	1.9	0.23	4.2	1.2	2.0
40	1.4	1.3	0.42	0.48	1.1	2.1	0.75
41	18.	3.6	2.9	2.8	7.4	4.5	9.4
42	11.	8.7	1.7	0.42	7.4	28.	6.0
43	2.7	3.2	1.2	5.8	8.8	7.2	3.1
44	0.29	29.	2.0	1.3	1.6	25.	100.
45	—	0.89	0.39	1.6	0.17	1.8	2.8
56	2.7	3.5	1.1	2.1	8.1	7.3	2.3
57	5.6	1.3	0.23	1.1	4.2	5.0	1.6
58	100.	100.	0.30	1.9	100.	100.	10.
59	3.6	3.9	0.02	0.08	3.9	3.9	0.41
71	—	0.36	0.04	0.04	0.58	1.0	0.39
72	—	19.	0.98	1.3	9.6	17.	2.3
73	0.41	31.	10.	10.	11.	23.	1.2
74	0.02	2.0	0.83	0.50	1.3	1.1	0.07

[a] Figure 4-3.

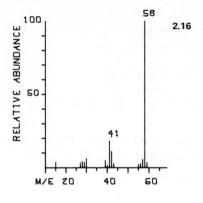

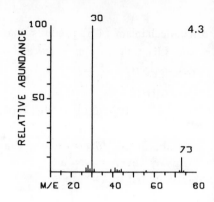

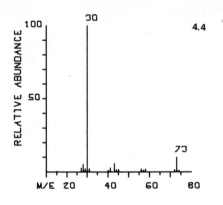

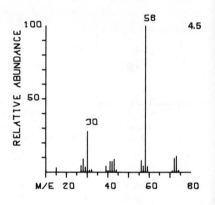

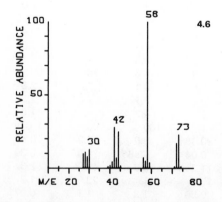

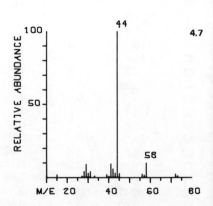

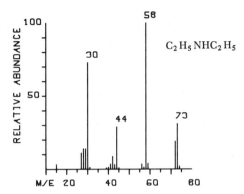

$C_2H_5NHC_2H_5$

FIGURE 4-3   Mass spectrum of diethylamine.

the possible amines of molecular weight 73. Start with the four spectra that have a base peak at m/e 58; which of your structures will show a ready loss of 15? (Thus, which have an α-methyl group?) You should have

$$(CH_3)_2\overset{\overset{\displaystyle CH_3}{|}}{C}NH_2, \quad C_2H_5\overset{\overset{\displaystyle CH_3}{|}}{C}HNH_2, \quad CH_3\overset{\overset{\displaystyle CH_3}{|}}{C}HNHCH_3, \quad CH_3CH_2NHC_2H_5, \text{ and } CH_3CH_2N(CH_3)_2$$

The spectrum of Unknown 2.16 should be familiar—it is of *tert*-butylamine, and is repeated for comparison. The mechanism for the secondary formation of m/e 30 is discussed later in the chapter; this helps to identify Figure 4-3 as the spectrum of diethylamine.

The other isomeric C_4 amines of Unknowns 4.3 through 4.7 contain the remaining three α-methylamines; yet in only two is mass 58 the base (largest) peak. Why? This should be obvious from the possible molecular structures.

To assign structures to Unknowns 4.3 through 4.7, try *predicting* the major ions in the spectra of all the isomeric C_4 alkylamines. The spectrum of one isomer is not included in these unknowns. Which one?

CHARGE SITE INITIATION (INDUCTIVE EFFECT, i):

$$OE^+: R\overset{\frown}{-}\overset{+\cdot}{Y}-R \xrightarrow{i} R^+ + \cdot YR$$

$$\underset{R}{\overset{R}{>}}C\overset{+\cdot}{=}Y \left(\longleftrightarrow \underset{R}{\overset{R}{>}}\overset{+}{C}-\ddot{Y}: \right) \xrightarrow{i} R^+ + R-\dot{C}=Y$$

$$EE^+: R\overset{\frown}{-}\overset{+}{Y}H_2 \xrightarrow{i} R^+ + YH_2$$

$$R\overset{\frown}{-}\overset{+}{Y}=CH_2 \xrightarrow{i} R^+ + Y=CH_2$$

Initiation of a cleavage reaction by the positive charge (which is generally less important than that by the radical site) involves *attraction of an electron*

attraction of electron pair

pair. The tendency for the formation of R^+ from RY is: halogens $> O, S \gg N,$ C; for elements of the same row of the periodic table this tendency parallels the inductive effect (i) of Y. Such charge site reactions will be designated with i over the arrow.

A saturated oxygen atom can thus initiate charge site as well as radical site reactions. In an aliphatic ether *attraction* of an electron pair initiated by the localized positive charge on the oxygen can form the alkyl ion and the alkoxyl radical; in this case the charge site is moved. Note that the bond cleaved

aliphatic ether

$$C_2H_5 \overset{\curvearrowright}{-} \overset{+\cdot}{O}C_2H_5 \xrightarrow{\; i \;} C_2H_5^+ + \cdot OC_2H_5 \qquad (4\text{-}9)$$
$$40\%$$

$(R'-CH_2 \not{+} OR)$ is *not* that cleaved by the radical site initiation $(R' \not{+} CH_2 - OR,$ reaction 4-3), nor is the charge retained by the heteroatom fragment as in $R - \overset{+}{\underset{\cdot\cdot}{S}} - R' \rightarrow R - S^+ + \cdot R'$ (reaction 4-2). For both *n*-alkanols and *n*-alkyl chlorides, RCH_2Y, $[(M - HY)^{+\cdot}] > [(M - Y)^+]$ (4-10); initial hydrogen trans-

n-alkyl chlorides

$$CH_3CH_2CH_2 \overset{+\overset{\curvearrowright}{\;}}{-CH_2 - \overset{\cdot\cdot}{Cl}} \xrightarrow{\; i \;} (M - HCl)^{+\cdot}, C_4H_9^+, C_3H_7^+ \qquad (4\text{-}10)$$
$$100\% \qquad 3\% \quad 30\%$$

$$(CH_3)_2CH - CH_2 \overset{+\overset{\curvearrowright}{\;}}{- \overset{\cdot\cdot}{Cl}} \xrightarrow{\; i \;} (M - HCl)^{+\cdot}, C_4H_9^+, C_3H_7^+ \qquad (4\text{-}11)$$
$$7\% \qquad 4\% \quad 100\%$$

fer to Y eliminates its radical site's tendency to strengthen the C—Y bond. The $(M - Y)^+$ ion is favored for Y = Br and I despite their lower electronegativities because of the substantial decrease in R—Br and R—I bond strengths. As is expected for an inductive effect, the influence of the charge site can affect a bond that is farther away if it has more polarizable electrons (reaction 4-11).

For even-electron ions decomposition to form another EE^+ ion and neutral molecule is favored (reaction 4-12), as discussed above. For decomposition of the primary EE^+ product of ethers this leads (reaction 4-13) to the same alkyl ion as reaction 4-9 above; for the purposes of structure elucidation the relative importance of these two pathways is immaterial.

even-electron ions

$$R \overset{\frown}{-CH_2} \overset{\curvearrowleft}{-} CH_2^+ \xrightarrow{\times} R - CH_2^+ + :CH_2$$
$$\xrightarrow{\; i \;} R^+ + CH_2 = CH_2 \qquad (4\text{-}12)$$

ethers

$$R' \overset{\frown}{-CH_2} \overset{\curvearrowright}{-} \overset{+\cdot}{O} - R \xrightarrow[\alpha]{-R' \cdot} CH_2 = \overset{+}{\overset{\frown}{O}} - R \xrightarrow{\; i \;} CH_2O + R^+ \qquad (4\text{-}13)$$

Alternative mechanisms are possible for reaction initiation by the charge site of unsaturated functional groups. Both reactions 4-14 and 4-15 predict the important alkyl ions found in ketone spectra. However, note that the reactions initiated by the radical (4-4) and charge sites (4-14, 4-15) involve

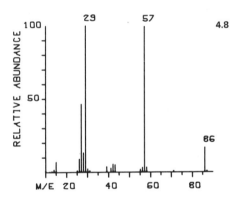

$$R' \underset{R'}{\overset{}{\diagdown}}C\overset{\cdot+}{\equiv}\ddot{O} \left(\longleftrightarrow R' \underset{R'}{\overset{}{\diagdown}}\overset{+}{C}-O\cdot \right) \xrightarrow{i} R^+ + R-\dot{C}=O \qquad (4\text{-}14)$$ *ketones*

$$R \underset{R}{\overset{}{\diagdown}}C=O \xrightarrow[\alpha]{-R'\cdot} R-\overset{+}{C}\equiv\overset{}{O} \xrightarrow{i} R^+ + CO \qquad (4\text{-}15)$$

cleavage of the same bond; *both* are α-cleavage reactions (in contrast to 4-9, which is *not* an α-cleavage). Thus aliphatic ketones would be expected to show four major ions from cleavage of the two bonds to the carbonyl group; the favored acylium ion should be the one formed through loss of the larger alkyl group, and the favored carbonium ion should be the more stable one. Unknowns 4.8 and 4.9 are the spectra of 3-pentanone and 3-methyl-2-butanone; which is which?

Unknown 4.8

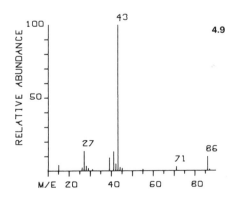

Unknown 4.9

In Unknown 4.10 the m/e 130 peak has the elemental composition $C_8H_{18}O$. Utilize the above mechanisms in elucidating the structure of this molecule. (*Hint:* The molecular ion information from Table A-4 is also valuable.)

Unknown 4.10

m/e	Relative abundance	m/e	Relative abundance
26	0.38	57	100.
27	6.1	58	4.5
28	1.6	59	2.2
29	15.	60	0.09
29.5	0.35	71	1.7
30	0.55	72	0.23
31	1.2	73	1.1
32	0.05	74	0.05
39	5.6	87	7.9
40	0.97	88	0.46
41	22.	89	0.03
42	2.9	101	0.74
43	9.8	102	0.05
44	1.0	115	0.24
45	3.6	130	2.1
46	0.10	131	0.21
55	2.3	132	0.01
56	4.8		

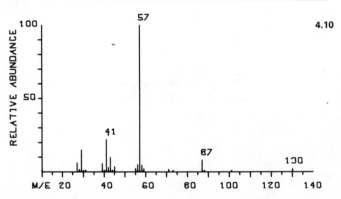

4.6   Rearrangement Reactions

As is often found in normal chemical reactions, mass spectral reactions can produce ions whose atoms have not retained the structural relationships of the original molecule. Some of these rearrangements reactions are very useful for structure elucidation; others give ambiguous structure information. It is obviously of importance to understand such reactions in interpreting mass spectra. As will be discussed in Chapter 8, kinetic as well as thermodynamic factors are important in determining the abundance of ions produced by rearrangement reactions.

Some of these rearrangements have been termed *random* because extensive molecular scrambling has occurred, or because no specific mechanism is apparent. Random rearrangements are exhibited mainly by ions whose bonds are relatively difficult to cleave and which do not have reactive radical or charge sites. Saturated hydrocarbons and polyhalocarbons are common examples; $(CH_3)_3CH$ shows a $C_2H_5^+$ ion and perfluorobenzene shows a CF_3^+ ion in their respective spectra. Hydrogen scrambling is even more common. The base peaks in the spectra of methylcyclohexane and toluene are $(M - CH_3)^+$ and $(M - H)^+$, respectively, as expected from the mechanisms cited above, yet from $C_6H_{11}CD_3$ the peaks $(M - CHD_2)^+$ and $(M - CH_2D)^+$ are larger than $(M - CD_3)^+$, and from $C_6H_5CD_3$ $(M - H)^+$ is more abundant than $(M - D)^+$. Similar effects are often observed in the mass spectra of other molecules when the electron energy is lowered to near the threshold for normal decompositions, which can increase the opportunity for isomerization.

Fortunately, many rearrangements occur through *specific* mechanisms which are now well understood, making such product ions actually valuable for structure determination. Radical and charge site initiation can also rationalize rearrangement processes; these can be viewed as an attack by the active site on another part of the ion. Steric factors can thus be of major importance, paralleling observations on intramolecular rearrangements in normal chemical reactions.

RADICAL SITE REARRANGEMENTS:

An unpaired electron can also be donated to form a new bond to an adjacent atom *through space* (4-16);* as in reaction 4-3, the second electron of this pair is supplied by transfer from the adjacent C—H bond, resulting in

$$
\begin{array}{ccc}
\text{CH}_3\text{HC}\overset{H}{\frown}\;\overset{+}{O} & & \text{CH}_3\text{HC}\cdot\;\overset{+}{O} \\
\text{H}_2\text{C}\underset{\text{H}_2}{\overset{\text{C}}{\diagdown}}\overset{\text{C}}{\diagup}\text{C}_2\text{H}_5 & \xrightarrow{r\text{H}} & \text{H}_2\text{C}\underset{\text{CH}_2}{\diagdown}\overset{\text{C}}{\diagup}\text{C}_2\text{H}_5
\end{array}\;\xrightarrow{\alpha}
$$

$$
\begin{array}{cc}
\text{CH}_3\text{HC} \\
\| \quad + \\
\text{H}_2\text{C}
\end{array}
\quad
\begin{array}{c}
\text{H}\diagdown\overset{+}{\text{O}} \\
\| \\
\cdot\text{CH}_2\diagup\overset{\text{C}}{}\diagdown\text{C}_2\text{H}_5
\end{array}
\left(
\longleftrightarrow
\begin{array}{c}
\text{H}\diagdown\overset{\cdot+}{\text{O}} \\
| \\
\text{H}_2\text{C}\diagup\overset{\text{C}}{}\diagdown\text{C}_2\text{H}_5
\end{array}
\right)
\qquad (4\text{-}16)
$$

m/e 72, 20% (m/e 57 = 100%)

its cleavage. In the aliphatic ketone shown, the 4-hydrogen atom† is transferred through a sterically favorable six-membered ring transition state. However, in this process the initial cleavage *does not result in the loss of part of the ion*, only in a change in the position of the radical site (*4.5*). The new radical site can now initiate an α-cleavage reaction resulting in fragmentation of the 2,3-carbon–carbon bond (and thus a "β-cleavage" for the carbonyl group) with loss of an olefin or other stable molecule to form the odd-electron ion; an OE‡ is formed because two bonds are cleaved to effect fragmentation in M‡ in this rearrangement reaction.

Note the concomitant *formation* of two bonds, accounting for the characteristically low activation energy of such reactions. Part of the driving force for this rearrangement is the resonance stabilization of the radical site in the product ion, which is isoelectronic with the allyl radical; note that this requires 2,3-bond cleavage in the second reaction step and thus necessitates 4-H transfer to produce the reactive intermediate.

Such hydrogen rearrangement through a six-membered ring intermediate yields *characteristic OE^{+} ions for a wide variety of unsaturated functional groups,* such as aldehydes, ketones, esters, acids, amides, carbonates, phosphates, sulfites, ketimines, oximes, hydrazones (4-17), olefins, and phenylalkanes (4-18).

$$
\begin{array}{c}
\text{CH}_3\overset{H}{\frown}\overset{\cdot+}{\underset{\diagdown}{\text{N}}}\text{-N(CH}_3)_2
\end{array}
\xrightarrow{r\text{H}}\;\xrightarrow{\alpha}\;
\begin{array}{c}
\text{CH}_3\text{---}\| \quad + \quad
\begin{array}{c}
\text{H}\diagdown\overset{+}{\text{N}}\text{-N(CH}_3)_2 \\
\| \\
\cdot
\end{array}
\end{array}
\qquad (4\text{-}17)
$$

(m/e 85 = 100%) 90%

---

* The most common type of rearrangement involves transfer of a hydrogen atom; these will be designated by "*r*H" over the arrow. Flatteringly, this has been referred to as the "McLafferty rearrangement."

† This is also commonly referred to as the γ-carbon atom. The latter nomenclature can cause confusion, however, with our definition of α-cleavage; in alkanones α-cleavage involves rupture of the 1,2-bond, *not* the α,β-bond.

$$C_2H_5 \cdots \longrightarrow C_2H_5 \cdots \xrightarrow{rH} \xrightarrow{\alpha} C_2H_5 \parallel + H \cdots$$

$$(m/e\ 91 = 100\%) \quad m/e\ 92,\ 60\%$$

$$(4\text{-}18)$$

Consecutive reactions of this type can give so-called "double hydrogen rearrangements."

$$R \cdots O \cdots C_3H_7 \xrightarrow{rH} \xrightarrow{\alpha} R \parallel + \overset{+}{HO} \cdots C_3H_7 \equiv \xrightarrow{rH} \xrightarrow{\alpha}$$

$$\overset{+}{HO} \underset{H_3C}{\diagdown} + \underset{H_2C}{\diagdown}^{CH_2} \qquad (4\text{-}19)$$

Unknown 4.11. What is the mass of the characteristic OE^{+} ion (or ions) which will be formed by this six-membered ring H rearrangement from each of the following M^{+}:

$$CH_3CH_2CH_2CH(C_2H_5)\overset{O}{\overset{\parallel}{C}}NH_2^{+}, \quad CH_3CH_2CH_2C(CH_3)=CH_2^{+}, \quad CH_3CH_2CH_2\overset{O}{\overset{\parallel}{C}}OCH_2CH_3^{+},$$

$C_2H_5OCH_2C_6H_5^{+}$, and $CH_3CH_2O\overset{O}{\overset{\parallel}{C}}OCH_2CH_3^{+}$? Draw out the mechanism, complete with "fishhooks," for each.

Unknowns 4.12 and 4.13 are the spectra of 3- and 4-methyl-2-pentanone; which is which? Does an odd-electron fragment ion aid in the solution of Unknown 4.14?

Unknown 4.12

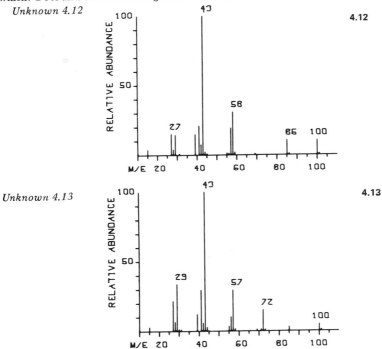

Unknown 4.14

m/e	Relative abundance	m/e	Relative abundance
15	0.34	63.5	0.05
26	1.2	64	1.0
27	11.	65	10.
28	1.1	66	0.74
29	3.9	67	0.07
30	0.09	76	0.62
38	1.2	77	5.9
39	10.	78	6.2
39.1 m	0.17	79	2.7
40	0.91	80	0.24
41	5.3	88.0 m	0.18
42	0.40	89	1.7
43	2.7	90.0 m	1.7
44	0.15	91	100.
44.5	0.02	92	55.
46.4 m	0.21	93	3.9
50	2.7	94	0.14
51	7.4	103	2.0
51.5	0.07	104	1.4
52	1.9	105	8.5
53	1.1	106	0.78
54	0.14	115	1.0
55	0.50	116	0.31
56	0.51	117	0.68
56.5	0.02	118	0.12
57	0.17	119	0.85
57.5	0.63	120	0.08
58	0.27	133	0.09
58.5	0.08	134	24.
59.4 m	0.05	135	2.6
63	3.3	136	0.12

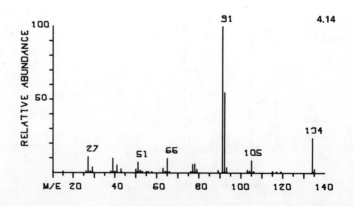

Such radical site rearrangements are also initiated by related structural moieties (reactions 4-20 to 4-24). The initial hydrogen transfer can occur through a smaller-ring

$$\xrightarrow{rH} \qquad \xrightarrow{\alpha} \quad \| \;+\; \tag{4-20}$$

$$\xrightarrow{rH} \quad \xrightarrow{\alpha} \quad H_2C=CH_2 + H{-}\overset{+\cdot}{S}{-}C_2H_5 \tag{4-21}$$
$$50\%$$

$$\xrightarrow{rH} \quad \xrightarrow{\alpha} \quad H_2C=C=O + H_2\overset{+\cdot}{N}C_4H_9 \tag{4-22}$$
$$20\%$$

$$\xrightarrow{\alpha} \quad \xrightarrow{rH} \quad \xrightarrow{\alpha} \quad HC \;+\; \begin{matrix} CH_3 \\ | \\ \cdot CH_2 \end{matrix} \tag{4-23}$$
$$100\%$$

$$\underset{rH}{\overset{rH}{\rightleftharpoons}} \qquad \xrightarrow{rH}$$

$$\xrightarrow{\alpha} \qquad + \tag{4-24}$$
$$(m/e\ 74 = 100\%) \qquad m/e\ 87,\,76\%$$

intermediate (reactions 4-21 to 4-23) if initiated by radical sites on saturated atoms. (An even-electron ion is formed from the cyclic ketone because three bonds of $M^{\dot{+}}$ are cleaved in the decomposition.) Rearrangement through seven- and eight-membered ring intermediates actually compete with reaction 4-16 for compounds with polar unsaturated functionalities. Stenhagen and Spiteller and their co-workers (*4.6*) have shown with deuterium labeling that 3,4-bond cleavage can proceed through a "reciprocal hydrogen rearrangement" (reaction 4-24) involving initial transfer of a 6- or 5-H. The preference observed for the former may be due to the fact that the second step (a six-membered ring transition state) competes more favorably with the reversal of the first step.

Increased lability of the hydrogen atom increases its tendency to rearrange. Transfer of a secondary hydrogen atom is favored over a primary one, and a tertiary hydrogen over a secondary. Transfer of a hydrogen atom is also favored from an atom adjacent to an unsaturated group (for example, an allylic hydrogen as in the second step of reaction 4-24), a positive charge site, or a heteroatom (for example, a hydroxyl hydrogen).

Note that for the unsaturated functional groups this rearrangement causes β-cleavage; the bond broken is further removed from the functional group than that broken in α-cleavage (although not for C=C double bonds, reactions 4-5 and 4-18). This rearrangement is thus a valuable means of identifying a 2-substituent, as you saw in Unknowns 4.12 and 4.13. Hydrogen rearrangement to a saturated heteroatom (reactions 4-21 and 4-22) results in rupture of a bond *to the heteroatom*, again a different bond than that ruptured by α-cleavage.

The radical site mechanism is supported by the similarity of this reaction to the photochemical "Norrish type 2" rearrangement. In a variety of cases this mass spectral rearrangement has also been shown to be a stepwise, not a concerted, reaction (*4.5*). The initial H-transfer step must compete with other possible decompositions of the precursor; the H-isomerized product must have a decomposition pathway that is more favorable than reverse isomerization back to the original precursor.

CHARGE MIGRATION.   After the initial hydrogen rearrangement step, other competitive reactions may also be possible. Thus a second step involving charge site initiation can be used to rationalize the concurrent formation of the ionized olefin product; the abundances of these competing (reaction 4-16 versus 4-25)* ion products generally reflect their relative

m/e 58, 5%

m/e 104, 100%

ionization potentials (see Table A-3). For example, the spectrum of $C_3H_7COOC_2H_5$ shows $[C_3H_7COOH^{+}] \gg [C_2H_4^{+}]$, while $C_3H_7COOC_3H_7$ and $C_3H_7COOCH(CH_3)_2$ show $[C_3H_6^{+}] > [C_3H_7COOH^{+}]$. An analogous reaction (4-26) at a saturated functional group Y, such as hydroxyl, accounts for common OE^{+} ion products formed through elimination of a stable molecule HY, or of HY and an olefin. In the intermediate species attraction of an electron pair can cause rupture of this single bond (in contrast to the behavior of the more stable double bond in 4-16) with transfer of the charge

* Hydrogen rearrangement to the phenyl ring also takes place; the corresponding m/e 92 and 70 peaks have abundances of 3% and 1%, respectively (*4.7*).

site. For groups containing a more electronegative element such as oxygen, charge retention requires a charge-stabilizing group on that element (reaction 4-21).

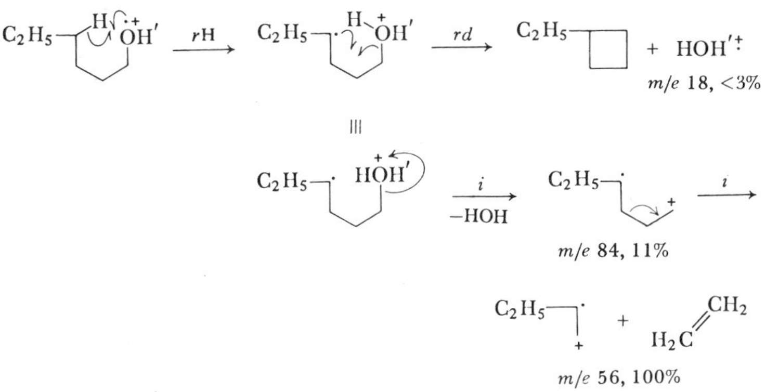

C_2H_5 ⟶ rH ⟶ C_2H_5 ⟶ rd ⟶ C_2H_5 ☐ + HOH$\cdot^+$ Charge retention (see 4-21)
m/e 18, <3%

|||

C_2H_5 · HOH
$\xrightarrow{i}$
$-HOH$
C_2H_5 ⟶ $\xrightarrow{i}$
m/e 84, 11%

C_2H_5 · + H_2C=CH_2 Charge migration (4-26)
m/e 56, 100%

1-Chloro- and 1-fluoroalkanes show prominent $(M - HX)^+$ as well as $(M - X)^+$ ions (4-27). In the so-called "ortho effect" this type of rearrangement can serve to characterize the ortho isomer for a variety of structures, such as that of reaction 4-28.

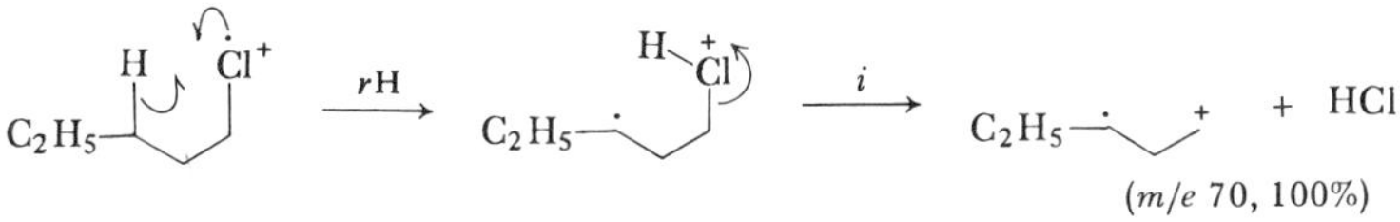

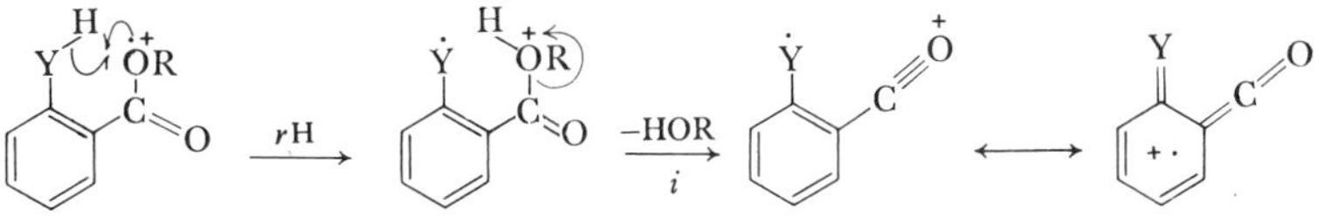

C_2H_5 H Cl$^+$ $\xrightarrow{rH}$ C_2H_5 · $\xrightarrow{i}$ C_2H_5 · + HCl   (4-27)
$(m/e\ 70, 100\%)$

Y OR $\xrightarrow{rH}$ Y OR $\xrightarrow{-HOR}{i}$ Y C≡O ⟷ Y C=O   (4-28)

YH = CH_3, OH, NH_2, OCH_3, CH_2OH

Reaction 4-25, like 4-16, often exhibits a marked specificity for H transfer through a six-membered ring transition state. This is not true of most reactions with a saturated ring transition state, such as 4-21, 4-26, and 4-27. Labeling shows that the transition state of HY loss from $n\text{-}C_5H_{11}Y^{\cdot+}$ varies with Y, but involves mainly five- and six-membered rings; some of these reactions even show stereospecificity (4.8). However, for structural elucidation purposes it is important to note that such reactions are often significant when only a four-membered ring can be formed, such as the $(M - H_2O)^{\cdot+}$ ion in ethanol.

CYCLIZATION–DISPLACEMENT REACTIONS. Rearrangement of other than hydrogen atoms apparently can also be initiated by the radical site. Cyclization to form a divalent chloronium ion with displacement of an alkyl group accounts for the largest peak

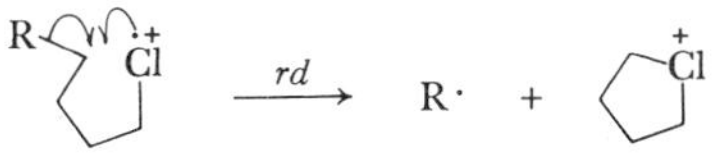

R Cl $\xrightarrow{rd}$ R· + ☐Cl   (4-29)

in the spectra of a number of n-alkyl chlorides; despite the poor electron-donating ability of chlorine, this pathway apparently is favored because formation of the new C—Cl bond can compensate for the energy required for R—C bond dissociation. In the spectrum of 2-bromoethylbenzene (*4.9*), such "anchimeric assistance" has been used also to explain the unusual abundance of $(M - Br)^+$; this ion presumably is formed through cyclization to produce the phenonium ion with displacement of bromine.

Steric requirements are less critical than for the 4-H rearrangement (reaction 4-16) and vary for the functional groups undergoing such cyclization rearrangement. The $C_nH_{2n}Y^+$ ions formed from n-alkyl chlorides, bromides, thiols, and ketones in reactions like 4-29 show maximum abundances at $n = 4$; from primary amines at $n = 5$; and from nitriles at $n = 5$ to 7. In the spectrum of 1-aminodecane, Figure 4-2*b*, this cyclization displacement reaction can thus account for the small but important peaks at m/e 72, 86, and 100. Stabilization of the radical site in the neutral product may also aid this reaction; this could account for the significant $(M - \cdot CH_2COOCH_3)^+$ peak in the spectra of methyl ω-amino-alkanoates. Such reactions are particularly important at low ionizing-electron energies and in metastable transitions (*4.10*).

Note that this is a concerted reaction cleaving a single bond to give an EE^+ ion, in contrast to the hydrogen rearrangement above. However, in unsaturated systems cleavage does not necessarily accompany cyclization, although bonds may be formed and broken at the same atom, as in reaction 4-30 (*4.11*). There are even cases which appear to be

$$\text{(4-30)}$$

cyclization-displacement reactions in which the charge site provides the reaction driving force (4-31) (*4.12*).

$$\text{(4-31)}$$

CYCLIZATION-ELIMINATION REACTIONS.   A variety of rearrangements can take place through the elimination of a stable, usually small, neutral moiety. These are more common for compounds containing unsaturated (especially aromatic) functionalities and for heteroatoms, especially those from below the second row of the periodic table, such as silicon and sulfur. Most of these can be viewed as a rearrangement of a group to either a radical or a charge site. Examples are given in Table 4-1 for common types of groups which are eliminated.

The elimination of a *saturated* molecule from any ion (except from some saturated ions formed by rearrangement) involves the rearrangement of a group to the neutral moiety. Elimination of a molecule of ethylene from a cyclohexane ion can be accomplished by the movement of only electrons, but the loss of a molecule of ethane from cyclohexane (or any other molecule) must be accomplished by the rearrangement of one or more atoms to the ejected neutral species, for example, $H-R-C_2H_5^+ \rightarrow R^+ + C_2H_6$. Small molecules that are eliminated easily are mainly limited to those containing an electronegative atom, such as HCl, H_2O, and H_2S (described above); abundant ions are generally not produced from

TABLE 4-1   *Examples of Other Rearrangement Reactions*

Neutral m/e	Eliminated Formula	Molecule (R = alkyl, Ar = aryl)
15	$CH_3\cdot$	$ArCH=CHAr$
18	H_2O	$C_{10}H_{21}OC_{10}H_{21}$
28	CO	$ROCOR$, $RCCH_2COR$, $ArOH$, $ArCAr$, $ArOAr$, $ArCCl$ (with C=O groups)
	N_2	$ArN=NAr$
	C_2H_4	$C_6H_5CH_2CH_2CH_2Br$
29	$CHO\cdot$	C_6H_5COH, $C_6H_5CH-CHC_6H_5$ (epoxide)
30	$NO\cdot$	$ArNO_2$
	CH_2O	$ROCH_2OR$, $C_3H_7-CH_2O-CC_2H_5$, $CH_3CCH_2OSO_2CH_3$
31	$CF\cdot$	$CHF=CFBr$, $CF_2=CFCl$
32-4	S, $\cdot SH$, SH_2	RSR, $RSAr$, $ArSAr$, $RSSR$
41	CH_3CN	$C_6H_5C(CH_3)=N-OH$,
43	HNCO	$ROCNHR$ (with C=O)
	$C_3^*H_7\cdot$	$C_{14}H_{29}(C^*H_2)_3COCH_3$, $R(C^*H_2)_3R$
44	CS	$ArSAr$
	CO_2	$R\underset{}{\overset{O}{C}}O$, $ROCOR$, $ROCSR$, $ArCOC(CH_3)_3$, $ArOCC(CH_3)_3$,
		phthalimide-NR
	C_2H_4O	$C_2H_5-CH(CH_3)O-CR$ (with C=O)
45	$HCO_2\cdot$	$ROCCH=CHCOR$, $C_6H_5OCCH_2C_6H_5$
50	CF_2	$C_6H_5CF_3$
54	C_4H_6	$HO-\!\!\bigcirc\!\!=O$
60	COS	$RSCOR$
	C_2H_4S	$C_2H_5-CH_2CH_2S-CR$ (with C=O)
64	SO_2	RSO_2R, $ArSO_2OR$
69	$C_5H_9\cdot$	$HO-\!\!\bigcirc\!\!-OH$, $HO-\!\!\bigcirc\!\!-OH$
98	H_3PO_4	$(ArO)_3P=O$

odd-electron ions by the loss of H_2, CH_4, and C_2H_6. The mechanism given above for the loss of H_2O, HCl, and similar heteroatom-containing molecules would predict this, as there is no site for formation of a new bond on an alkyl group. Long-chain branched alkanes are an apparent exception, the mass spectra of $R-CHR'R''$ showing $(M - RH)^{\ddagger}$ as well as $(M - R)^{+}$.

   CHARGE SITE REARRANGEMENTS.   Although they are often difficult to observe experimentally, isomerizations of even-electron ions involving hydrogen rearrangement to the charge site are probably common, such as $CH_3CH_2CH_2^+ \rightarrow CH_3C^+HCH_3$ and $CH_3CH(OH)CH_2^+ \rightarrow (CH_3)_2C=\overset{+}{O}H$ (*4.16*). These reactions generally lead to more stable ions and can involve transition states of several ring sizes.

   There are isolated examples of mass spectral reactions that appear to involve rearrangements of other than hydrogen atoms to charge sites. Methyl migration to a charge site, such as reaction 4-32, is analogous to the known behavior of carbonium ions in solution. Some

(4-32)

of the reactions of Table 4-1 could also involve charge site initiation; however, the requirements for this are poorly understood. For example, the rearrangement observed in the mass spectrum of 4,4,5-trimethyl-Δ^2-cyclohexenone (reaction 4-32) is virtually absent in that of 4,4-dimethyl-Δ^2-cyclohexenone (*4.13*).

EVEN-ELECTRON ION REARRANGEMENT AT AN "INCIPIENT RADICAL SITE"

   The decomposition of an even-electron ion to produce another even-electron ion and a stable molecule can also be accomplished through hydrogen rearrangement. In the two most common types of this reaction the hydrogen rearranges either to an unsaturated center containing a heteroatom to eject a C_nH_{2n} or similar molecule, or to a saturated heteroatom (Y) to eject a saturated molecule containing the heteroatom (HY, HYR).

   Even-electron ions ostensibly contain no radical site. However, in these rearrangements the charge site does *not* appear to provide the driving force; many of these reactions exhibit a striking similarity to rearrangements initiated by the radical site. For example, reactions 4-16 and 4-33 (*4.14*) both

(4-33)

involve only 4-H migration. We shall view these rearrangements, even those at a charge site, as caused by *incipient radical site initiation*, in which the donated electron is unpaired in an excited state, analogous to photochemical reactions of neutral molecules. However, *the decompositions of even-electron ions are poorly understood and should be used with caution for structure determination.*

There are several ways in which these rearrangements differ from the charge-site reactions described above. The charge site of an EE^+ product ion should already be favorably located for ion stability; apparently the high activation energy necessary to move the charge site in an EE^+ ion thus makes radical site reactions requiring the unpairing (or at least polarization) of electrons competitively favorable. (Such unpairing must take place in the loss of a radical from an even-electron ion, which, although rare, can occur in special cases such as the formation of the abundant $C_6H_4^+$ ion in the spectrum of *p*-dinitro-benzene.) Rearrangements appear to be initiated by unpairing of either *n*- or π-electrons; it might be expected that the influence of structure on the tendency for this would parallel the structural effects on ionization potentials.

Rearrangement reactions of EE^+ are commonly initiated at *the site of an unsaturated functionality*, a site which often was not present in the molecular ion. These resemble the C=C induced reactions in $OE^{\ddagger}$ ions, such as the retro-Diels-Alder reaction and specific rearrangements, which produce small stable unsaturated molecules as the neutral product. Paralleling the radical site rearrangements, if the double bond is in the ring of the cyclic transition state involved in rearranging the hydrogen atom, a six-membered ring is commonly the minimum requirement. Only a four-membered ring is necessary if the double bond is exocyclic, although larger ring sizes may be favored when they are possible. For the new double bond in an EE^+ "onium" ion this gives four general types of rearrangement that must be considered (reactions 4-34 to 4-37). A variety of other

$$(4\text{-}34)$$

$$(4\text{-}35)$$

$$(4\text{-}36)$$

$$(4\text{-}37)$$

reactions appear to be possible, at least for oxygen-containing ions. For example, four isomeric $C_3H_7O^+$ ions show favored loss of C_2H_4 to yield CH_3O^+. For $CH_3CH_2\overset{+}{O}=CH_2$ and $CH_3CH_2CH=\overset{+}{O}H$ this should be due to reactions 4-36 and 4-37, respectively; for $(CH_3)_2C=\overset{+}{O}H$ and $CH_3CH=\overset{+}{O}CH_3$ the rearrangements involved are more complex (*4.15*, *4.16*). The even-electron ion $HCO\overset{+}{O}=CHR$ found in formate mass spectra also appears to be a special case; loss of the stable molecule CO yields an analogous hydrogen rearrangement involving a three-membered ring intermediate.

Driving forces for these reactions include the loss of larger C_nH_{2n} molecules, the lability of the hydrogen atom rearranged, and the stability of the product ion. For example, reaction 4-34 is less favorable for alcohols because of the tendency for the intermediate $R'\overset{\cdot}{C}HCH_2CH_2\overset{+}{C}HOH_2$ to dehydrate. In contrast to the $OE^{+\cdot}$ rearrangements such as 4-16, 4-21, and 4-22, these may be concerted reactions; if they were stepwise, the intermediate would be a diradical. The limited labeling data available indicate source specificity of the migrating hydrogen atom in particular cases for reactions 4-34–4-36. For metastable ion decompositions Williams and co-workers (*4.17*) find that $CH_3CD_2\overset{+}{N}H=CH_2$ specifically loses $C_2H_2D_2$ (reaction 4-36), but that $CH_3CD_2CH=\overset{+}{N}H_2$ (reaction 4-37) and $CD_3C(CH_3)=\overset{+}{N}H_2$ undergo complete H/D scrambling in the loss of ethylene.

Characteristic reactions of aliphatic amines and esters deserve special mention, as in these cases such rearrangement (4-36) provides reliable and valuable evidence of structure. This reaction gives the second-largest peak in the spectrum of diethylamine, Figure 4-3 (reaction 4-38). The transition state

$$CH_3CH_2\overset{+}{N}H\overset{\frown}{-}CH_2-CH_3 \xrightarrow{-CH_3\cdot} \overset{H}{\underset{H_2C-CH_2}{\overset{\overset{+}{N}H=CH_2}{|}}} \xrightarrow{rH} H_2C=CH_2 + H_2\overset{+}{N}=CH_2$$

$$(4\text{-}38)$$

size requires an ethyl or larger group on the nitrogen for this rearrangement. Reaction 4-34 has been observed for longer-chain amines; reactions 4-35 and 4-37 do not appear to be competitive in amine spectra.

Unknown 4.15.   Predict the principal peaks in the mass spectrum of N-methyl-N-isopropyl-N-*n*-butylamine (*1.3*).

Rearrangement of two hydrogen atoms (sometimes called the "McLafferty + 1" rearrangement) is a characteristic decomposition of esters and similar functional groups that can be rationalized (reaction 4-39) using a

$$(4\text{-}39)$$

transfer of the second hydrogen by a mechanism analogous to reaction 4-36. An added driving force is the resonance stabilization of the EE^+ product ion (three bonds are cleaved in the reaction).

$[R'C(OH)_2^+]/[R'CO(OH)^+]$ is increased for propyl and higher esters, as cyclopropyl or allylic stabilization of the resulting neutral radical is possible ($R\dot{C}HCH=CH_2 \leftrightarrow RCH=CH-\dot{C}H_2$). However, $[RCH=CH_2^+]/[R'CO(OH)^+]$ also increases for higher esters, and in general $[RCH=CH_2^+] > [R'C(OH)_2^+]$. This rearrangement is characteristic of related functional groups such as thioesters, amides, and phosphates, and two hydrogens can migrate similarly even in the M^+ reactions of longer chain acids, methyl esters, primary amides, sulfides, and ketones (reaction 4-40; compare with reactions 4-24 and 4-26) (1.3).

$$(4\text{-}40)$$

Kinstle and co-workers have reported (4.18) a siliconium ion rearrangement that is highly specific (reaction 4-41). It thus appears more analogous to reactions 4-21 and 4-36, and less

$$(4\text{-}41)$$

analogous to the behavior of the corresponding carbonium ion.

One of the above mechanisms should help in the elucidation of Unknown 4.16.

Unknown 4.16

m/e	Relative abundance	m/e	Relative abundance
15	0.21	80	0.34
27	3.6	104	0.67
28	2.5	105	100.
29	5.1	106	8.3
39	2.4	107	0.49
40	0.33	120	0.20
41	6.0	121	0.28
42	0.34	122	17.
43	0.87	123	68.
50	3.0	124	5.3
51	1.1	125	0.45
52	0.77	134	0.21
55	2.7	135	1.3
56	19.	136	0.44
57	1.5	149	0.34
63	0.19	161	0.52
65	0.40	163	0.34
76	2.0	178	2.0
77	37.	179	0.26
78	3.0	180	0.02
79	5.1		

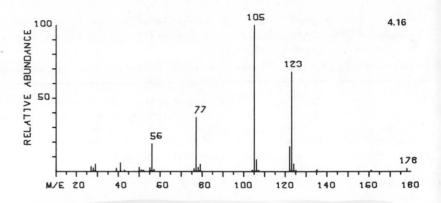

4.16

REARRANGEMENTS AT INCIPIENT RADICAL SITES OF SATURATED HETEROATOMS

$$M^{\ddot{+}} \xrightarrow{-X\cdot} \left(R - \begin{matrix} H \\ \diagdown \\ (CH_2)_n \end{matrix} \ddot{Y}R \right)^{+} \xrightarrow{rH} H\ddot{Y}R + \left(R \diagup (CH_2)_n \right)^{+}$$

The loss of small molecules containing a heteroatom, such as H_2O, HCN, or HX, is common from even-electron ions. For structure determination this reaction is probably of greatest importance for compounds containing multiple functionalities. For example, the base peak of 1,1-dichlorobutane (m/e 55, Figure 4-4) arises from $(M - Cl - HCl)^{+}$ and, possibly, $(M - HCl - Cl)^{+}$.

$$\begin{matrix} CH_3 \\ | \\ Cl-CHCH_2CH_2Cl \end{matrix} \xrightarrow[i]{-Cl\cdot} CH_3\overset{+}{CH}-\begin{matrix} H & \ddot{Cl} \\ | & | \\ CH-CH_2 \end{matrix} \xrightarrow{rH} CH_3\overset{+}{CH}CH=CH_2 + HCl \quad (4\text{-}42)$$

$n\text{-}C_3H_7CHCl_2$

FIGURE 4-4   Mass spectrum of 1,1-dichlorobutane.

This incipient radical site reaction also appears to parallel closely its radical site counterpart (see equations 4-26 and 4-27), except for a reduced probability and specificity. The product ion abundance for the loss of HY is approximately in the order Y = halogens, $CN > SH$, OH, SZ, $OZ > NH_2$, CH_3, H. The abundance is usually reduced when Z is an electron-donating group such as alkyl, but the abundance is favored if Z is an electron-attracting group such as acyl (for example, the loss of CH_3COOH from acetoxy EE^+ ions).

Deuterium labeling indicates that the transition state of such reactions can have a wide variety of ring sizes. For the dihalo-*n*-butanes the value of $[(M - HY_2)^+]$ is little affected by the position of substitution (reaction 4-42). Loss of NH_3 usually requires special activation, such as the substitution of alkyl or aryl groups on the β-carbon atom, although this is the most common decomposition pathway for the $CH_3CH_2CH=NH_2$ ion (*4.17*). The losses of H_2 and CH_4 (which must use bonding electrons as the incipient radical site) are usually important only from smaller ions, but the possibility of this occurrence needs to be recognized to avoid assigning peaks from such reactions to other, more structurally significant, sources.

For functional groups of intermediate electronegativity and electron-donating ability, such as SH, SR, OH, and OR, this reaction (4-43) should occur in competition with the rearrangements 4-34 through 4-37 in which the charge site remains on the heteroatom.

$$RCH_2(CH_2)_n CH=Y + {}^+CHR'CH_3 \quad (4\text{-}14)$$

$$\xrightarrow[(n=2)]{rH} RCH=CH_2 + CH_2=CH\dot{Y}HCHR'CH_3 \quad (4\text{-}34)$$

$$\xrightarrow{rH} RH_2C(CH_2)_n CH=\overset{+}{Y}H + CHR'=CH_2 \quad (4\text{-}36)$$

$$\xrightarrow{rH} RHC{-\!-\!-}\overset{+}{CH} + HYCHR'CH_3 \quad (4\text{-}43)$$

Reaction 4-14 can also compete, and should be favored by ion stabilizing groups on the $CHR'CH_3$ moiety and ion destabilizing groups on the rest of the precursor. Other examples are shown in reactions 4-44 and 4-45.

$$H_2\overset{+}{N}=CHCH=CH_2 + HSCH_3 \quad (4\text{-}44)$$

$$\xrightarrow{rH} CH_4 + HC\equiv\overset{+}{O} \quad (4\text{-}45)$$

The migration of a large group which results in the elimination of a stable molecule ("*re*") has been observed in EE^+ as well as $OE^{\ddagger}$ ions (see Table 4-1). Examples of such EE^+

$$(CH_3)_3 Si \quad O=Si(CH_3)_2 \xrightarrow{re} O\overbrace{\hspace{2em}}^{(CH_2)_n}CH_2 + (CH_3)_3 SiO=Si(CH_3)_2 \quad (4\text{-}46)$$

$$CH_3O\,CH=\overset{+}{O}CH_3 \xrightarrow{re} CH_2=CHOCH_3 + CH_3O-CH=\overset{+}{O}CH_3 \quad (4\text{-}47)$$
$$H_2C-CHOCH_3$$

$$\xrightarrow{re} (CH_3\overset{O}{\overset{\|}{C}})_3 O^+ \quad (4\text{-}48)$$

ion rearrangements are shown in reactions 4-46 to 4-48; the trimethylsilyl and methoxy (*4.19*) groups are among the most common which tend to undergo such rearrangement.

4.7 Summary of Types of Reaction Mechanisms

The following is intended to underscore the relationships of the common types of reactions which ions can undergo, using examples from Sections 4.5 and 4.6. You should use this as a checklist when you are attempting to predict the spectrum of a molecule; to use it effectively, however, you will have to understand the material of the preceding section and go to the original literature for details.

R indicates an alkyl group, but this could also contain another functionality; if a species contains more than one R group, these are not necessarily identical. Y indicates a heteroatom functionality, but it is not limited to the valence indicated (thus "YR" might actually be a chlorine atom). ∪ indicates a saturated connecting chain of two or more atoms; ▽ indicates a stable cyclic or unsaturated molecule. In reactions in which an alkyl group is lost, the loss of the largest is generally favored.

Sigma Electron Ionization (σ):

			See equations
Alkanes: R^+CR_3	$\xrightarrow{\sigma}$	$R\cdot + \overset{+}{C}R_3$	4-1
S, Si, etc.: R^+YR	$\xrightarrow{\sigma}$	$R\cdot + \overset{+}{Y}R$	4-2

Charge site initiation (inductive effect, i): Halogens $> O$, $S \gg N$, C. Attracts electron pair, cleaves bond, moves + site; formation of most stable R^+ favored; less important than radical site initiation.

$$OE^+: \; R-\overset{\cdot+}{Y}-R \xrightarrow{\;i\;} R^+ + \cdot YR \qquad\qquad 4\text{-}9$$

$$EE^+: \; R-\overset{+}{Y}H_2 \xrightarrow{\;i\;} R^+ + YH_2 \qquad\qquad 4\text{-}12,\; 4\text{-}25\text{-}4\text{-}27$$

$$\cdot R-\overset{+}{Y}=CH_2 \xrightarrow{\;i\;} R^+ + Y=CH_2 \qquad\qquad 4\text{-}13,\; 4\text{-}15$$

Radical site initiation (alpha cleavage, α): $N > S,\, O,\, \pi,\, R\cdot > Cl > Br > I$. Donates an electron, forms a new bond to an adjacent atom concomitant with cleavage of a bond to that atom, moves radical site; loss of largest R group favored.

Saturated group:
$$R-CR_2-\overset{\cdot+}{Y}R \xrightarrow{\;\alpha\;} R\cdot + CR_2=\overset{+}{Y}R \qquad 4\text{-}3,\; 4\text{-}8$$

$$\overset{+}{Y}R-CH_2-\overset{\cdot}{C}H_2 \xrightarrow{\;\alpha\;} YR^+ + CH_2=CH_2$$

Unsaturated heteroatom:
$$R-CR=\overset{\cdot+}{Y} \xrightarrow{\;\alpha\;} R\cdot + CR\equiv\overset{+}{Y} \qquad 4\text{-}4$$

Alkene (allylic cleavage):
$$R-CH_2-CH\overset{\cdot+}{=}CH_2 \xrightarrow{\;\alpha\;} R\cdot + CH_2=CH-\overset{+}{C}H_2 \qquad 4\text{-}5$$

Retro-Diels-Alder (double α-cleavage): 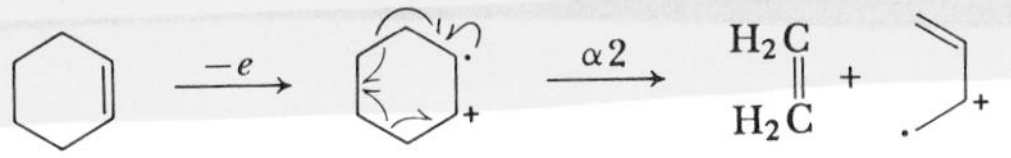
$$4\text{-}7$$

Rearrangements (r): radical and "incipient radical" site initiation. Formation of a new bond from the radical site to another atom *through space* concomitant with cleavage of a bond to that atom; a subsequent reaction is usually required for loss of the neutral. The transition state size is influenced by the stabilities of the products and of the bonds formed and cleaved, and by steric factors; in most cases a six-membered ring is the minimum size if there is a double bond in the ring, and a four-membered ring is the minimum if there is none.

H rearrangement, saturated ring transition state

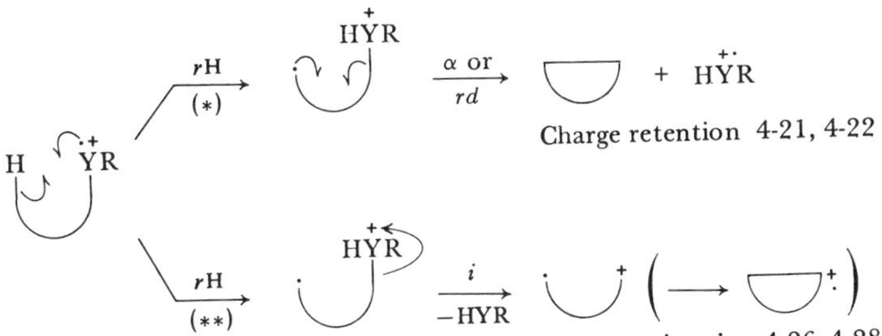

Charge retention 4-21, 4-22

Charge migration 4-26-4-28

(*) also

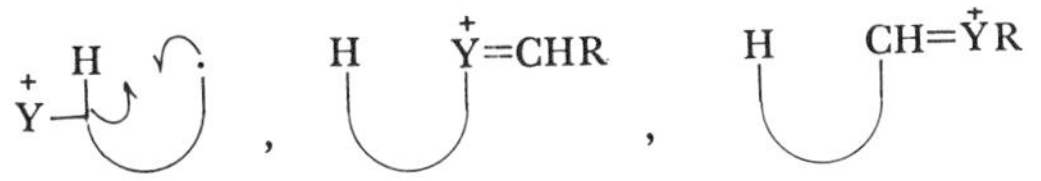

4-23, 4-24
4-36-4-38

(**) also

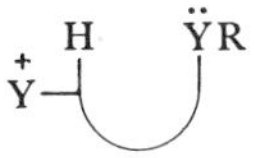

4-42-4-46

H rearrangement, unsaturated ring transition state

$\xrightarrow{rH}$ $\xrightarrow{\alpha}$ Charge retention 4-16, 4-17, 4-19

$\xrightarrow{i}$ Charge migration 4-25,

also   ,   ,   ,   ,   4-18, 4-33–4-35

2 H rearrangement: $\xrightarrow{rH}$ $\longleftrightarrow$ $\xrightarrow{rH}$ 4-39–4-41

Charge site rearrangement (r+): $R'\!-\!\!\!\bigcirc\!\!\!\bigcup$ $\xrightarrow{r+}$ $R'\!-\!\!\!\bigcup\!-\!R$ 4-32

Displacement (rd): $R\!-\!\!\!\bigcup\ \overset{\cdot}{Y}R$ $\xrightarrow{rd}$ $R\cdot\ +\ \bigcup\overset{+}{Y}R$ 4-29, 4-30

$\overset{+}{Y}\!-\!\!\!\bigcup\ \overset{\cdot\cdot}{Y}R$ $\xrightarrow{rd}$ $Y\ +\ \bigcup\overset{+}{Y}R$ 4-31

Elimination (re): $R\bigcup\overset{+}{R}Y$ $\xrightarrow{re}$ $\bigcirc\ +\ R\!-\!R\overset{+}{Y}$ Table 4-1, 4-46–4-48

$H_n R\ \ R\overset{+}{Y}$ $\xrightarrow{re}$ $H_n R'Y\ +\ R\!=\!R\overset{+}{Y}$ Table 4-1
$\ \ \ \ \ R'Y$

Cyclization (rc) followed by either rd or re: $R\!-\!\!\!\bigcup\ \overset{+}{Y}R$ $\xrightarrow{rc}$ $R\!-\!\!\!\bigcup\overset{+}{Y}R$ $\xrightarrow[(rd)]{\alpha}$ $R\cdot\ +\ \bigcup\overset{+}{Y}R$ 4-30

5

POSTULATION OF MOLECULAR STRUCTURES

There are several major kinds of general structure information available in the mass spectrum. These are particularly helpful if you have no information from other sources concerning the unknown molecule. The overall appearance of the spectrum and the low mass peaks can give a general indication of the type of compound. Furthermore, the neutral fragments lost in forming the high mass peaks can provide information on specific structural functionalities. The fragmentation behavior of the indicated type of molecule is then used to postulate structures, as will be discussed in Chapter 6, for the unknown. Be sure to examine the unknown spectrum for each of the types of information described here, as outlined in Table A-1.

5.1   General Appearance of the Spectrum

A brief inspection of the bar graph spectral presentation can tell the experienced interpreter a substantial amount about the unknown molecule. You have already seen how the mass and relative abundance of the molecular ion indicate the size and general stability of the molecule (Section 3.5). In addition, the number of abundant ions in the spectrum and their distribution in the mass scale are indicative of the type of molecule and the functional groups present. For example, a glance at the spectrum of Unknown 5.1 should tell you that this is a highly stable molecule. Determine its elemental composition and value for rings plus double bonds; is the latter consistent with this stability? Not only are there no weak bonds in the molecule, but apparently the main fragmentation pathways are of approximately the same low probability. What is a possible structure?

Another typical spectral pattern that you should be able to recognize on sight is that of an *n*-alkane. Figures 5-1 and 5-2 show the bar graphs of

Unknown 5.1

m/e	Relative abundance	m/e	Relative abundance
38	1.8	64.5	1.1
39	3.9	65	0.24
40	0.19	66	0.02
41	0.01	74	4.7
42	0.06	75	4.9
42.67	0.10	76	3.3
43	0.16	77	4.1
43.5	0.02	78	2.7
49.5	0.24	79	0.19
50	6.4	87	1.4
50.5	0.09	88	0.22
51	12.	89	0.73
51.5	0.37	90	0.06
52	1.6	101	2.7
53	0.27	102	7.1
54	0.04	103	0.64
55	0.14	104	0.15
55.5	0.03	110	0.06
56	0.12	111	0.09
56.5	0.06	112	0.02
61	1.4	113	0.18
61.5	0.08	125	0.85
62	2.7	126	6.1
62.5	0.20	127	9.8
63	7.4	128	100.
63.5	0.95	129	11.
64	10.	130	0.52

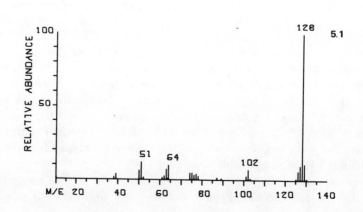

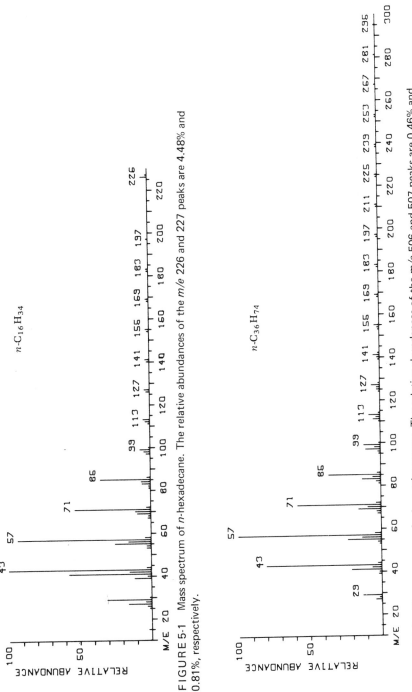

FIGURE 5-1   Mass spectrum of *n*-hexadecane. The relative abundances of the *m/e* 226 and 227 peaks are 4.48% and 0.81%, respectively.

FIGURE 5-2   Mass spectrum of *n*-hexatriacontane. The relative abundances of the *m/e* 506 and 507 peaks are 0.46% and 0.18%, respectively. The relative abundances of the $C_nH_{2n+1}^{+}$ peaks decrease regularly from *m/e* 309 = 0.7% to *m/e* 505 = 0.1%.

*C*_{*n*}H⁺_{2*n*+1} alkyl series

n-hydrocarbons

n-hexadecane, $C_{16}H_{34}$, and *n*-hexatriacontane, $C_{36}H_{74}$. Note the striking similarity to each other and to the spectrum of *n*-decane, Figure 4-2a. All the "important" (see Section 4.3) peaks except M‡ are even-electron ions. The regular distribution of the ions results from the fact that most of the carbon–carbon bonds are of nearly the same energy, as are the carbon–hydrogen bonds. Thus, the rates of the initial decomposition reactions of the molecular ion involving cleavages of the different carbon–carbon bonds are comparable to each other, as are the secondary decompositions of the primary product ions. This accounts for the regular increase in abundances with decreased sizes of the alkyl ions. The possibility of rearranged products of greater stability becomes higher with the secondary reactions, so that the structures of the smaller ions, such as $C_3H_7^+$ and $C_4H_9^+$ are largely the more stable branched carbonium ion structures. Thus the distribution of ions is maximized in the C_3 and C_4 region of higher *n*-alkanes.

The same $C_nH_{2n+1}^+$ alkyl ion series can also be recognized in the spectrum of methyl octadecanoate (Figure 5-3). This has an even more striking

Unknown 5.2

m/e	Relative abundance	m/e	Relative abundance	m/e	Relative abundance	m/e	Relative abundance
27	1.3	74	2.0	105	100	153	1.8
28	1.0	75	1.7	106	7.8	154	1.4
38	0.37	75.5	0.21	107	0.48	155	0.16
39	1.1	76	4.3	119	0.02	164	0.06
50	6.2	76.5	0.33	126	0.63	165	0.44
51	19.	77	62.	127	0.40	166	0.06
52	1.4	78	4.2	128	0.13	181	8.2
53	0.29	79	0.13	139	0.17	182	60.
63	1.3	91	0.08	151	1.1	183	8.5
64	0.61	104	0.48	152	3.4	184	0.71
65	0.09						

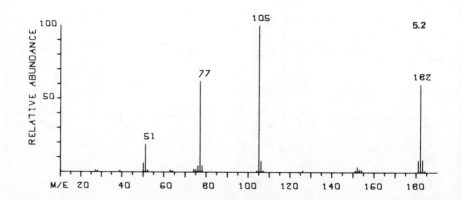

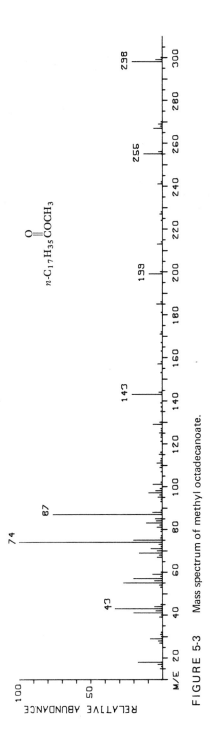

FIGURE 5-3   Mass spectrum of methyl octadecanoate.

sequence of ions of the formula $C_nH_{2n}COOCH_3^+$; however, instead of decreasing regularly, the abundances of such straight-chain esters show local maxima at $n = 2, 6, 10 \cdots$ (discussed in Section 6.4). Despite this difference, these two long series of peaks separated by 14 mass units should immediately suggest the presence of a large saturated hydrocarbon moiety.

Unknown 5.2 has a molecular ion of substantial abundance and two prominent fragment peaks; the remainder of the spectrum is very weak and bears no relationship to Figures 5-1 to 5-3.

A few prominent ions generally mean that there are only a few favored decomposition pathways. This is usually caused by the lability of one or a few bonds compared to the rest in the molecule, and (or) the stability of one or a few products compared with the other possibilities.

In the spectrum of Unknown 5.3 the m/e 43 peak is by far the most prominent in the spectrum. The bond that is cleaved in the formation of this ion would be expected to be the weakest in the molecule from its known chemical reactivity.

Unknown 5.3

m/e	Relative abundance	m/e	Relative abundance
13	3.2	43	100.
14	10.	44	2.4
15	34.	45	0.22
16	0.55	56	0.26
26	2.0	57	0.10
27	1.4	71	0.01
28	1.0	86	11.
29	2.0	87	0.47
41	1.8	88	0.06
42	7.2		

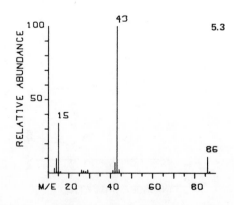

5.2   Low Mass Ion Series

Although the *specific* structural information of the low mass ions is relatively ambiguous, these can indicate *general* structural features of the molecule (for example, Figures 5-1 and 5-2). For this purpose the use of low mass ions has certain advantages. Both the isobaric (ions of the same nominal mass but different elemental composition) and isomeric structural possibilities for ions at a particular mass increase exponentially with m/e. A sizable m/e 15 peak almost always is CH_3^+, while both $C_2H_5^+$ and CHO^+ are common at m/e 29, and a number of ions besides $C_3H_7^+$ can cause an abundant m/e 43. Identifications are also simpler at the low mass end because the abundant low mass ions are usually even-electron. The structural implications of these ions can often indicate the most probable of the isomeric and isobaric possibilities for the high mass ions when the latter are studied.

SERIES SEPARATED BY CH_2 GROUPS.   Many structural features give rise to a significant homologous series of ions starting at the low mass end of the spectrum, such as the continuous series of alkyl ions, $C_nH_{2n+1}^+$, in *n*-paraffin spectra (Figures 5-1 and 5-2). The high probability of rearrangement on forming the lowest mass ions produces a much more complete homologous series with much less variation in ion abundances than at higher masses. The hydrocarbon $(CH_3)_3CC(CH_3)_3$ (Figure 5-4) does not contain a C_2H_5 or C_3H_7 grouping, yet it gives the ion series CH_3^+, 5.6%; $C_2H_5^+$, 16%; $C_3H_7^+$, 17%; and $C_4H_9^+$, 100%. Thus a quick inspection of the spectrum starting at the low mass end of Figure 5-4 indicates the presence of an alkyl moiety. The fact that the $C_nH_{2n+1}^+$ ions can be traced from CH_3^+ to $C_7H_{15}^+$ is a valuable indication (although not a proof) of the size of the alkyl moiety.

m/e	Relative abundance	m/e	Relative abundance
15	5.6	56	26.
26	0.43	57	100.
27	8.3	58	4.3
28	1.6	59	0.06
29	16.	69	1.4
30	0.31	70	0.12
39	8.5	71	0.33
40	1.4	72	0.03
41	27.	83	0.77
42	1.5	84	0.33
43	17.	85	0.03
44	0.60	98	0.04
45	0.01	99	6.1
53	1.3	100	0.47
54	0.28	101	0.02
55	4.1	114	0.03

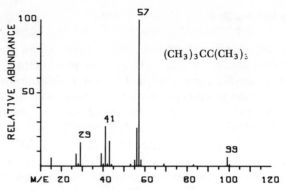

FIGURE 5-4   Mass spectrum of 2,2,3,3-tetramethylbutane.

A substituted alkyl group will produce a homologous series of displaced mass—for example, amines, 30, 44, 58, $\cdots$; alcohols, 31, 45, 59, $\cdots$; ketones, 43, 57, 71, $\cdots$ (unfortunately —CO— corresponds to —C_2H_4— in

Unknowns 5.4 and 5.5

m/e	Relative abundance 5.4	Relative abundance 5.5
15	2.8	3.2
16	0.03	1.1
26	1.4	0.52
27	10.	2.7
28	5.2	4.4
29	6.0	2.3
30	0.33	100.
31	4.5	1.5
37	1.2	0.09
38	1.9	0.33
39	5.8	0.57
40	1.0	1.0
41	7.2	2.5
42	4.2	5.4
43	19.	7.1
44	3.9	3.7
45	100.	0.09
46	2.3	—
47	0.19	—
57	0.41	0.27
58	0.20	0.60
59	4.3	3.6
60	0.51	5.2
61	0.03	0.17

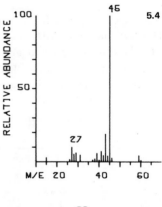

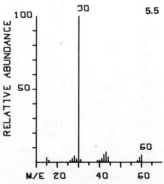

mass, causing overlap with the alkyl series); and chloroalkanes, 49, 63, 77, $\cdots$. A variety of such ion series is listed in Table A-6, along with the most probable types of molecular structures in whose spectra they are found.

Many of the common series can be confused by the possibility of isobaric multiplets, so that the accurate determination of elemental composition greatly improves the usefulness of this table. Some of these functionalities can hold more than one alkyl group, so that the length of the ion series only indicates the total alkyl content; although Figure 4-3 shows the $C_nH_{2n+2}N^+$ series 30, 44, 58, 72 (m/e 72 = $C_4H_{10}N^+$), it does not have four *contiguous* carbon atoms (Figure 4-3 is diethylamine). Unknown 4.10 was made difficult by the fact that the relative abundances of the peaks at highest mass are insufficient for an accurate determination of elemental composition. The possibilities for this, however, are narrowed rapidly with the assignment of the low mass ions to logical even-electron series.

In Unknown 5.4 the use of Table A-6 should clear up any confusion about the identity of the molecular ion. In Unknown 5.5, however, the search for an even-electron ion series could lead to quite different conclusions.

For more complex molecules, there may well be a number of series of even-electron ions. Try to account for all major even-electron ions in the lower half of the mass spectrum. Following the series does not have to be limited to the lower half of the spectrum, however; in Unknown 4.10 and Figures 5-1 and 5-4 an ion series can be carried nearly all the way to the molecular ion. Note also that attempts to continue the series should not be abandoned if the next higher member happens to be of low abundance.

As was mentioned above, homologous series can be found at higher masses than those listed in Table A-6, such as the $(CH_2)_nCOOCH_3^+$ series (87, 101, 115, $\cdots$) of aliphatic esters of Figure 5-3; of course there is also a much wider variety of compound types which can give a higher mass ion series. The maximum mass of the structural moiety attached to the alkyl group is indicated by the lower limit of the ion series; assignment of this limit may be difficult owing to interference, however.

The rules on relative peak importance (Section 4.3) apply to the significance of ion series; the presence of an important homologous ion series decreases the significance of a series in the same mass range that is lower by 2 and, to a lesser extent, 4 mass units. Thus in Unknown 4.10 the presence of the 31, 45, 59, 73, 87, 101, 115 ($C_nH_{2n+1}O^+$) ion series affects the significance of the 29, 43, 57, 71 ($C_nH_{2n+1}^+$) series. The latter is surely important through m/e 57, the base peak in the spectrum. However, there is no $C_5H_{11}^+$ contribution to the m/e 71 peak; this is entirely due to $C_4H_7O^+$. In Figure 5-4 the C_nH_{2n-1} series of fair abundance does *not* indicate the presence of olefinic or cycloalkyl structures as might be deduced from Table A-6. Note, however, that a multiply unsaturated or cyclic molecule, such as C_nH_{2n-4}, will also give even-electron ions that are *less* hydrogen-deficient; cyclohexene, C_6H_{10}, gives the ion series CH_3^+, $C_2H_5^+$, $C_3H_7^+$ (rearrangements) and $C_2H_3^+$, $C_3H_5^+$, $C_4H_7^+$, in addition to the expected C_2H^+ (small), $C_3H_3^+$, $C_4H_5^+$, $C_5H_7^+$, $C_6H_9^+$. Thus the rings-plus-double-bonds value is best indicated by the series extending to the highest m/e value.

Remember that at the higher masses of a series the peaks will arise from more specific processes, so that substantial alternations in abundance may be indicative of a specific structural feature. It is also possible, although much rarer, that abundant odd-electron ions can appear in a homologous series; possibilities are listed in Table A-7. For example, the spectrum of 1-octanol (Figure 5-5) shows a prominent OE^+ series corresponding to $C_nH_{2n}^+$

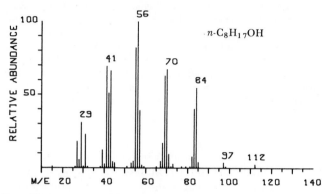

FIGURE 5-5   Mass spectrum of 1-octanol.

in which the peaks at m/e 56, 70, 84, and 112 are more important than those at adjacent masses; these ions presumably are formed by reaction 4-26.

OTHER ION SERIES.   Compounds with a low hydrogen-to-carbon ratio, such as Unknown 5.1, do not have sufficient hydrogen atoms for such a series of ions spaced at 14 mass unit intervals. In aromatic hydrocarbons the fragment ions 39, 50, 51, 52, 63, 64, 65, 75, 76, 77 (roughly $C_nH_{0.5n}$ to C_nH_n) are typical (Table A-6). Heterocyclic compounds containing ring oxygen and nitrogen atoms show similar m/e fragments plus additional significant peaks at masses 40, 53, 66, and 78 due to replacement of C by N or O.

The substitution of hydrogen atoms by halogen atoms, X, changes the homologous series spacings by CHX or CX_2, causing a marked change in the appearance of the spectrum. Additionally, the electronegative halogen atoms are much more easily lost than hydrogen atoms, so that ions separated by X and HX in mass are also found. For chlorine and bromine, these are easily identified because of the "isotope clusters". Fluorine and iodine have only one natural isotope each—^{19}F and ^{127}I— but these can usually be recognized by the very unusual mass differences they cause.

In Unknowns 5.6 to 5.9 attempt to derive as much information as possible from the ion series.

Unknown 5.9 is a methyl-esterified component of butterfat identified by Stenhagen and his co-workers (ref. *1.16*, p. 217). It is also found in the liver fat of patients suffering from Refsum's disease.

Unknown 5.6

m/e	Relative abundance	m/e	Relative abundance
12	13.	50	25.
14	2.1	51	0.31
19	2.0	69	100.
24	2.7	70	1.08
26	11.	76	46.
27	0.14	77	1.2
31	22.	95	2.4
32	0.28	96	0.06
38	6.2		

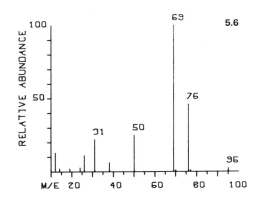

Unknown 5.7

m/e	Relative abundance	m/e	Relative abundance
37	2.7	65	0.80
37.5	0.12	65.5	0.05
38	3.7	73	1.0
38.5	0.05	74	7.1
39	4.8	75	9.9
40	0.62	76	9.0
40.5	0.10	77	3.8
41	0.38	78	2.5
42	0.11	79	0.45
43	0.48	80	0.20
43.5	0.03	81	0.42
44	1.6	86	0.42
44.5	0.02	87	0.94
45	0.10	88	0.35
49	2.0	89	0.26
49.5	0.64	90	0.16
50	12.	97	0.33
50.5	0.47	98	1.2
51	19.	99	0.91
51.5	1.0	100	0.94
52	4.2	101	5.6
53	0.41	102	24.
61	1.8	103	7.6
61.5	0.07	104	0.62
62	3.2	126	0.15
62.5	0.07	127	1.8
63	5.8	128	16.
63.5	0.14	129	100.
64	1.5	130	10.
64.5	3.9	131	0.46

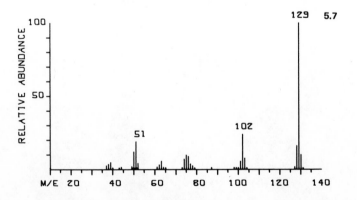

Unknown 5.8

m/e	Relative abundance	m/e	Relative abundance	m/e	Relative abundance	m/e	Relative abundance
15	0.66	55	34.	87	0.10	121	0.56
26	1.3	56	17.	91	0.15	122	0.05
27	18.	57	21.	92	0.04	123	0.40
28	3.5	58	0.96	93	1.2	133	0.04
29	18.	69	6.0	94	0.05	134	0.04
30	0.40	70	0.53	95	1.2	135	50.
39	11.	71	0.53	105	0.28	136	2.2
40	2.1	79	0.19	106	0.64	137	49.
41	37.	80	0.10	107	5.0	138	2.1
42	14.	81	0.19	108	0.73	139	0.05
43	100.	82	0.13	109	4.7	164	2.2
44	3.4	83	0.74	110	0.14	165	0.15
45	0.05	84	0.66	119	0.25	166	2.2
53	2.1	85	49.	120	0.05	167	0.13
54	1.1	86	3.2				

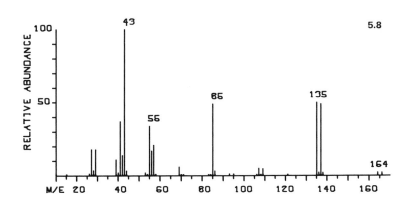

Unknown 5.9

m/e	Relative abundance	m/e	Relative abundance	m/e	Relative abundance	m/e	Relative abundance
29	0.33	87	4.3	141	0.82	223	0.36
41	1.7	88	0.20	143	6.2	227	0.21
42	0.51	89	0.03	144	0.58	237	0.16
43	3.9	93	1.0	145	0.04	241	3.2
44	0.12	94	0.27	149	2.7	242	0.53
53	2.0	95	4.3	150	0.82	250	1.5
54	1.2	96	2.6	151	0.86	252	3.7
55	33.	97	15.	153	1.2	253	1.6
56	10.	98	4.0	155	0.52	254	0.32
57	29.	99	2.7	157	0.47	255	0.85
58	2.0	100	0.42	163	1.3	256	0.14
59	14.	101	100.	165	1.0	261	0.81
60	0.43	102	5.7	167	3.6	262	0.17
67	4.2	103	0.51	168	0.39	269	1.7
68	2.5	107	0.92	171	18.	270	0.30
69	23.	108	0.14	172	2.0	271	0.03
70	6.3	109	2.8	173	0.18	276	2.7
71	19.	110	1.3	181	1.3	277	1.7
72	1.2	111	11.	182	1.0	278	0.23
73	6.0	112	2.5	183	0.55	279	2.0
74	58.	114	0.38	185	1.2	280	0.39
75	19.	115	1.7	186	0.15	281	0.04
76	0.65	116	0.12	197	1.1	283	0.78
77	0.12	123	1.6	198	0.62	284	0.16
79	1.2	125	3.0	199	0.96	295	0.77
80	0.32	126	1.6	200	0.13	296	0.16
81	4.6	127	1.3	209	3.0	311	2.0
82	1.2	128	0.39	210	0.47	312	0.44
83	11.	129	2.0	211	0.04	313	0.05
84	1.7	130	0.16	213	5.0	326	8.7
85	7.0	139	3.0	214	0.70	327	2.0
86	1.2	140	1.7	215	0.07	328	0.25

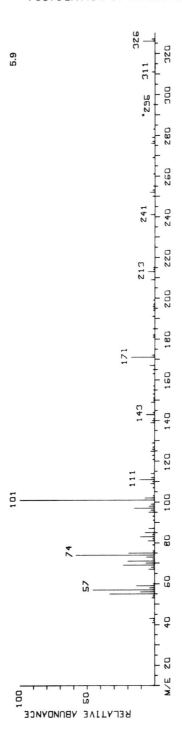

5.3   Small Neutral Losses

Perhaps the most simple and positive assignments that can be made in the spectrum are for the small neutral species lost in the formation of the fragment ions of highest mass in the spectrum, especially those formed directly from the molecular ion. For example, the ions at masses $(M - 1)^+$, $(M - 15)^+$, $(M - 18)^+$, and $(M - 20)^+$ almost always represent the losses of H, CH_3, H_2O, and HF, respectively, from the molecular ion. Because formation of such large primary ions involves the lowest probability of a randomizing rearrangement, such "small neutral loss" peaks are of major significance in determining the molecular structure. Thus an abundant peak corresponding to $(M - 1)^+$ indicates a labile hydrogen atom (and the absence of other labile substituents), and an abundant peak corresponding to $(M - 15)^+$ indicates a methyl group on a substituted carbon or similar position from which it can be readily lost. A list of common small neutral fragments lost in the formation of important spectral peaks is set forth in Table A-5; their use as tests for the molecular ion was discussed in Section 3.4.

As the neutral fragments increase in mass, the isobaric or isomeric possibilities cause an increasing probability of confusion in assignments. It also becomes more difficult to determine from which particular ion the fragment ion in question is formed. For example, in a spectrum containing abundant $(M - CH_3)^+$ and $(M - C_3H_7)^+$ ions, the latter could be formed either by the loss of the propyl radical as nominally indicated, or by the loss of an ethylene molecule from the $(M - CH_3)^+$ ion. Metastable ions are a valuable indication of such secondary processes; their use will be discussed in Section 7.1.

As was discussed in Section 4.3, *important* high mass peaks may be of relatively low abundance, even <0.1%. You must attempt to account for all the peaks in the high mass region; these can give very valuable structure clues. Be sure you do this in Unknown 5.10. This has been isolated as an impurity from blood recirculated through an artificial heart-lung device.

Unknown 5.10

m/e	Relative abundance	m/e	Relative abundance
27	3.6	45	0.89
28	1.2	50	4.3
29	5.9	51	1.9
31	0.22	52	1.0
39	1.9	63	0.47
40	0.39	64	0.74
41	0.32	65	7.8
42	0.29	66	3.2
43	0.53	74	0.79
44	0.12	75	1.1

Unknown 5.10 (continued)

m/e	Relative abundance	m/e	Relative abundance
76	6.4	135	0.46
77	3.2	136	0.09
78	0.39	147	0.31
79	0.17	148	0.44
89	0.22	149	100.
90	0.14	150	10.
91	0.63	151	1.0
92	0.37	163	0.31
93	6.2	164	0.40
94	0.39	165	0.54
103	0.42	166	0.37
104	4.9	167	0.15
105	8.3	176	9.0
106	1.0	177	28.
107	0.09	178	3.3
119	0.19	179	0.34
120	0.11	194	0.71
121	5.3	195	0.44
122	2.9	196	0.05
123	0.27	221	0.12
132	2.2	222	3.0
133	0.49	223	0.40
134	0.13	224	0.04

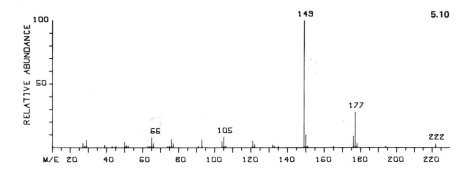

5.4   Characteristic Ions

The mass (or elemental composition) of a larger ion actually represents *two* pieces of structural information; the mass (or elemental composition) of the ionic portion of the original molecule can provide valuable information in addition to that from the mass of the neutral portion of the molecule. Deduction of the structural information from a larger ion is more difficult because of the larger number of theoretically possible assignments for it. Despite this, for many particular mass (and, especially, elemental composition) values there are only a few characteristic structural groupings that commonly give rise to the corresponding peak in mass spectra. Such "characteristic ions" are surprisingly helpful in suggesting possible fragments of the molecule. You should already be familiar with some of these, like the m/e 30 from amines, m/e 74 from methyl alkanoates, and m/e 91 from compounds containing the benzyl group.

Unknown 5.10 above provides a classic example. In solving this the low mass ion series and the neutral loss of 27 should have soon led you to postulate an aromatic ethyl ester; deducing a phthalate structure probably took substantially more effort. However, the experienced interpreter would immediately *suspect* a phthalate from the presence of the base peak at m/e 149. (In an *Eight Peak Index* of 17,124 mass spectra (*5.1*), over half of the compounds giving a m/e 149 base peak are phthalates.) Phthalates are ubiquitous impurities found in mass spectra, as they are common components of plasticizers (tubing, cap liners, gaskets), vacuum pump oil, and chromatographic column packings.

Thus the next step in the interpretation of the spectrum is to note the possible structural significance of all important peaks. Where more than one possible interpretation exists, be sure to note all of them; then if other evidence in the spectrum eliminates one or more of these possibilities, the others will be much more meaningful. Possible assignments for even-electron ions are given as part of the ion series of Table A-6; Table A-7 lists common odd-electron fragment ions. The *Eight Peak Index of Mass Spectra* (*5.1*) provides a listing of compounds which give a particular m/e value as the largest, second largest, etc., peak in their spectra; scanning this list can give valuable ideas as to possible structural moieties for a particular peak.

Mass Spectral Correlations (*5.2*) shows what elemental compositions and structures are possible for a peak, and what the *relative* probability is for each of these postulations. Its use is illustrated in Figure 5-6 by a copy of its data on the ions of m/e 43. This shows that mass 43 ions of elemental formulas CHNO, C_2H_3O, CH_3N_2, C_2H_5N, and C_3H_7 are all possible at mass 43. High resolution or other elemental composition information could distinguish these. Figure 5-6 also shows that ions of a particular formula can arise from a number of general types of compounds. Thus, the ion $C_2H_3O^+$ is abundant in the spectra of methyl ketones, acetates, and acetamides, and can even arise from compounds that do not bear the obvious acetyl group, such as vinyl and cyclic ethers. The table thus has a considerable value for the beginner in avoiding the quick conclusion that the presence of an abundant $C_2H_3O^+$ ion must signify an acetyl group in the molecule.

The relative probability of a particular structural significance for an ion is shown in the columns of numbers. The tabulation was prepared by the examination of the major peaks in the mass spectra of 4000 different compounds. In the column headed 1, the figure shown signifies the number of times that an ion of this particular origin gives the largest peak in the spectrum. In the column headed 2, the entry similarly signifies the number of times that the same ion was the second most abundant in the spectrum. Obviously, a

m/e	Formula	Structural significance	Relative probability 1	2	3	Total
43.0058	CHNO	$R-O\ddagger CONH\ddagger H$, $R_2N\ddagger CONH\ddagger H(?)$	4		1	5
43.0184	C_2H_3O	$CH_3CO\ddagger R$	30	4	14	48
		$CH_3CO\ddagger OR$	36	7	11	54
		$CH_3CO\ddagger NR_2$	2	5	17	24
		Cyclic ethers	4	11	4	19
	Other	Other satd. ROH, ROR, mixed	5	7	15	27
		$CH_2=CHO\ddagger R$		2	3	5
		Other		1	2	3
43.0296	CH_3N_2	$CH_3N=N\ddagger CH_3$		1		1
43.0421	C_2H_5N	Cyclic amines	2			2
		Other	3			3
43.0547	C_3H_7	$(CH_3)_2CH\ddagger C_nH_{2n+1}$	29	8		37
		Other $(CH_3)_2CH\ddagger R$, $(CH_3)_2CH\ddagger RY$	31	20	20	71
		$CH_3CH_2CH_2\ddagger CHRR'$, $\ddagger CRR'R''$				
		(branched)	9	3	1	13
		$CH_3CH_2CH_2\ddagger R$ (R = $-C-C=C$, $-C-Ph$)	2	1	1	4
		Other $CH_3CH_2CH_2\ddagger C_nH_{2n+1}$	43	33	20	96
		Cpds. with large satd. h.c. groups	26	82	80	188
		C_3H_7-Y (Y = $-COOR$)	9	4		13
		(Y = $-CONR_2$)		1	1	2
		(Y = $-COR$)	5	1		6
		(Y = $-NR_2$)			1	1
		(Y = $-SR$ or $-SSR$)	4		4	8
		(Y = $-OR$)	10	4	2	16
		(Y = $-OCOR^*$)	4	5	3	12
		(Y = X)	5			5
		(Y = $-NO_2$)	2			2
		P.I.D. and unclassified	13	9	5	27
		Total	279	210	203	692

FIGURE 5-6   Data on *m/e* 43 from *Mass Spectral Correlations* (*5.2*).

molecule containing a number of functional groups or structural moieties would yield ions characteristic of each of these groups in competition, so that a distribution of entries in this column would be expected.

Most of the types of information discussed in this chapter should be useful for the solution of Unknown 5.11.

Unknown 5.11

m/e	Relative abundance	m/e	Relative abundance	m/e	Relative abundance
15	0.35	61	0.62	93	1.6
26	0.92	62	1.2	94	100.
27	14.	63	19.	95	6.6
28	1.1	64	2.0	96	0.40
29	0.22	65	15.	105	0.32
37	0.62	66	12.	106	0.11
38	2.2	67	0.72	107	29.
39	14.	68	0.21	108	2.2
40	2.1	73	0.24	109	0.13
41	0.33	74	0.90	119	0.19
42	0.17	75	0.68	120	0.40
43	0.38	76	0.69	121	1.6
49	0.28	77	22.	122	0.13
50	3.0	78	1.8	123	0.01
51	10.	79	5.0	156	41.
52	0.91	80	0.51	157	3.7
53	0.55	91	1.5	158	13.
55	1.5	92	0.58	159	1.2
				160	0.07

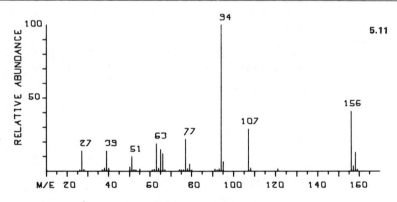

5.5   Assignment of the Most Probable Structure

All the information and postulations gathered above must now be utilized to deduce the most logical structure. It is difficult to outline a generally applicable pathway from these to such a deduction, for each case is usually dependent on the particular spectrum and the other available information. Although practice and experience are invaluable in finding the most logical and efficient pathways, some particulars may be helpful.

Molecular structure determination by most spectroscopic techniques involves the basic method of postulating a particular structure, predicting its spectrum, and then comparing this with the unknown spectrum. A main reason for the first eight steps of Table A-1 is that these will generally suggest structures for examination. Thus at this point you should review the information and postulations from these steps and the possible molecular structures which they suggest. Before each of these structures is examined critically, a real effort should be made to list *all* that appear possible, although there is usually sufficient information in the mass spectrum to narrow the structural possibilities rapidly. The elimination of all but one possibility for the molecular structure of course does not prove that this one is correct, unless a reference spectrum of the compound can be obtained.

Comparison with reference spectra should be made for all probable assignments, if possible. Tabular data on 6652 mass spectra are listed in the *Atlas of Mass Spectral Data* (*5.3*), and bar graph spectra of 19,000 different compounds are assembled in the *Registry of Mass Spectral Data* (*5.4*); these are arranged according to the exact molecular weight and structure of the compound. If the reference spectrum is not available, try to predict it by using the rules in Chapter 4 and the correlations of Chapter 6. Special techniques are discussed in Chapter 7.

Follow the outline of Table A-1 in attempting to assign structures to Unknowns 5.12 to 5.14.

Unknowns 5.12–5.14

m/e	Relative abundance			m/e	Relative abundance		
	5.12	5.13	5.14		5.12	5.13	5.14
39	8.9	3.9	8.5	74	1.2	4.4	0.60
40	0.79	0.25	0.71	75	1.3	2.2	0.56
41	4.4	0.24	3.3	76	1.0	3.7	0.47
42	0.38	0.99	0.21	77	13.	74.	3.2
43	1.4	15.	0.09	78	5.3	7.7	6.1
46.4 m	0.03	–	0.15	79	9.5	0.33	1.3
50	4.5	7.6	2.4	80	0.61	–	0.09
50.5	0.14	–	0.04	89	0.84	0.86	1.6
51	12.	22.	6.0	90	0.24	0.26	0.84
51.5	0.65	0.32	0.07	91	5.2	1.3	100.
52	3.3	2.6	1.6	92	0.69	0.07	10.
52.5	1.3	1.5	0.03	93	0.05	–	0.47
53	1.5	0.34	0.64	101.0 m	0.59	–	–
56.5 m	0.09	–	–	103	5.9	0.17	1.0
57	0.33	–	0.24	104	2.2	0.27	0.59
57.5	0.71	–	0.77	105	100.	100.	3.3
58	1.0	–	0.52	106	8.5	7.8	0.33
58.5	0.08	–	0.09	107	0.32	0.49	0.04
59	1.1	–	–	115	0.88	–	1.0
59.4 m	0.30	–	–	116	0.17	–	0.27
62	1.0	1.8	1.0	117	0.44	–	0.59
63	2.9	2.4	3.1	118	0.16	–	0.12
64	0.54	0.52	0.79	119	0.83	–	0.17
65	2.4	2.1	9.3	120	25.	28.	21.
66	0.29	0.08	0.61	121	2.4	2.5	2.0
69.0 m	0.02	–	0.13	122	0.10	0.15	0.09
73	0.16	0.91	0.09				

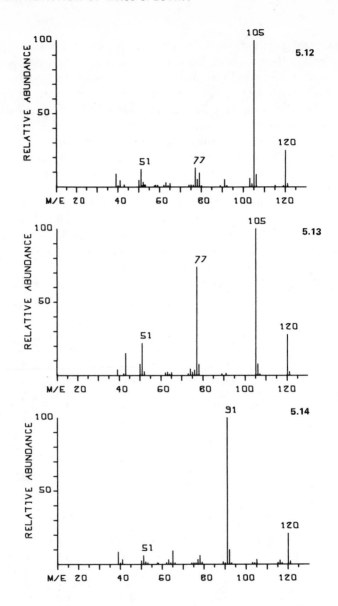

6

MASS SPECTRA OF COMMON COMPOUND CLASSES

Now we shall attempt to apply the principles set forth above to the interpretation of the spectra of common types of organic compounds. It is important for you to gain an appreciation of the reliability—and lack of reliability—of the various types of mass spectral information in providing evidence concerning various structural features. Note that there is an exponential increase in the number of possible fragmentation pathways with an increase in the number of reaction-initiating sites; this can be seen by comparing the behavior of esters with that of either ketones or ethers.

This chapter is intended to illustrate how the mechanisms can be applied to particular compounds, *not* to give a comprehensive catalog of the mass spectral behavior of organic structures. Detailed correlations have now been published of the mass spectra of a wide variety of molecular classes. In many of these studies isotopic labeling and other special techniques have been employed to elucidate mechanistic pathways. An excellent summary of this literature to 1967 is available in the comprehensive volume of Budzikiewicz, Djerassi, and Williams (*1.3*). This is recommended as a basic reference; the compound classifications in this chapter are patterned after it. A wealth of specific material is to be found in the specialized journals *Organic Mass Spectrometry* (Heyden, London) and *International Journal of Mass Spectrometry and Ion Physics* (Elsevier, Amsterdam), and thorough cross-referencing of the current literature is given in the *Mass Spectrometry Bulletin* (AWRE, Aldermaston, England).

A special note of caution is necessary for the unknowns of this chapter. Some are very difficult; for some a complete structure elucidation is not possible from the mass spectral data. Do not struggle too long without reading part of the solution; the solutions are an important aspect of the book's instruction.

COMPOUNDS CONTAINING MORE THAN ONE FUNCTIONAL GROUP.   There are great differences in the overall ability of a particular functional group to influence the fragmentation of a molecular ion. For example, although in the spectrum of $C_2H_5CH(OCH_3)(CH_2)_6CH_3$ the α-cleavage peak, $C_2H_5CH\overset{+}{=}OCH_3$, is more than twice as high as any other in the spectrum, it is <10% of the height of the $C_2H_5CH\overset{+}{=}NH_2$ peak in the spectrum of $C_2H_5CH(OCH_3)(CH_2)_4CH(NH_2)C_2H_5$. Spiteller (*4.4*) gives the following ranking of substituents in order of their increasing effectiveness: CO_2H, CH_2OH, OH, Cl, Br, CO_2CH_3, SH, C=O, SCH_3, OCH_3, I, ethylene ketal, NH_2, and $N(CH_3)_2$ (Section 4.5). Also, synergistic effects are common; a molecule containing two functional groups can undergo reactions that are not found for those with either group alone. To reiterate the precautions given above, always check the actual mass spectral behavior of compounds closely related to your proposed structure.

6.1   Hydrocarbons

Hydrocarbons, unfortunately, exhibit a substantial tendency to undergo *random rearrangements* in which the hydrogen atom positions and, to a lesser extent, the carbon skeletal arrangement are scrambled. This is the most pronounced in alkanes, in which the σ-electron ionization and C—C bond cleavages are higher-energy processes, producing more highly excited ions which have a higher tendency for isomerization and rearrangement decompositions. This is reduced by the presence of chain branching and unsaturation; the addition of a polar functional group changes the spectrum dramatically (see Figure 4-2).

SATURATED ALIPHATIC HYDROCARBONS.   As shown in the spectra of *n*-decane (Figure 4-2*a*), *n*-hexadecane (Figure 5-1), and *n*-hexatriacontane (Figure 5-2), straight-chain alkanes show weak molecular ions and typical series of $C_nH_{2n+1}^+$, and to a lesser extent $C_nH_{2n-1}^+$, ions with abundance maxima around C_3 or C_4. Chain branching causes a decrease in $[M^+]$ and characteristic increases in the abundances of $C_nH_{2n+1}^+$ and $C_nH_{2n}^+$ ions through cleavage and charge retention at the branched carbon, with the loss of the largest alkyl group favored (reaction 6-1, see also 4-1). (An

$$C_nH_{2n+1}R_2C\text{—}CH_2R' \xrightarrow{-e} C_nH_{2n+1}R_2C^+CH_2R' \begin{cases} \xrightarrow{\sigma} C_nH_{2n+1}R_2C^+ + \cdot CH_2R' \quad (6\text{-}1) \\ \xrightarrow{rH} C_nH_{2n}CR_2^+ + CH_3R' \end{cases}$$

apparent exception is the preferential loss of the isopropyl radical from simple 2-methylalkanes, reaction 6-2, which apparently forms the primary carbonium

$$C_nH_{2n+1}CH_2CH(CH_3)_2^{\ddagger} \xrightarrow{\sigma} C_nH_{2n+1}CH_2^+ + C_3H_7 \cdot \quad (6\text{-}2)$$

ion.) This general behavior is illustrated in the spectrum of pristane (Figure 6-1) which has been identified with the aid of mass spectrometry in such various sources as skin, hair, ovarian cysts, shark liver oil, and ancient geological sediments (*6.1*). Often the tendency to lose alkane molecules as well as alkyl radicals by cleavage at more branched carbon atoms is more pronounced than in this spectrum (for example, *m/e* 112) (*6.2*).

The tendency for rearrangement of such hydrocarbons makes absolute structural assignments difficult (see the spectra of *neo*-pentane and 2,2,3,3-tetramethylbutane, Figures 4-1 and 5-4). Useful information is often easily obtained, however; try Unknowns 6.1 to 6.3 which are $C_{16}H_{34}$ isomers.

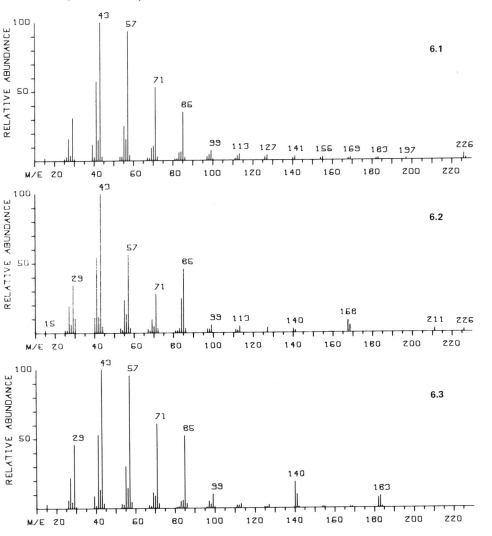

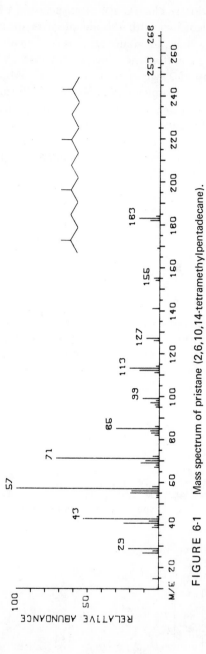

FIGURE 6-1   Mass spectrum of pristane (2,6,10,14-tetramethylpentadecane).

UNSATURATED ALIPHATIC HYDROCARBONS.   The addition f a double bond to an alkane increases the abundance of the $C_nH_{2n-1}^+$ and $C_nH_{2n}^+$ ion series, as shown in the spectrum of 1-hexadecene (Figure 6-2).

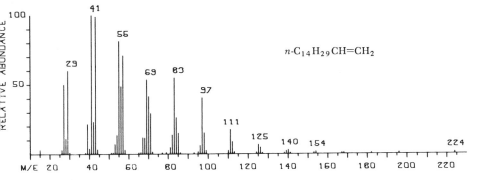

FIGURE 6-2   Mass spectrum of 1-hexadecene.

Note the increasing importance of the $C_nH_{2n+1}^+$ alkyl ion series at lower masses. Adding a double bond increases [M^+] only for compounds of lower molecular weight. Cis and trans isomers usually have very similar mass spectra.

Alkene ions exhibit allylic cleavage (reactions 4-5 and 6-3), but also show a strong tendency to isomerize through migration of the double bond. The mass

$$R'\!-\!CH_2\!-\!CH\!=\!CHR \xrightarrow{\ \alpha\ } R'\cdot + CH_2\!=\!CH\!-\!\overset{+}{C}HR \longleftrightarrow \overset{+}{C}H_2\!-\!CH\!=\!CHR \quad (6\text{-}3)$$

spectra of alkenes, and especially polyenes, tend to be independent of double bond position unless the double bond is highly substituted or a number of double bonds act together, as in benzylic cleavage, $C_6H_5CH_2 \!+\! R$. Thus allylic cleavage to produce the $C_5H_9^+$ ion in *allo*-ocimene is retarded because the cleaved bond is also vinylic, but enhanced in myrcene in which the cleaved bond is doubly allylic (6-4).

$$\begin{array}{c}CH_3\\ |\\ CH_2\!=\!CHC\!=\!CH\!-\!CH_2\!-\!CH\!-\!\overset{+}{C}(CH_3)_2\end{array} \xrightarrow{\ \times\ } C_5H_7\cdot + CH_2\!=\!CH\!-\!\overset{+}{C}(CH_3)_2$$
allo-Ocimene

$$\begin{array}{c}CH_2\\ \|\\ CH_2\!=\!CHC\!-\!CH_2\!-\!CH_2\!-\!CH\!-\!\overset{+}{C}(CH_3)_2\end{array} \xrightarrow{\ \alpha\ } C_5H_7\cdot + CH_2\!=\!CH\!-\!\overset{+}{C}(CH_3)_2 \quad (6\text{-}4)$$
Myrcene

Henneberg reports that the spectra of branched unsaturated alkenes, $RCH=C(CH_3)CH_2R'$ and $RCH_2C(CH_3)=CHR'$, show abundant RCH_2^+ ions which appear to arise by initial migration of the double bond away from the position of branching (6.2). In homosqualene, cleavage at the doubly allylic position produces an abundant $(M-83)^+$ ion, but the characteristic

$(M - 57)^+$ ion involves double bond migration to the conjugated position followed by allylic cleavage.

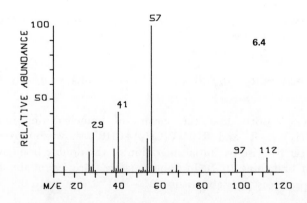

$$\text{(M − 83)} \qquad \longrightarrow \qquad \text{(M − 57)} \qquad (6\text{-}5)$$

Unknown 6.4

m/e	Relative abundance	m/e	Relative abundance
15	3.9	56	18.
16	0.16	57	100.
27	14.	58	4.3
28	3.8	59	0.07
29	27.	67	1.0
29.5 m	0.15	68	0.27
30	0.59	69	5.0
31.2 m	0.07	70	0.52
37.1 m	0.11	71	0.04
38	1.0	80	0.09
39	16.	81	0.77
40	2.5	82	0.13
41	41.	83	0.09
42	2.0	84	0.14
43	2.5	97	9.5
44	0.09	98	0.71
51	1.5	99	0.03
52	0.61	112	9.7
53	3.5	113	0.80
54	0.82	114	0.03
55	23.		

Elimination of an olefin molecule through γ-hydrogen rearrangement with formation of an odd-electron ion (reaction 6-6; see also reaction 4-18) is

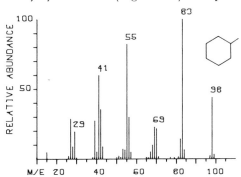

$$(6\text{-}6)$$

found in the spectra of substituted alkenes. Note that the *same* bond is ruptured in this rearrangement as in simple allylic cleavage. Skeletal rearrangements of surprising specificity have been reported recently (*6.3*).

A recent detailed study of acetylenic compounds (*6.4a*) indicates that their fragmentation behavior resembles that of olefins.

SATURATED ALICYCIC HYDROCARBONS.   Although the molecular ions of cycloalkanes are more abundant than those of their acyclic counterparts, their spectra are often more difficult to interpret. Skeletal decompositions must involve cleavage of at least two bonds, which may contribute to the increased randomization observed with these compounds. In the spectrum of methylcyclohexane (Figure 6-3) isotopic labeling shows that

FIGURE 6-3   Mass spectrum of methylcyclohexane.

the prominent $(M - CH_3)^+$ peak is due to loss of the methyl substituent. However, only half of the corresponding peak in methylcyclopentane arises in this manner (indicating a greater degree of endocyclic cleavage in the five-membered ring), and cyclohexane itself shows a $(M - CH_3)^+$ ion which is 27% of the base peak. The $(M - C_2H_4)^+$ peak of methylcyclohexane can be rationalized on the basis of initial ionization at the endocyclic branched sigma bond (6-7); labeling indicates that 60% of the peak arises from the elimination

$$(6\text{-}7)$$

of C_2H_4 originating in this position.

However, careful spectral correlation can give valuable structural information on such compounds; the detailed studies of Djerassi and his students
(*6.4b*) on the steroid hydrocarbon skeleton provides a classic case. For
example, in the mass spectrum of 5-α-pregnane (Figure 6-4) the $(M - CH_3)^+$
arises from the loss of the angular methyl groups (mainly C19). Loss of C_2H_5
by the exocyclic fragmentation of the 17–20 bond is negligible because of
favored 13–17 cleavage of the D ring producing the stable tertiary carbonium
ion. Radical site reactions of this species can proceed either through reciprocal
hydrogen transfer (equation 6-8) and 14–15 cleavage to yield the characteristic OE$^+$ *m/e* 218 ion, or through electron donation to the neighboring bond
resulting in the *m/e* 232 peak through 15–16 cleavage (reaction 6-9). A

$$(6\text{-}8)$$

m/e 218
$+ CH_2\text{=}CHCH_2R$

substantial part of the base peak at *m/e* 217 is due to C19 methyl loss from
m/e 232; a possible mechanism is shown (6-9). Finally, the *m/e* 149 ion is

$$(6\text{-}9)$$

m/e 232   *m/e* 217

composed mainly of rings A and B, but is formed in a complex mechanism
operating in conjunction with a triple hydrogen transfer. Despite this apparent
degree of randomness, the stereochemistry of the A/B rings has a characteristic effect on this process; in mass spectrum of the 5-β-(cis)-isomer, the [*m/e*
149]/[*m/e* 151] is much lower than in that of the 5-α-isomer. This effect is
relatively independent of the C17 substituent and has been used by Seifert
and his co-workers (*6.5*) to establish the presence of stereoisomers of

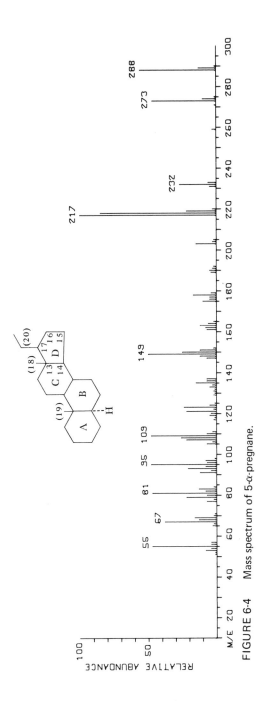

FIGURE 6-4   Mass spectrum of 5-α-pregnane.

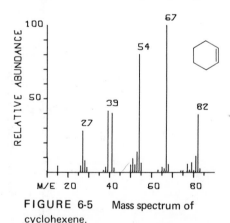

m/e 149

$C_{22}-C_{24}$ steroid acids in highly complex petroleum mixtures; animal contribution to the genesis of this petroleum is proposed because the bile acids of mammals are genetically related to the particular steroid acids identified.

UNSATURATED ALICYCLIC HYDROCARBONS. For many types of cycloalkenes the position of the double bond has little effect on the mass spectrum. Ten isomers of C_5H_8, which can have no larger than a cyclopentene ring, show similar spectra, as do a variety of C_7H_{10} (three rings + double bonds) isomers and other compounds with a high degree of unsaturation. Monoterpenoid hydrocarbons ($C_{10}H_{18}$, two rings + double bonds) containing a cyclohexane ring and an exterior double bond exhibit spectra which are consistent with initial isomerization to a cyclohexene structure, plus other rearrangements such as methyl migration.

Cyclohexene derivatives, on the other hand, can undergo quite specific fragmentations, as illustrated by the spectrum of cyclohexene itself (Figure 6-5). The base peak can be rationalized by a hydrogen abstraction mechanism

FIGURE 6-5 Mass spectrum of cyclohexene.

transferring the unpaired electron to an allylic radical site (reaction 6-10) followed by methyl loss. The significant odd-electron ion of *m/e* 54 which arises through a retro-Diels–Alder reaction (4-7, 6-11) is a convenient characteristic of the cyclohexene structure. This reaction produces a diene and

$$m/e \; 67$$
$$(6\text{-}10)$$

$$m/e \; 54$$

$$(6\text{-}11)$$

monoene fragment; as in the case of many hydrogen rearrangement reactions, the products compete for the positive charge. Tetrahydrocannabinol produces a significant m/e 246 peak corresponding to the ionized monoene through loss of C_5H_8; reaction 6-12 is one possible rationalization of the electron shifts

| m/e 314 | m/e 246 | m/e 231 |

$$(6\text{-}12)$$

involved. Note that CH_3 loss from the $OE^{\ddagger}$ m/e 246 ion gives the base peak, consistent with the aromatic stabilization achieved in this EE^+ product ion. The retro-Diels–Alder reaction is also a common decomposition mode of even-electron ions, so that a substantial part of the m/e 231 peak may be formed by C_5H_8 loss from the $(M - CH_3)^+$ ion.

As with other hydrocarbon fragmentation reactions, the retro-Diels-Alder reaction will be important only if no preferable fragmentations are possible. Thus the addition of a functional group can dramatically reduce the abundance of ions from this reaction. An excellent example from Biemann (*1.2*) illustrates this. Unknowns 6.5 and 6.6 show the spectra of α- and β-ionone. Pair the structures and spectra, and justify your choice.

α-Ionone   β-Ionone

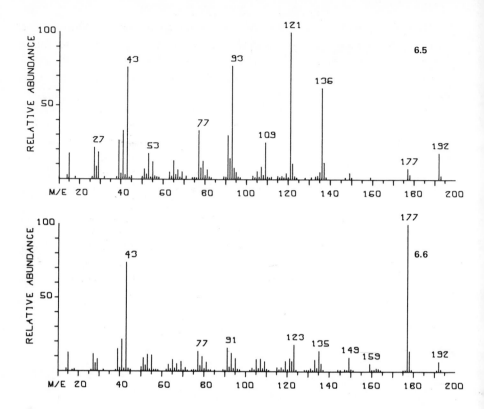

AROMATIC HYDROCARBONS. (The spectra of *n*-propylbenzene, iso-propylbenzene, *n*-butylbenzene and naphthalene are given in Unknowns 5.14, 5.12, 4.14 and Figure 5-1, respectively.) The addition of an aromatic nucleus substantially influences the mass spectrum, as can be seen in Figure 6-6, the

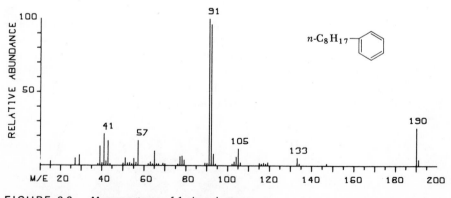

FIGURE 6-6   Mass spectrum of 1-phenyloctane.

spectrum of 1-phenyloctane. Molecular ion peaks are higher than those of the corresponding alkanes, and doubly charged ions are usually abundant. Aromatic ring cleavage processes usually require relatively high energies and are accompanied by a high degree of hydrogen and even skeletal scrambling; this leads to the characteristic "aromatic ions series" (Table A-6). The ions $C_n H_{0.5n}$ – $C_n H_{0.8n}$ ($n = 3$ to 6) often predominate if the ring contains electronegative substituents; the series $C_n H_{0.9n}$ – $C_n H_{1.2n}$ is more typical of the presence of electron donating substituents or heterocyclic compounds. Also the *ring* position of alkyl substitution usually has little influence on the spectrum (for example, *o*-, *m*-, and *p*-xylene have very similar mass spectra).

Another characteristic homologous ion series of phenylalkanes can be seen in Figure 6-6 at masses corresponding to $C_6 H_5 (CH_2)_n^+$ (*m/e* 77, 91, 105, 119, $\cdots$); the abundances of the individual ions are much more dependent on the structure of the molecule than those of the low mass ion series. However, ions stabilized by the aromatic nucleus can be formed through a variety of fragmentation pathways, so that the presence of a large peak, such as *m/e* 91, only signifies that the molecule contains one or more of several different structural features.

The most characteristic ion of this series in Figure 6-6 corresponds to rupture of the benzylic bond of the largest alkyl group; thus 1-phenylalkanes exhibit an abundant $C_7 H_7^+$ ion (reaction 6-13). The resonance-stabilized

$$(6\text{-}13)$$

m/e 91

benzyl ion is depicted as the $C_7 H_7^+$ product, but in particular cases the similarly stabilized tropylium ion has been shown to be the chief product (for most interpretive mechanisms it is not important to make this distinction). For example, in toluene the molecular ion undergoes ready isomerization to a cycloheptatriene-like ion, so that most of the $C_7 H_7^+$ from hydrogen loss has the tropylium (equation 6-14, R = H), not the benzyl structure (*6.6*). In

$$(6\text{-}14)$$

polyalkylaromatics this can account for some competing cleavage at the ring-alkyl bond, such as for the prominent $(M - CH_3)^+$ peak in dimethyl-benzenes (equation 6-14, $R = CH_3$). Olefin elimination from the primary benzyl ion product can also give $C_6H_5(CH_2)_n^+$ ions of significant abundance (reaction 6-15). (It has been postulated that the m/e 119 ion of 6-15

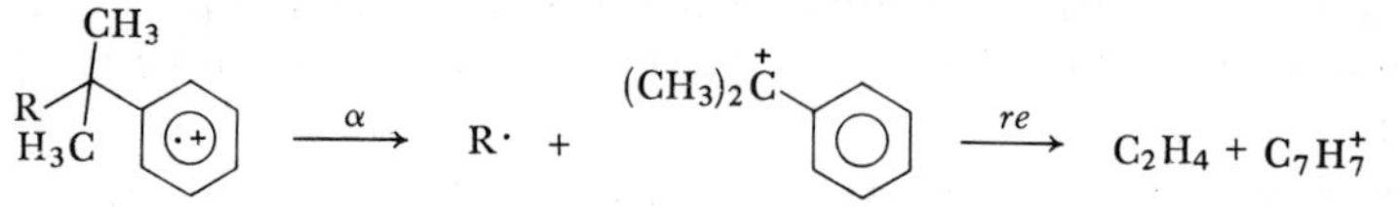

$$(6\text{-}15)$$

decomposes through a "phenylated cyclopropane" intermediate; in the α-^{13}C-labeled analog, 65% of the ^{13}C is lost in forming $C_7H_7^+$) (6.6).

When the alkyl side chain is propyl or larger, hydrogen rearrangement through a six-membered ring transition state can produce the characteristic $OE^{+\cdot}$ ion (reaction 4-18, 6-16).

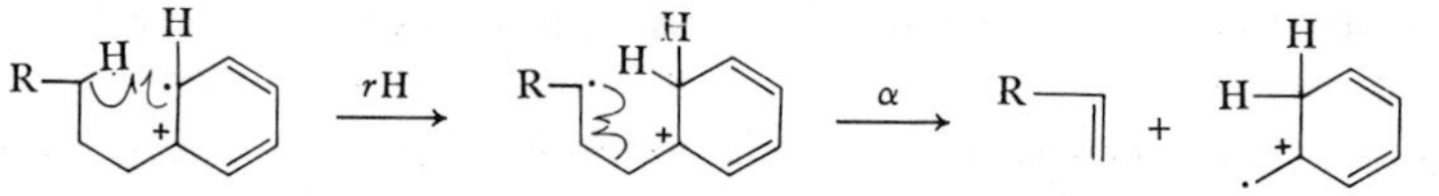

$$(6\text{-}16)$$

Note that the *same* bond is ruptured in reaction 6-16 as in simple benzylic cleavage, reaction 6-13, which is not the case of the analogous reactions of polar unsaturated functionalities, equations 4-16 and 4-4. In some cases the ratio of these competing reactions can be rationalized in terms of the relative charge stabilization in their initiating canonical forms. The relative abundances of the corresponding rearrangement ion, $C_8H_{10}^+$, in the mass spectra of

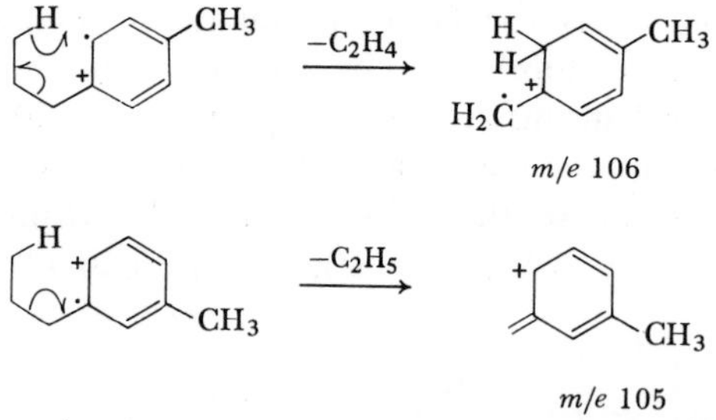

m/e 106

m/e 105

m-tolyl- and p-tolyl-1-propane are 5.5% and 0.9%, respectively, compared to the abundances of the ion from benzylic cleavage, $C_8H_9^+$. The rearrangement is unfavorable when either the γ-position or the ortho-positions are completely substituted, the latter presumably because of steric interference.

The presence of heteroatoms in the aromatic ring or small functional groups directly substituted on the ring usually do not obscure reactions such as the characteristic alkyl side-chain cleavages. This can be seen in Unknowns 6.7 to 6.9, which are isomeric alkylphenols.

m/e	Relative abundance 6.7	6.8	6.9	m/e	Relative abundance 6.7	6.8	6.9
15	0.09		0.06	92	0.30	0.38	0.24
27	0.67	0.88	0.85	93	0.27	0.69	0.13
28	0.28	0.90	0.53	94	0.12	0.12	0.52
29	2.8	2.3	2.2	95	0.51	0.22	3.2
39	1.4	1.0	1.7	103	0.62	1.5	0.35
40	0.15	—	0.20	104	0.20	0.38	0.07
41	5.7	2.8	5.8	105	1.1	1.4	0.49
42	0.22	—	0.23	106	0.21	0.20	0.41
43	0.65	0.59	0.98	107	2.3	3.9	9.2
51	1.2	0.67	0.50	108	0.22	0.33	0.74
52	0.59	0.22	0.16	109	0.15	—	0.16
53	0.86	0.75	0.58	115	2.1	2.0	0.55
54	0.07	—	0.06	116	0.74	0.65	0.16
55	1.3	1.7	1.3	117	1.0	1.2	0.18
56	0.09	—	0.14	118	0.23	0.24	0.14
57	18.	4.7	8.2	119	0.88	0.76	1.6
57.5	0.23	—	—	120	0.26	0.41	0.56
58	1.1	0.29	0.38	121	0.94	5.9	0.77
59	0.22	—	—	122	0.11	0.60	0.07
60	2.4	—	—	128	1.2	0.8	0.09
60.5	0.22	—	—	129	0.72	1.4	0.06
63	0.50	0.37	0.31	130	0.17	0.94	—
63.5	0.09	—	—	131	0.67	1.0	0.23
64	0.90	0.23	0.16	132	0.28	0.40	0.10
64.5	0.15	—	—	133	1.1	2.9	0.57
65	1.1	0.92	1.2	134	0.45	0.73	2.2
65.5	0.11	—	0.03	135	1.7	1.7	100.
66	1.6	0.21	0.30	136	0.20	0.19	10.
66.5	0.19	—	—	147	1.4	3.00	0.08
67	0.64	0.28	0.16	148	0.59	5.0	0.04
71	0.09	—	0.07	149	0.86	1.3	0.74
72	0.78	—	0.03	150	0.12	0.13	0.19
72.5	0.33	—	—	161	1.3	1.6	—
73	3.6	—	—	162	0.20	1.1	—
73.5	0.86	—	—	163	4.6	3.2	—
74	7.9	—	—	164	0.60	0.39	—
74.5	0.88	—	—	165	0.07	—	—
75	0.22	—	0.09	175	3.1	1.1	0.09
76	0.15	0.14	—	176	0.55	—	—
77	1.9	2.2	2.2	177	0.33	100.	—
78	0.48	0.50	0.42	178	—	13.	—
79	1.0	—	0.67	190	0.31	—	—
87	0.15	—	—	191	100.	4.0	0.21
87.5	0.90	—	—	192	14.	0.59	0.03
88	3.5	—	—	193	1.2	—	—
88.5	0.46	—	—	194	0.09	—	—
89	0.36	0.26	0.21	205	0.15	0.81	—
90	0.10	—	0.09	206	15.	15.	3.8
91	2.7	3.1	2.2	207	2.3	2.4	0.60
				208	0.20	0.21	0.06

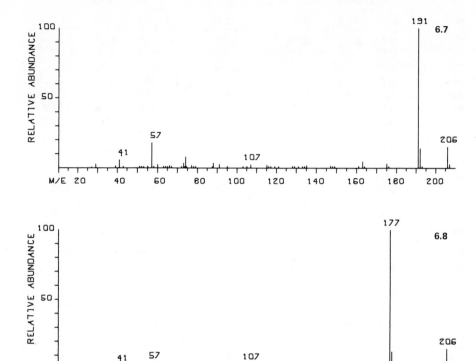

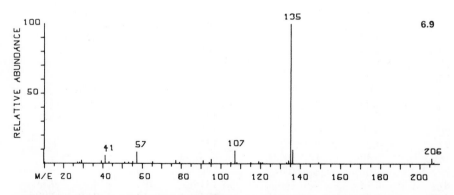

POLYARYL AND POLYCYCLIC AROMATIC COMPOUNDS. The behavior of higher aromatic hydrocarbons can be viewed as an extrapolation of that of alkylbenzenes described above. The molecular and doubly charged ions are of higher abundance. Similar characteristic alkyl side-chain cleavages occur; decomposition in the unsaturated system is subject to severe hydrogen and skeletal scrambling.

Unknown 6.10

m/e	Relative abundance	m/e	Relative abundance	m/e	Relative abundance	m/e	Relative abundance
38	0.16	75.5	0.43	102	1.0	154	0.06
39	1.0	76	10.	103	1.1	163	0.70
40	0.05	76.5	1.3	115	0.54	164	0.20
50	1.0	77	1.1	126	2.7	165	0.07
51	2.3	78	0.22	127	0.89	174	0.53
52	0.67	87	1.3	128	0.64	175	2.3
53	0.06	87.5	0.19	129	0.08	176	14.
63	3.6	88	3.6	139	2.3	177	10.
63.5	0.19	88.5	0.62	140	0.41	178	100.
64	0.38	89	7.4	150	3.9	179	15.
65	0.41	89.5	1.4	151	7.9	180	1.1
74	1.8	90	0.21	152	8.4	181	0.05
75	2.4	91	0.13	153	1.0		

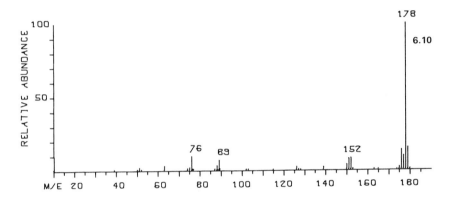

6.2   Alcohols

SATURATED ALIPHATIC ALCOHOLS.   The mass spectrum of 1-octanol was given in Figure 5-5; that of the isomeric 3-methyl-3-heptanol is shown in Figure 6-7.

Addition of a hydroxyl group to an alkane lowers the ionization potential, but the molecular ion abundance decreases (and often is not observable, as in the spectrum of Figure 6-7) despite this stabilization because of the increased ease of decomposition through reactions initiated at the ionized hydroxyl group. Offsetting this lack of M^+, alcohols do undergo ion–molecule reactions to give a pressure-dependent $(M + H)^+$ peak which is useful for molecular weight determination (*3.6*). Thermal and catalytic dehydrogenation and dehydration of the sample, especially in metal reservoir systems, can give spurious peaks such as $(M - 2)^+$, $(M - 18)^+$, and $(M - 20)^+$, although these can also arise through electron-impact induced fragmentation (the presence of the corresponding metastable ion provides a convenient proof of the latter). A substantial peak at m/e 18 has little meaning because of the high possibility of the presence of H_2O from desorption in the inlet system or as an impurity.

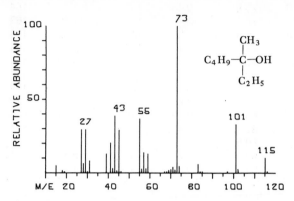

FIGURE 6-7   Mass spectrum of 3-methyl-3-heptanol.

Both the radical site and the charge site of the hydroxyl group are intermediate in their capability for reaction initiation, so that mass spectra of alcohols exhibit many of the types of reactions outlined in Chapter 4. Tertiary alcohols contain the largest, and primary alcohols the smallest, total abundance of oxygen-containing ions in their spectra. In all but the spectra of 1-alkanols, α-cleavage (reaction 4-3) is the most useful characteristic reaction. In the spectrum of 3-methyl-3-heptanol (Figure 6-7) this produces the important peaks at m/e 73, 101, and 115 (6-17), whose abundance reflects

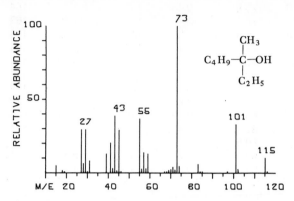

the size of the alkyl groups lost. Formation of such $C_n H_{2n+1} O^+$ ions through the cyclization–displacement reaction 4-29 should be of little importance.

There are a number of possible paths for further decomposition of these EE^+ ions. (The only simple cleavage which could yield another EE^+ ion, reaction 4-13, gives only H^+.) Rearrangement of hydrogen to the carbon atom of the oxonium double bond to eliminate $C_n H_{2n}$ (equation 4-37) can account for the m/e 31, 45, 59, and 87 peaks; the most abundant of these is that predicted for the loss of the largest $C_n H_{2n}$ molecule from the most abundant primary product ion. Further, rearrangement 4-34 could also yield m/e 59 and 73 ions.

The main competitive decomposition of the EE^+ $C_n H_{2n+1} O^+$ ions is dehydration, which contributes to the formation of the m/e 55, 83, and 97 peaks (reaction 4-42). Part of the abundant m/e 29 and 43 peaks are due to CHO^+ and $C_2 H_3 O^+$, which also may arise from decomposition of the $C_n H_{2n+1} O^+$ ions; obviously, care should be exercised in using products of secondary EE^+ ion reactions, such as these and those of 6-17, as evidence of structure.

The other major decomposition pathway possible for alcohol molecular ions leads to the loss of $H_2 O$ and of $(H_2 O + C_n H_{2n})$ $(n \geq 2)$, reaction 4-26. As can be seen from the abundances of the predicted m/e 112 and 42 peaks, this reaction is less competitive in branched alcohols. In contrast, most of the spectra of straight-chain alcohols, such as 1-octanol (Figure 5-5) and 1-hexadecanol (Figure 6-8), show products which would result from such a primary

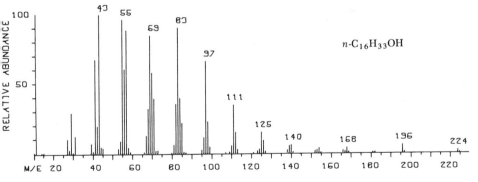

FIGURE 6-8   Mass spectrum of 1-hexadecanol.

dehydration of the molecular ion. The $C_n H_{2n+1} O^+$ ions which would arise from simple α-cleavage (m/e 31) and displacement (reaction 4-29) are minor. The rest of the spectrum closely resembles that of the corresponding alkene, as can be seen by comparing the spectra of 1-hexadecanol (Figure 6-8) and 1-hexadecene (Figure 6-2). The prominent $C_n H_{2n-1}^+$, $C_n H_{2n}^+$, and $C_n H_{2n+1}^+$ ion series of 1-alkanols (which could arise in part directly from M^+) can give evidence of branching or other structural features of the carbon skeleton; this fragmentation behavior generally follows that outlined for the corresponding hydrocarbons.

Unknown 6.11

m/e	Relative abundance	m/e	Relative abundance
15	0.72	69	100.
17	0.25	70	8.4
18	1.1	71	3.7
19	0.99	72	7.1
27	20.	73	61.
28	2.0	74	2.8
29	12.	75	0.16
30	0.60	83	1.6
31	11.	84	0.86
32	0.13	85	1.7
39	6.4	86	5.6
40	1.0	87	57.
41	34.	88	3.4
42	4.0	89	0.20
43	33.	96.5 m	0.05
44	9.2	97	0.25
45	11.	99	0.20
46	0.26	111	0.08
55	86.	112[a]	7.4
56	6.6	113	0.98
57	14.	114	0.01
58	3.6	127	0.29
59	1.0	128	0.50
67	1.0	129[a]	0.94
68	0.56	130	0.09

[a] The elemental compositions of the *m/e* 112 and 129 ions are C_8H_{16} and $C_8H_{17}O$, respectively, by high-resolution mass spectrometry.

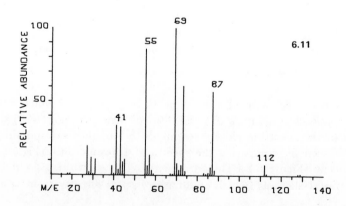

CYCLIC ALIPHATIC ALCOHOLS.   The spectrum of 2-methylcyclo-
hexanol is shown in Figure 6-9. Alpha cleavage (reaction 4-3) is favored at the

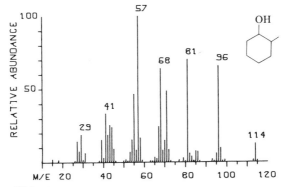

FIGURE 6-9   Mass spectrum of 2-methylcyclohexanol.

more substituted ring bond (6-18 > 6-19). No neutral is lost in this cleavage,

however. Further reaction through olefin elimination gives characteristic OE⁺
ions at m/e 44, 58, 72, and 86. However, this reaction is not as favorable as
hydrogen abstraction, in which a secondary radical site is formed. Elimination
of an alkyl radical gives the stable $C_3H_5O^+$ (6-18) or $C_4H_7O^+$ (6-19) ions. A
minor process, reaction 6-20, indicated by labeling studies involves abstraction
of the hydroxyl hydrogen (a favored type of hydrogen for rearrangement) by
the initial radical product to give the heptanal molecular ion; further

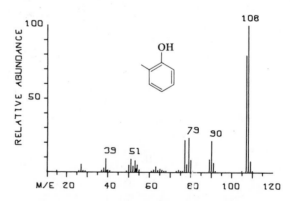

$$\text{(6-20)}$$

decomposition of this and the analogously formed 2-methylhexanal will also contribute to peaks such as m/e 44 and 58.

As in the mass spectra of acyclic alcohols, loss of H_2O (reaction 4-25) provides the other major pathway for $M^{\ddagger}$ decomposition. This largely involves the hydrogen atoms attached to carbons 3, 4, and 5 which would be expected from a *cis*-stereochemistry of the eliminated groups in the boat-form transition state. The spectrum's hydrocarbon-type ions are consistent with those expected from further decomposition of such bicyclic dehydration products; the m/e 68 and 54 $OE^{\ddagger}$ ions would represent elimination of a bridging group as the stable C_2H_4 or C_3H_6 (note that the "rule" of loss of the largest alkyl *radical* does not apply to the elimination of molecules; in this case the $C_5H_8^{\ddagger}$ ion should be more stable and thus more abundant than the alternative $C_4H_6^{\ddagger}$ ion).

PHENOLS.   The spectrum of *o*-methylphenol (Figure 6-10) illustrates a number of fragmentations characteristic of the hydroxyl group on an

FIGURE 6-10   Mass spectrum of *o*-methylphenol.

aromatic ring. The odd-electron $(M - CO)^{\ddagger}$ peak, which is usually accompanied by $(M - CHO)^+$, is especially useful in recognizing this functionality. The apparent mechanism (6-21) involves elimination of oxygen with its adjacent ring carbon, as shown by ^{13}C labeling studies of phenol (6.7); deuterium labeling studies indicate that CHO loss is accompanied by substantial hydrogen scrambling.

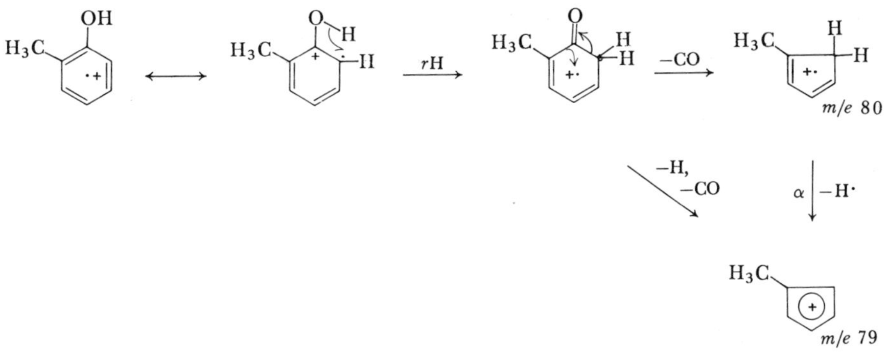

(6-21)

The characteristic OE^{+} ion at $(M - 18)^{+}$ in this spectrum is an example of the "ortho effect" (6-22; see reaction 4-28); the abundances of the $(M - 18)^{+}$

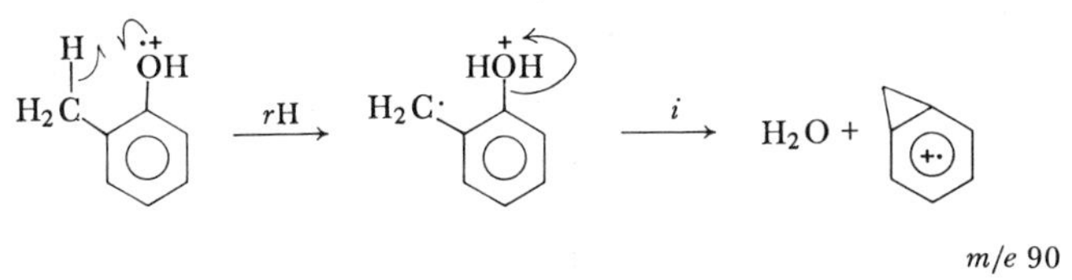

(6-22)

peak in the corresponding meta and para isomers are only 3% and 2%, respectively. The large $(M - 1)^{+}$ peak arises from the loss of the benzylic hydrogen atom.

ALCOHOLS CONTAINING OTHER FUNCTIONAL GROUPS.   The hydroxyl hydrogen exhibits a high tendency for transfer to a radical site. In a phenol the hydroxyl hydrogen atom can thus act as a ready donor for an ortho effect rearrangement. The base peak of methyl salicylate is due to the loss of methanol (6-23), while the corresponding abundances for the meta and

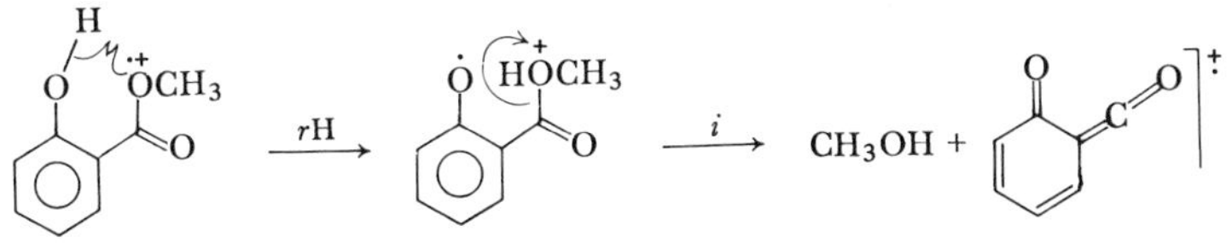

(6-23)

para isomers are <1%. Isomeric structures other than those shown are possible for the product ions of 6-22 and 6-23. Can you utilize these correlations for Unknown 6.12?

Unknown 6.12

m/e	Relative abundance	m/e	Relative abundance	m/e	Relative abundance
15	0.23	74	2.1	133	0.13
26	0.59	75	3.9	135	0.09
27	3.2	76	3.5	143	4.0
28	1.7	77	1.6	144	0.69
29	5.5	78	0.58	145	4.0
30	0.12	79	0.15	146	0.70
31	0.09	91	1.4	147	0.08
38	3.2	92	1.9	155	2.7
39	6.1	93	17.	156	0.33
40	0.22	94	1.1	157	2.8
41	0.18	95	0.06	158	0.31
42	0.07	103	0.17	159	0.15
43	0.36	104	0.41	172	100.
45	0.13	105	0.24	173	6.7
50	4.0	106	0.33	174	98.
51	1.3	107	0.02	175	6.5
52	0.23	116	0.19	176	0.36
53	1.3	117	2.2	185	0.33
54	0.10	118	0.27	186	0.03
55	0.27	119	2.2	187	0.32
62	2.5	120	0.72	188	0.02
63	7.8	121	0.20	200	42.
64	4.5	122	0.02	201	3.7
65	17.	128	0.09	202	42.
66	1.2	129	0.28	203	3.8
67	0.13	130	0.10	204	0.22
73	0.41	131	0.32		

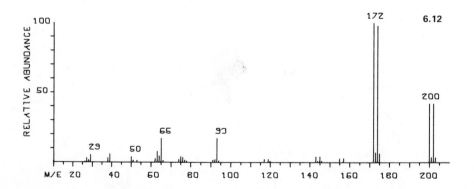

6.3   Aldehydes and Ketones

ALIPHATIC ALDEHYDES AND KETONES.   The mass spectra of 3-pentanone,   3-methyl-2-butanone,   4-methyl-2-pentanone,   3-methyl-2-pentanone, and 2,3-butanedione have been given as Unknowns 4.8, 4.9, 4.12,

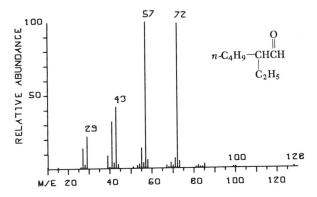

FIGURE 6-11   Mass spectrum of 2-ethylhexanal.

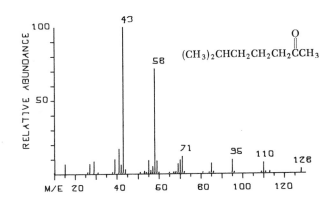

FIGURE 6-12   Mass spectrum of 6-methyl-2-heptanone.

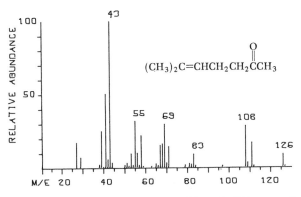

FIGURE 6-13   Mass spectrum of 6-methyl-5-heptene-2-one.

4.13, and 5.3; those of 2-ethylhexanal, 6-methyl-2-heptanone, and 6-methyl-5-heptene-2-one (*6.8*) are shown in Figures 6-11 to 6-13.

Addition of a carbonyl group to an alkane lowers the ionization potential substantially; typical values (Table A-3) of 9.4 to 9.8 eV are below those of the corresponding aliphatic alcohols. The molecular ion of even larger aldehydes and ketones with some degree of chain branching is usually of observable abundance.

The characteristic peaks in the spectra of carbonyl compounds provide examples of many of the major types of fragmentation pathways discussed in Chapter 4, as shown in equations 4-4, 4-14, 4-15, 4-16, 4-19, 4-23, 4-25, 4-31, 4-33, 4-41, and Table 4-1. Many of these are utilized in reactions 6-24 and 6-25 to rationalize the formation of the characteristic peaks in 2-ethylhexanal (Figure 6-11) and 6-methyl-2-heptanone (Figure 6-12). The α-

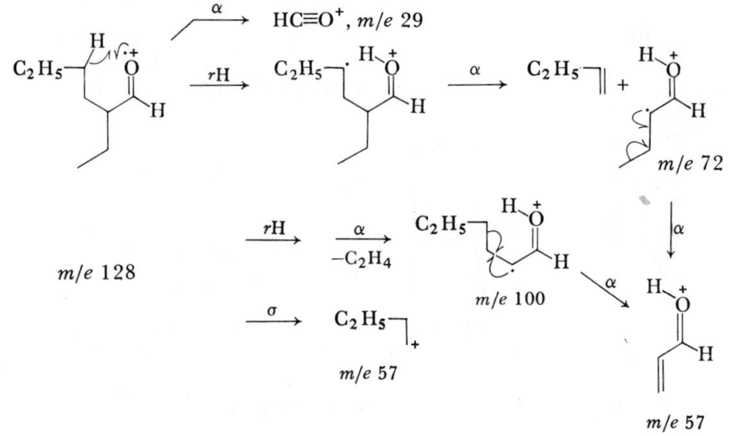

(6-24)

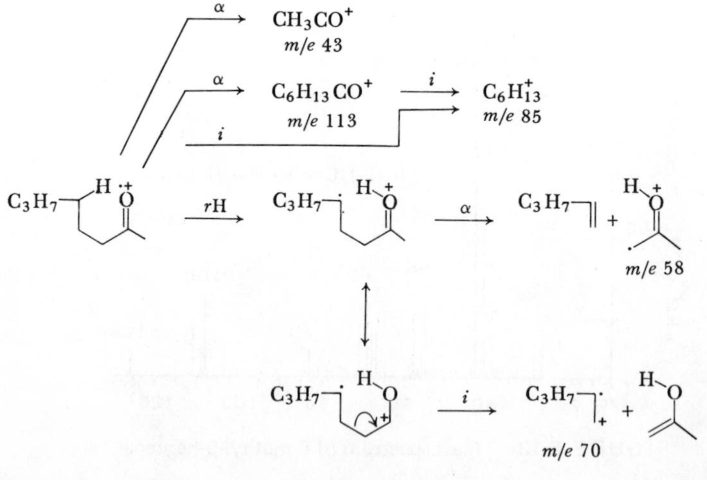

(6-25)

cleavage reaction is generally much less important for aldehydes than for ketones. The CHO^+ (m/e 29) peak is prominent only for smaller aldehydes and those with highly electronegative functionalities, such as C_3F_7CHO. The alternative α-cleavage yielding $(M - H)^+$ appears to be appreciable only when the RCO^+ ion which is formed is substantially stabilized, as for aromatic aldehydes. Alpha cleavage is much more prominent in aliphatic ketones, yielding a pair of acylium ions (m/e 113 and 43 in Figure 6-12) and a pair of alkyl ions (m/e 85 and 15). The more abundant acylium ion is usually formed by the loss of the larger alkyl group, while the more abundant alkyl ion is usually the more stable. Unknowns 4.8 and 4.9 gave further examples of this.

Ions of the general formula $C_nH_{2n+1}CO^+$ can also arise, however, through cleavages at other bonds. "Reciprocal hydrogen rearrangement" (*4.6*), reaction 4-24, may provide an important driving force for this. Aldehydes and ketones show the characteristic ion series 15, 29, 43, 57, $\cdots$ due to both $C_nH_{2n+1}CO^+$ and $C_nH_{2n+1}^+$ ions. Although these are best distinguished by high-resolution data, the absence of a particular $C_nH_{2n+1}^+$ ion can sometimes be demonstrated by a low $[(A+1)^+]/[A^+]$ value (Section 2.3). Such ions can also be formed by displacement reactions, for example:

$$\text{(structure)} \xrightarrow{rd} H_3C\cdot + \text{(structure)}$$

This low-energy reaction is important only in metastable decompositions, possibly because precursor ions of the required energy (see Chapter 8) are formed in low abundance by electron impact ionization (*4.10*).

Initial rearrangement of a γ-hydrogen atom followed by β-cleavage can give an enol ion (m/e 72 and 100 in Figure 6.11 and m/e 58 in Figure 6.12) and its complementary alkene ion, reactions 4-16 and 4-25. The relative abundances of these competitive products are reflected by their ionization potentials (Table A-3); enols generally have lower ionization potentials than n-alkenes, making these ions more abundant. Further α-cleavage of either OE^+ enol ion from 2-ethylhexanal will produce the resonance-stabilized $C_3H_5O^+$ ion. As was also illustrated in Unknowns 4.12 and 4.13, comparison of the products of the α-cleavage and the β-cleavage reactions thus provides evidence of substituents at the α-position(s). If a ketone contains γ-hydrogen atoms in both chains, both hydrogen atoms can be rearranged with losses of both olefin molecules (see reaction 4-19).

Ions corresponding to $(M - C_2H_4)^{+\cdot}$ have also been reported for larger n-alkyl aldehydes. Both aliphatic aldehydes and ketones can exhibit anomalous $(M - 18)^{+\cdot}$ peaks from the loss of water.

Unknowns 6.13 to 6.15 are spectra of isomeric compounds.

Unknowns 6.13–6.15

m/e	Relative abundance 6.13	6.14	6.15
14	2.1	4.7	2.0
15	4.4	6.0	14.
26	10.	21.	3.1
27	34.	45.	4.8
28	62.	25.	4.7
29	100.	80.	3.0
30	6.4	24.	0.15
31	3.5	60.	0.51
37	3.3	6.8	1.7
38	3.5	9.4	1.9
39	7.3	39.	4.2
40	1.2	11.	0.83
41	2.8	7.6	1.9
42	3.2	2.1	6.7
43	3.9	6.0	100.
44	0.12	0.20	2.4
45	0.01	0.01	0.22
55	2.3	6.2	0.35
56	0.98	8.1	0.03
57	18.	100.	1.1
58	64.	26.	37.
59	2.4	1.1	1.2
60	0.16	0.08	0.09

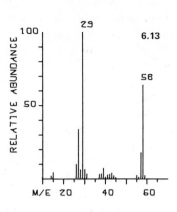

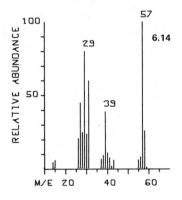

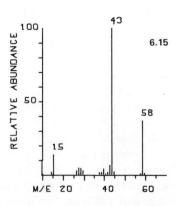

UNSATURATED KETONES.   If the γ-hydrogen is vinylic, this can drastically reduce the formation of ions from hydrogen rearrangement and subsequent β-cleavage. Thus these OE$\cdot^{+}$ peaks are of very low abundance in 4-methyl-6-hepten-3-one and 4-methyl-4-penten-2-one (6-26). However, in 6-methyl-5-hepten-2-one (Figure 6-13) isomerization of the double bond to a more favorable position is possible (reaction 6-26), and the $C_3H_6O^{+}$ and

$$\text{(6-26)}$$

$C_5H_8\cdot^{+}$ rearrangement ions are observed in fair abundance, although [$C_3H_6O\cdot^{+}$] is less than that in the saturated derivative. Paralleling the behavior of alkenes (reaction 6-5), double-bond isomerization apparently has not occurred in all M^{+}; the m/e 69 ion, which would be the product of allylic cleavage, is more abundant than the α-cleavage m/e 83 ion (*6.9*).

In certain cases displacement reactions appear to be possible at the carbonyl group; such a reaction (6-27) accounts for the base peak corresponding to $(M - CH_3)^{+}$ in the spectrum of β-ionone (Unknown 6.6) (*6.10*).

$$\text{(6-27)}$$

Unknown 6.16 can be formed from β-ionone by opening the ring. Try to devise a structure that is consistent with its mass spectrum (*6.8*).

Unknown 6.16

m/e	Relative abundance	m/e	Relative abundance
27	11.	105	2.3
29	6.0	106	1.6
39	13.	107	2.9
41	75.	108	1.3
42	4.2	109	34.
43	49.	110	2.9
44	1.4	111	0.25
45	0.11	121	1.7
53	11.	122	0.78
54	1.8	123	1.4
55	4.4	124	22.
57	0.51	125	2.0
58	0.25	126	0.12
67	7.2	133	0.53
68	1.9	134	1.5
69	100.	135	1.1
70	6.6	136	0.45
71	0.57	149	3.1
79	9.5	150	0.34
80	12.	159	0.90
81	47.	160	0.12
82	4.5	174	0.43
83	1.0	175	0.06
91	5.4	177	1.6
92	1.4	178	0.21
93	3.6	192	3.6
94	0.92	193	0.52
95	2.0	194	0.04
96	0.24		

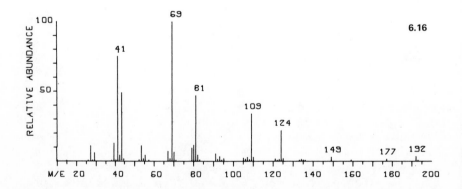

6.16

ALICYCLIC KETONES.   The mass spectrum of isophorone (Figure 6-14) illustrates major additional fragmentation pathways found for cyclic

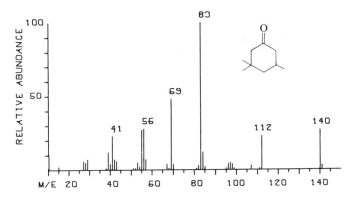

FIGURE 6-14   Mass spectrum of 3,3,5-trimethylcyclohexanone.

ketones (reaction 6-28); these are similar to those discussed for cyclic alcohols.

$$(6-28)$$

AROMATIC ALDEHYDES AND KETONES.   Fragmentations in these spectra (for those of acetophenone and benzophenone see Unknowns 5.13 and 5.2) in general follow expected pathways; for example, benzaldehydes show characteristic $(M - H)^+$ and $(M - CHO)^+$ ions. Loss of CO can occur (Table 4-1), especially if the carbonyl group is endocyclic, such as in anthraquinone. The abundances of RCO^+ ions from $YC_6H_4COR^+$ have been shown to obey linear free energy $(\sigma\rho)$ correlations, although (6.11) a number of substituent-affected factors control $[RCO^+]$.

When the pesticide DDE, $Cl_2C=C(p\text{-}C_6H_4Cl)_2$, is irradiated in air, a compound is formed (6.12) whose mass spectrum is shown as Unknown 6.17.

Unknown 6.17

m/e	Relative abundance	m/e	Relative abundance
61[a]	4.5	124	4.9
61.5	4.9	125	3.6
62	6.5	126	0.5
63	2.8	149	11.
73	10.0	150	37.
73.5	2.4	151	5.1
74	13.1	152	0.31
74.5	4.5	184	6.5
75	19.8	185	20.
75.5	4.1	186	4.4
76	3.0	187	6.9
92	12.	188	1.0
92.5	12.	213	4.9
93	6.0	214	0.70
93.5	5.1	215	1.8
95	2.4	220	22.
97	4.1	221	2.8
98	6.5	222	15.
99	7.7	223	2.3
100	2.8	224	2.3
109.5	16.	225	0.31
110	4.5	248	100.
110.5	11.	249	14.
111	2.6	250	64.
111.5	1.6	251	9.2
112	3.6	252	9.9
121	1.2	253	1.5
122	3.2	254	0.10
123	5.7		

[a] Data below m/e 60 were not recorded.

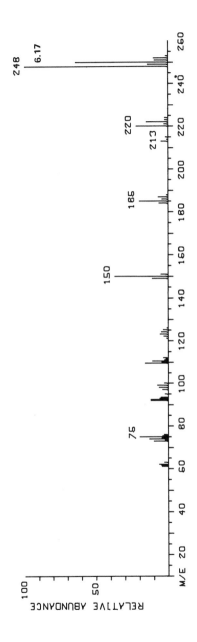

Unknown 6.18 was found as the principle constituent of a defensive secretion of the willow-feeding larva *Coleoptera chrysomelidae* (*6.13*). Can you identify it?

Unknown 6.18

m/e	Relative abundance	m/e	Relative abundance
27	2.0	64	2.6
28	0.59	65	27.
29	3.6	66	8.5
31	1.0	67	1.1
37	3.3	68	0.42
38	7.2	74	1.9
39	27.	75	1.4
40	6.6	76	19.
46	1.4	77	2.3
46.5	0.50	92	1.8
47	4.3	93	18.
50	5.4	94	5.8
51	3.4	95	0.39
52	0.77	104	13.
53	4.9	105	1.0
54	0.51	106	0.04
55	1.6	121	89.
61	2.9	122	100.
62	2.8	123	7.9
63	5.6	124	0.67

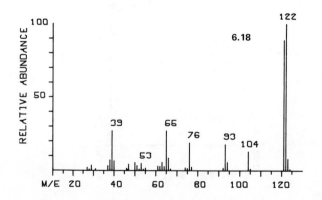

6.4   Esters

ALIPHATIC METHYL ESTERS.   The classic studies of Stenhagen and
his co-workers in the 1950's on the mass spectra of fatty acid esters (6.14)
was probably the first clear demonstration of the value of mass spectrometry
for structure determination of complex natural product molecules. The mass
spectrum of methyl octadecanoate is shown in Figure 5-3; Unknown 5.9 is
methyl 3,7,11,15-tetramethyloctadecanoate. Molecular ions of appreciable
abundance are observable even for methyl esters of high-molecular-weight
n-aliphatic acids; $[M^+]$ actually increases at higher molecular weights ($>C_6$),
although it decreases with chain branching.

Both the carbonyl oxygen and the saturated oxygen atom of esters can act
as sites for reaction initiation to give reaction paths expected from the
separate behavior of these functionalities and, in addition, new reactions
apparently due to their combined effects.

Methyl esters which do not contain an additional functionality show the
expected reactions of the carbonyl group—α-cleavage (reaction 6-29) and
β-cleavage with γ-hydrogen rearrangement (reaction 6-30) (6.15). For methyl
n-alkanoates, such as Figure 5-3, α-cleavage gives characteristic $(M - 31)^+$ and
59^+ ions whose abundances decrease with increasing molecular weight. The
$(M - 59)^+$ alkyl ion and the CH_3O^+ ion are very small except for low-
molecular-weight esters. Further decomposition of the alkyl moiety produces
the characteristic $C_nH_{2n+1}^+$ and $C_nH_{2n-1}^+$ ion series.

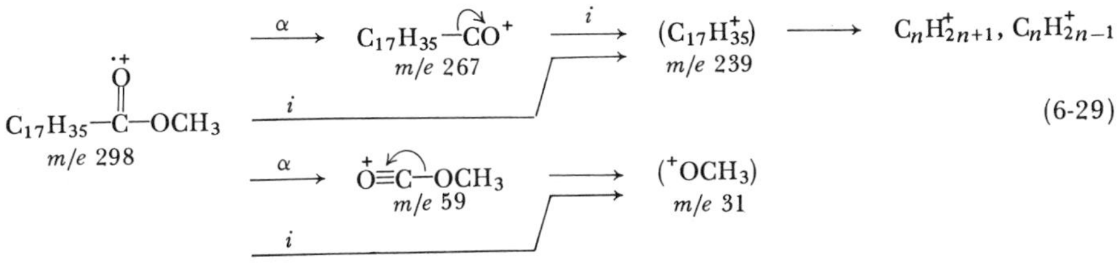

(6-29)

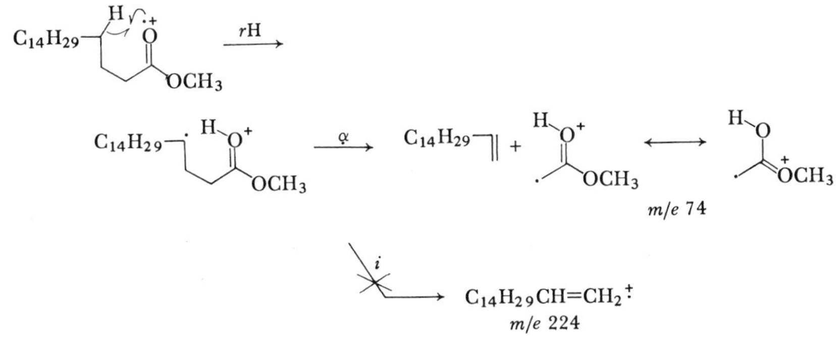

(6-30)

Chain branching produces characteristic changes in the $CH_3OCO(CH_2)_n^+$ ion series, m/e 59, (73), 87, 101, $\cdots$, through increased cleavage at the tertiary carbon. However, the straight-chain alkanoates show an unusual periodicity in the $CH_3OCO(CH_2)_n^+$ ion series that is quite different from the regular abundance decrease with increasing molecular weight found for the $C_nH_{2n+1}^+$ series of n-alkanes. Note in Figure 5-3 the unusually high abundances in this series for m/e 87, 143, 199, and 255 (n = 1, 5, 9, and 13). These arise mainly (*6.15*) through initial migration of the δ- or ε-hydrogen, with reciprocal hydrogen transfer to produce the radical site on the α-carbon (reaction 6-31). Appreciable hydrogen scrambling indicates multiple transfers, so that the tendency for the m/e 87, 143, 199, $\cdots$ ions may be due to the favored loss of the allylic α-hydrogen and favored six-membered ring transition states. Another unusual rearrangement yielding $C_nH_{2n+1}CO^+$ ions identified by Stenhagen and his co-workers involves the formation of $(M - C_3H_7)^+$, possibly through two displacement reactions (6-32; see Table 4-1).

Beta cleavage with hydrogen rearrangement produces the characteristic $CR_2C(OH)OCH_3^+$ peak; for methyl octadecanoate (Figure 5-3) this is the base peak at m/e 74 (reaction 6-30). The companion $(M - CR_2C(OH)OCH_3)^+$ peak is weak for saturated esters but can be substantial if its ionization potential is lowered such as by the addition of a double bond. There is also some tendency for a double hydrogen rearrangement in methyl esters of longer-chain acids, here yielding m/e 75 (see reaction 4-39). If the size of the alcoholic alkyl group R is indicated by the $(M - OR)^+$ and $ROCO^+$ ions, the mass of the rearrangement ion $CR_\alpha R'_\alpha C(OH)OR^+$ thus defines the size of the α-substituents. If an R_α group is ethyl or larger, secondary β-bond cleavage can give a conjugated EE^+ ion (6-33).

$$R\!-\!CH_2\dot{C}R'_\alpha C(OH)=\overset{+}{O}R \quad \xrightarrow{\alpha} \quad R\cdot + CH_2=CR'_\alpha C(OH)=\overset{+}{O}R \qquad (6\text{-}33)$$

ETHYL AND HIGHER ESTERS.   The molecular ion peak of RCOOR' generally becomes relatively small when R' is larger than butyl. The spectrum of *sec*-butyl acetate (Figure 6.15) illustrates the additional reactions

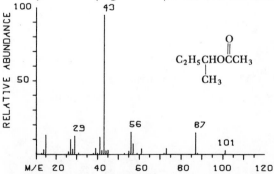

FIGURE 6-15   Mass spectrum of *sec*-butyl acetate. The M^+ peak at m/e 116 has an abundance of 0.1%.

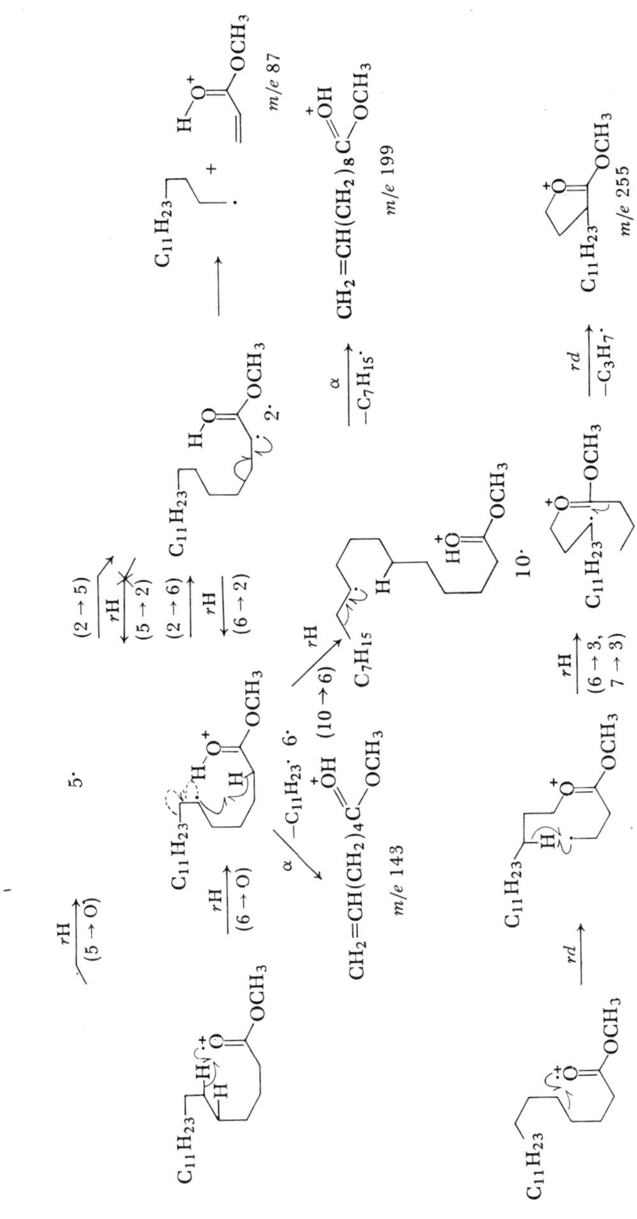

$C_{11}H_{23}$

$m/e\ 87$ (6-31)

$CH_2{=}CH(CH_2)_8C\overset{+}{\underset{OH}{C}}{\diagdown}OCH_3$
$m/e\ 199$

α
$-C_7H_{15}^{\cdot}$

$C_{11}H_{23}$ OCH$_3$ 2·

$(2 \rightarrow 5)$ / rH / $(5 \rightarrow 2)$
$(2 \rightarrow 6)$ rH $(6 \rightarrow 2)$

5·

rH $(5 \rightarrow O)$

rH $(6 \rightarrow O)$

$C_{11}H_{23}$ OCH$_3$

α $-C_{11}H_{23}^{\cdot}$ 6·

$CH_2{=}CH(CH_2)_4C\overset{+}{\underset{OH}{C}}{\diagdown}OCH_3$
$m/e\ 143$

$(10 \rightarrow 6)$

C_7H_{15}

rH

$C_7H_{15}^{\cdot}$

HO OCH$_3$ 10·

$C_{11}H_{23}$ OCH$_3$

rH $(6 \rightarrow O)$

rH $(6 \rightarrow 3,\ 7 \rightarrow 3)$

$C_{11}H_{23}$ OCH$_3$

rd

$C_{11}H_{23}$ OCH$_3$

rd $-C_3H_7^{\cdot}$

$C_{11}H_{23}$ OCH$_3$
$m/e\ 255$

(6-32)

that are possible with such esters. Rearrangement of one (reaction 4-25) and two (reaction 4-39) hydrogen atoms is highly characteristic (reaction 6-34).

$$ (6\text{-}34) $$

$$ (6\text{-}35) $$

For the former reaction alkene ion formation predominates for propyl and higher esters, consistent with the ionization potentials of acids and alkenes. Although the double hydrogen rearrangement produces an even-electron ion of only moderate abundance, you should be able to recognize it from its low rings-plus-double-bonds value and because it occurs in a rather unusual ion series $(47, 61, 75, \cdots)$.

Alpha cleavage (6-35) at the carbonyl group yields the large m/e 43 ion; the alternative $(M - CH_3)^+$ peak at m/e 101 is small. This latter peak actually can also be produced by an additional α-cleavage reaction initiated by the saturated oxygen atom; a similar cleavage with loss of the largest group produces the significant m/e 87 peak, providing a means to distinguish this spectrum from that of n-butyl acetate, in which this α-cleavage gives a peak at m/e 73. Note that the ion series m/e 59, 73, 87, $\cdots$ can be due to either $C_nH_{2n+1}O^+$ or $C_nH_{2n+1}COO^+$. A large peak in formate esters is formed by α-cleavage followed by CO loss ($HCOOCHR_2^+ \overset{\alpha}{\to} HCO\overset{+}{O}=CHR \overset{re}{\to} HOCHR^+ +$ CO).

Charge site initiation at the saturated oxygen, $RCOO-R'^+ \to RCOO\cdot + R'^+$, can give important peaks when R is small and R'^+ is stable. Thus for the n-, sec-, and $tert$-butyl acetates the values of $[(M - CH_3COO)^+]/\Sigma_{ions}$ are 1%, 3%, and 17%, respectively. A reaction like 4-26 predicts that $C_nH_{2n+1}CH_2CH_2OCOR^{+}$ should yield $C_nH_{2n}^+$ as well as $C_{n+2}H_{2n+4}^+$ ions.

A rather unusual OE^+ ion can arise from the elimination of the oxygen and α-carbon of the alcohol moiety as an aldehyde molecule. (This mechanism is not important in the spectrum in Figure 6-15.) Thioesters, $R-C_2H_4S-COR$, can give a significant $(M - C_2H_4S)^{+}$ ion (Table 4-1).

If both the ester and acid chains are of sufficient length (ethyl butanoate or larger), the hydrogen rearrangements 6-31 and 6-34 can occur sequentially; these characteristic ions will appear at m/e 60 and 61 if the acid's α-carbon atom is not substituted.

ESTERS CONTAINING OTHER FUNCTIONAL GROUPS.   As was mentioned above, the saturated oxygen atom of the ester group is also capable of acting as a site to which a hydrogen atom can be transferred. In reaction 4-28 of benzoate esters the presence of an α-hydrogen on an ortho substituent gives a characteristic product ion corresponding to the loss of an alcohol molecule; the addition of a 9,10-double bond to methyl octadecanoate gives $(M - CH_3OH)^{+}$ as the largest peak in its spectrum. A labile hydrogen attached to the C-6 position of a methyl alkanoate often gives characteristic $(M - 32)^{+}$ and $(M - 76)^{+}$ peaks (6.16) (reaction 6-36). The loss of ROH from M^{+}

apparently is favored only if the radical site is stabilized; this OE^+ ion often then loses CO (for example, ortho-substituted benzoate esters) or CH_2CO. The requirement of radical site stabilization is also met in EE^+ and some

OE$^+$ *fragment* ions of other esters that contain a labile hydrogen atom. Hydrogen activation is caused by groups such as keto, amino, ether, hydroxy (reaction 6-37), and trimethylsilyloxy (*6.17*), as well as by chain branching and unsaturation.

$$(6\text{-}37)$$

The mass spectra of alkenoate esters are relatively independent of the double bond position, which apparently migrates readily; for example, methyl alkenoates usually show the m/e 74 and 87 ions characteristic of methyl alkanoates. Cyclization can apparently cause displacement at the δ-position (reaction 6-38). Unsaturated methyl and ethyl esters exhibit peaks from the

$$(6\text{-}38)$$

elimination of CO_2 and $HCO_2\cdot$ (Table 4-1). Enol acetates and other unsaturated acetates give ions corresponding to the loss of ketene. Polyacetoxy compounds can show characteristic peaks such as $(CH_3CO)_3O^+$ (reaction 4-48) whose formation must involve acetyl migration.

AROMATIC ESTERS.   The common ester reactions cited above are found for aromatic esters (see the mass spectrum of n-butyl benzoate, Unknown 4.16); not surprisingly, charge retention on the aryl-containing fragment is strongly favored. If the aromatic ring contains alkyl groups, these undergo the typical fragmentations of arylalkenes described above. "Ortho" effects (reaction 4-28) are useful in identifying such ring isomerism.

A variety of new reaction pathways are made possible by the ability of the aromatic ring to reduce bond dissociation energies (reactions 4-28 and 6-36), stabilize the ion and radical sites (reaction 4-28), and provide an unsaturated site for rearrangement and cyclization (reactions 4-30 and 6-39) reactions. For

$$(6\text{-}39)$$

example, $(M - CH_2CO)^+$ is a peak characteristic of aryl acetate spectra $(C_6H_6O^+$ is the base peak in the spectrum of $C_6H_5OCOCH_3)$.

The spectrum of diethyl phthalate was given as Unknown 5.10. In addition to the expected fragmentations, phthalates give a highly characteristic peak at m/e 149. Its formation is rationalized in reaction 6-40 for di-n-butyl phthalate.

$$(6\text{-}40)$$

Unknown 6.19 is the spectrum of a simple ester prepared from an acid isolated from the preen gland secretion of the Peiping duck. What is its structure?

Unknown 6.19 (6.18)

m/e	Relative abundance	m/e	Relative abundance	m/e	Relative abundance
15	0.82	70	13.	104	0.03
27	11.	71	5.1	111	2.0
28	4.4	72	0.60	112	2.4
29	26.	73	22.	113	0.57
39	7.9	74	10.	115	0.84
40	1.4	75	2.8	125	3.2
41	24.	81	5.1	129	25.
42	7.1	82	0.79	130	2.0
43	33.	83	16.	131	0.18
44	1.7	84	2.3	139	1.4
45	8.2	85	3.7	141	29.
46	0.16	87	1.7	142	2.8
55	32.	88	73.	143	0.79
56	13.	89	7.9	157	5.4
57	29.	90	0.57	158	0.82
58	1.4	97	8.2	159	0.84
59	4.3	98	6.5	171	0.82
60	14.	99	15.	172	0.08
61	13.	100	1.1	185	0.29
67	3.1	101	100.	186	1.7
68	1.1	102	12.	187	0.21
69	9.9	103	1.1	188	0.03

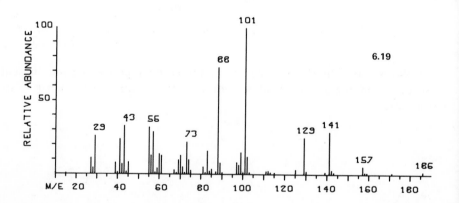

Unknown 6.20 is the spectrum from a trace of white powder found in the pocket of a suspected smuggler. Is the mass spectrum consistent with that which you would expect from 2β-methoxycarbonyl-3β-benzoyloxytropane (cocaine)?

Unknown 6.20 (6.19)

m/e	Relative abundance	m/e	Relative abundance	m/e	Relative abundance
40	1.1	79	1.9	138	1.0
41	7.0	80	3.2	140	1.1
42	23.	81	12.	150	2.0
43	1.9	82	95.	151	1.3
44	4.0	83	41.	152	2.4
45	0.91	84	4.0	153	1.0
50	2.0	91	2.9	154	1.1
51	7.6	92	1.0	155	1.8
52	1.1	93	3.7	166	3.2
53	3.0	94	33.	167	1.0
54	2.1	95	5.0	168	3.1
55	8.2	96	27.	169	0.29
56	3.0	97	17.	180	1.0
57	4.8	98	1.3	181	5.0
58	1.0	105	35.	182	100.
59	3.7	106	3.2	183	12.
65	2.3	107	1.0	184	0.96
66	1.0	108	3.3	198	11.
67	5.0	109	1.0	199	1.2
68	4.7	119	1.8	200	0.12
69	2.2	120	1.1	272	9.0
70	2.0	121	1.0	273	1.6
71	0.82	122	12.	274	0.21
76	1.4	123	1.9	303	25.
77	31.	124	6.0	304	4.8
78	3.0	125	0.92	305	0.63

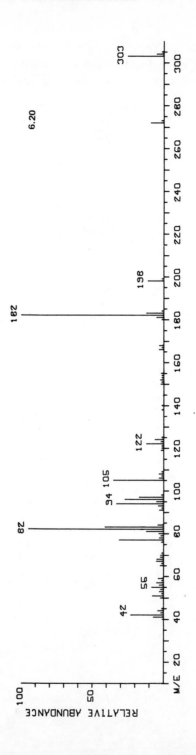

Each of the incomplete spectra of Unknowns 6.21, 6.22, and 6.23 is due to one of these compounds:

(a) $CH_2=C(CH_3)\overset{\overset{\displaystyle O}{\|}}{C}OCH_3$ (b) $CH_3CH_2CH_2CH_2CH_2\overset{\overset{\displaystyle O}{\|}}{C}H$ (c) $CH_3\overset{\overset{\displaystyle O}{\|}}{C}C(CH_3)_3$

(d) $CH_3CH_2CH_2CH_2OCH=CH_2$ (e) $CH_3\overset{\overset{\displaystyle O}{\|}}{C}OCH_2CH=CH_2$

(All these have a molecular weight of 100.) Assign the proper structure to each spectrum.

Unknowns 6.21–6.23

	Relative abundance		
m/e	6.21	6.22	6.23
29	32.	4.0	3.4
41	51.	100.	11.
42	3.7	5.3	2.7
43	37.	2.1	100.
44	0.86	3.6	2.6
55	4.3	6.3	0.76
56	7.0	2.7	0.18
57	100.	1.0	7.9
58	4.9	0.85	11.
59	2.3	9.2	0.44
60	0.33	0.37	0.21
61	0.19	0.17	2.7
69	0.87	83.	0.06
70	0.39	4.2	0.02
71	0.27	0.57	0.37
85	4.9	4.7	0.33
99	0.37	10.	0.02
100	26.	51.	0.25

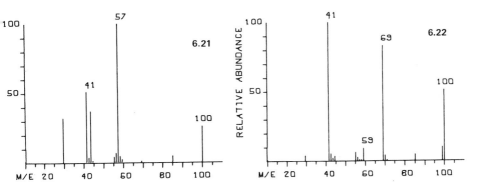

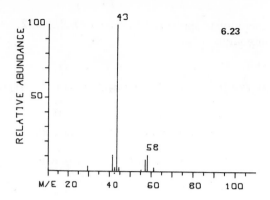

6.5   Acids and Anhydrides

Acids generally show distinctive molecular ions which increase in relative abundance with increasing molecular weight for n-alkanoic acids above C_6. In polycarboxylic acids M^+ is weak or absent, but in these the molecular weight can often be determined from the $(M + 1)^+$ ion formed by an ion–molecule reaction.

ALIPHATIC ACIDS.   The mass spectra of aliphatic acids (6.15) resemble closely those of methyl esters and primary amides; compare the spectrum of n-octadecanoic acid (Figure 6-16) with those of the methyl ester (Figure 5-3) and amide (Figure 6-25). The mass of the prominent γ-hydrogen-rearrangement peak, $CRR'C(OH)_2^+$, indicates the α-branching (m/e 60 for R = R' = H; this reaction is discussed in Section 6.4). The $C_nH_{2n}COOH^+$ series is characteristic of chain branching and also arises through mechanisms analogous to reactions 6-31 and 6-32. The $(M - OH)^+$ is somewhat less abundant than the $(M - OCH_3)^+$ of methyl esters, but is diagnostically useful for higher and unsaturated acids. The spectrum of 3-bromo-3-phenylpropionic acid even shows a hydroxyl group rearrangement in the decomposition of the $(M - Br)^+$ ion paralleling the methoxyl rearrangement of reaction 4-47. Formation of $(M - H_2O)^{\ddagger}$ in acid spectra appears to be important only under the special conditions outlined for the formation of $(M - CH_3OH)^{\ddagger}$ peaks in methyl esters. The loss of CO_2 is often found in the spectra of dicarboxylic and substituted acids; however, this can also arise from thermal decarboxylation. Aliphatic dicarboxylic acids sometimes show characteristic losses of 38 (H_4O_2) and 46 (CH_2O_2).

AROMATIC ACIDS.   Aromatic acids give spectra showing prominent OH loss followed by CO loss. A labile hydrogen on an ortho substituent causes a dominant $(M - H_2O)^{\ddagger}$ peak by the "ortho" effect, which is again followed by CO loss. Both thermal dehydration and decarboxylation are common for aromatic acids. Are these correlations applicable to Unknown 6.24?

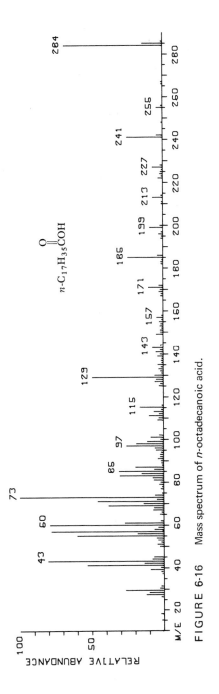

FIGURE 6-16   Mass spectrum of *n*-octadecanoic acid.

Unknown 6.24

m/e	Relative abundance	m/e	Relative abundance	m/e	Relative abundance
40	1.6	73	4.5	119	3.6
41	4.5	74	20.	120	2.0
42	1.4	75	16.	121	27.
43	5.9	76	16.	122	4.8
44	7.6	77	12.	123	0.41
45	23.	78	1.7	136	3.3
46	0.25	79	0.78	137	1.0
47	0.11	80	0.34	138	2.2
49	4.0	81	1.4	139	0.16
50	34.	82	0.73	140	0.02
51	23.	91	5.0	148	0.38
52	5.4	92	1.8	149	100.
53	7.3	93	4.3	150	9.0
54	0.70	94	0.67	151	0.97
55	4.1	102	0.72	152	0.05
62	2.7	103	3.8	165	0.52
63	4.7	104	4.9	166	86.
64	1.9	105	6.2	167	7.9
65	43.	106	0.46	168	1.0
66	4.6	107	0.03	169	0.06

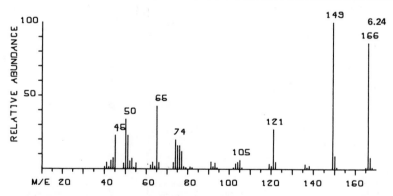

ANHYDRIDES. The mass spectrum of succinic anhydride is shown in Figure 6.17. The anhydrides of aliphatic acids show only a small or negligible molecular ion peak, but again the useful $(M + 1)^+$ ion can be formed at higher sample pressures. $[M^+]$ is usually significant in unsaturated anhydrides. For mixed anhydrides, RCO—O—COR′, the acylium ions RCO^+ and $R'CO^+$ are generally the largest peaks, and these lose CO as expected. A characteristic peak in the mass spectra of cyclic anhydrides of dicarboxylic acids is $(M - CO_2)^+$, which often fragments further by the ejection of $C_n H_{2n}$ or CO. The $(M - CO)^+$ peak is much less common.

Unknown 6.25 was a major component of the stomach washings from a comatose baby.

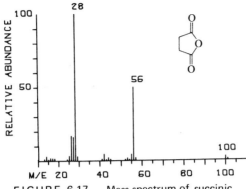

FIGURE 6-17   Mass spectrum of succinic anhydride.

Unknown 6.25

m/e	Relative abundance	m/e	Relative abundance
15	22.	62	4.5
27	3.9	63	12.
29	6.2	64	11.
31	2.2	65	10.
37	2.8	66	1.9
38	6.5	73	1.1
39	13.	74	3.9
40	1.6	81	2.5
41	3.1	91	1.9
42	10.	92	37.
43	92.	93	6.2
44	3.9	94	1.6
45	19.	119	1.4
46	0.23	120	100.
47	0.09	121	8.2
49	1.1	122	0.66
50	7.3	138	44.
51	11.	139	3.4
51.5	0.85	140	0.38
52	2.2	180	6.7
53	5.0	181	0.69
61	2.8	182	0.08

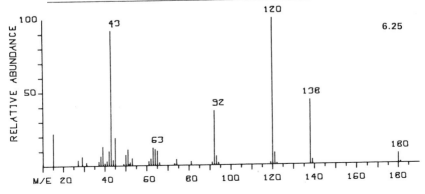

6.6 Ethers

ALIPHATIC ETHERS.   The mass spectrum of diisobutyl ether is given in Unknown 4.10 and that of isopropyl *n*-pentyl ether in Figure 6-18.

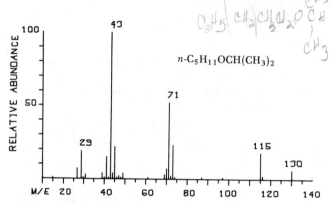

FIGURE 6-18   Mass spectrum of isopropyl *n*-pentyl ether (*6.20*). (The relative abundance of *m/e* 131 increases with increasing sample pressure.)

The molecular ion peak from an aliphatic ether tends to be more abundant than that from a structurally similar alcohol of comparable molecular weight, but the M^{+} peak is still weak to negligible. Again, ion–molecule formation of the $(M + 1)^{+}$ peak can be useful for molecular weight information (*3.6*).

The fragmentation of ethers resembles that of amines, but with a smaller propensity for α-cleavage and a much larger tendency for charge site cleavage, as expected from the higher inductive withdrawal of electrons by oxygen. The important primary cleavages of isopropyl *n*-pentyl ether (Figure 6-18) are due to these two types of cleavage (reaction 6-41). For the competing α-cleavages, the loss of methyl from the tertiary carbon yielding *m/e* 115 is almost as favorable as the loss of the larger butyl group from the secondary carbon. Secondary product ions in the same $C_nH_{2n+1}O^{+}$ ion series (*m/e* 31, 45, 59, ⋯) can be formed by rearrangement loss of an olefin molecule from these ions (reaction 4-36, but not 4-35). In contrast to the spectra of amines, the most abundant ions, $C_3H_7^{+}$ and $C_5H_{11}^{+}$, are produced by charge-site initiated reactions. Deuterium-labeling (*6.20*) indicates that 40% of the base $C_3H_7^{+}$ peak arises from further decomposition of $C_5H_{11}^{+}$.

Important odd-electron ions are notably lacking in this spectrum. Higher straight-chain ethers do show abundant $C_nH_{2n}^{+}$ ions; mechanism 4-26 can account for abundant ions of this type in particular cases. For example, ethyl

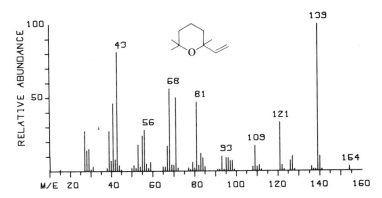

$$(6\text{-}41)$$

n-hexyl ether and di-*n*-hexyl ether exhibit prominent *m/e* 56 and 84 peaks in their spectra. (Charge retention in reaction 4-26 would give $C_nH_{2n+1}OH^{\ddagger}$, whose abundance should be low by analogy to that of the corresponding alkanol molecular ion.) Another source of $C_nH_{2n}^{+}$ ions is loss of H_2O which yields weak $(M - H_2O)^{\ddagger}$ peaks in higher *n*-alkyl ethers. *n*-Hexyl and higher ethers undergo rearrangement of two hydrogen atoms yielding $R\overset{+}{O}H_2$ ions (for example, *m/e* 103 from *n*-hexyl ether), which on decomposition provide another source of R^+ ions.

ALICYCLIC AND UNSATURATED ETHERS (*1.17*).   An illustrative example of such compounds given by Seibl (*6.21*) is 2,6,6-trimethyl-2-vinyltetrahydropyran (Figure 6.19). A rationale of the formation of the

FIGURE 6-19   Mass spectrum of 2,6,6-trimethyl-2-vinyltetrahydropyran.

principal peaks is given in reaction 6-42; additional pathways are possible, such as through charge site initiation.

AROMATIC ETHERS. The mass spectrum of methyl phenyl ether shows characteristic peaks for $(M - CH_3)^+$, $(M - CH_3 - CO)^+$, $(M - CH_2O)^+$, $(M - OCH_3)^+$, and $(M - CHO)^+$ (minor—but important in some derivatives) which is typical of the mass spectral behavior of methoxyaryl compounds. Ethyl and higher aryl ethers give a highly characteristic OE^+ ion from the elimination of C_nH_{2n}: $C_6H_5OC_nH_{2n+1}^+ \rightarrow C_6H_5OH^+$. (This probably involves hydrogen rearrangement to the oxygen atom, similar to charge retention in reaction 4-26, although formulating it as 4-18 correctly predicts the product ion composition. Look again at the spectrum of 1-phenoxy-2-chloroethane, Unknown 5.11.) Benzyl ethers similarly give a significant $C_6H_5CH_2OH^+$ peak as well as a $C_6H_5CH_2^+$ peak.

KETALS AND ACETALS.   The presence of two alkoxyl groups on the same carbon provides a powerful reaction initiating site. The activation energy for α-cleavage, $R{-}CH(OR')_2^+ \rightarrow R'O{-}CH{=}\overset{+}{O}R' \leftrightarrow R'\overset{+}{O}{=}CHOR$, is substantially lowered by the resonance stabilization of the product ion. Unfortunately, this also causes the molecular ion for simple acetals and ketals to be negligible. Some reactions are observed which are due to the second functionality, such as the elimination of H_2CO from formaldehyde acetals (Table 4-1). However, in general the ion decomposition pathways outlined above for ethers are applicable; use them to attempt the solution of Unknown 6.26.

Unknown 6.26

m/e	Relative abundance	m/e	Relative abundance
13	2.0	46	2.3
14	6.5	47	3.5
15	41.	48	0.06
28	2.8	57	0.05
29	46.	58	0.09
30	3.4	59	0.09
31	13.	60	0.02
32	0.83	61	0.01[a]
33	0.23	75	44.
43	0.96	76	1.4
44	2.3	77	0.19
45	100.		

[a] A real peak in the spectrum; not due to background.

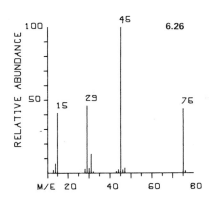

An interesting example is the striking influence of the ethylene ketal moiety on steroid mass spectra, as shown in the classic work of Fétizon and Djerassi and their co-workers. The spectrum of 5α-androstan-3-one ethylene ketal is shown in Figure 6-20. Mechanisms for the formation of the two major

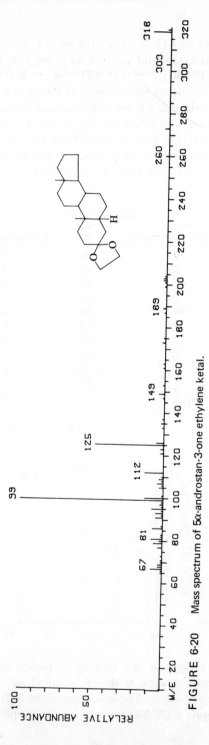

FIGURE 6-20   Mass spectrum of 5α-androstan-3-one ethylene ketal.

peaks are given in 6-43; interestingly, these are directly analogous to the fragmentation of the corresponding 3-aminosteroid. Can you account for the m/e 112 peak?

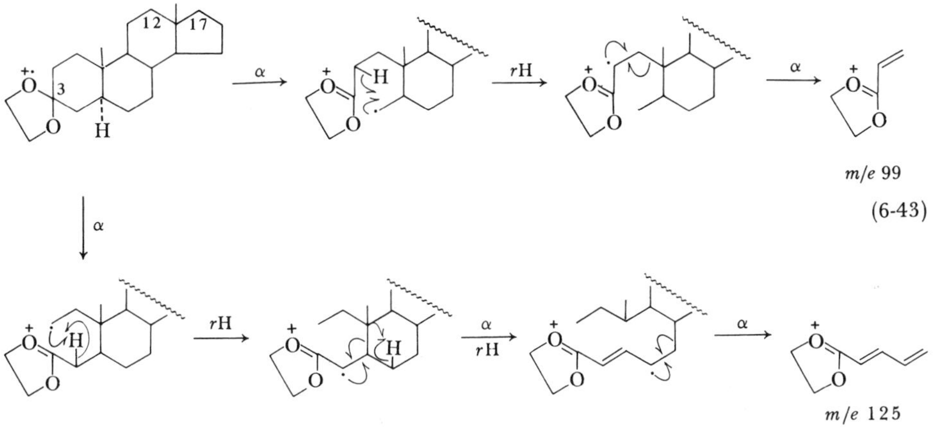

m/e 99

(6-43)

m/e 125

Unknown 6.27.   A compound is either a 12- or 17-ketosteroid (see 6-43). The $C_5H_7O_2^+$ peak in the mass spectrum of its ethylene ketal is large. Which compound is it?

What can you deduce about the structure of Unknown 6.28?

Unknown 6.28 (4.4)

m/e	Relative abundance	m/e	Relative abundance
31	3.2	73	100.
41	16.	74	4.5
42	3.1	75	0.28
43	8.5	83	1.5
44	1.2	84	0.09
45	15.	111	8.1
46	0.32	112	0.73
55	12.	113	0.03
56	1.3	140	1.1
57	2.9	141	0.13
58	0.72	143	31.
59	2.1	144	3.0
69	35.	145	0.20
70	1.8	172	0.14
71	2.8	173	0.02
72	1.2		

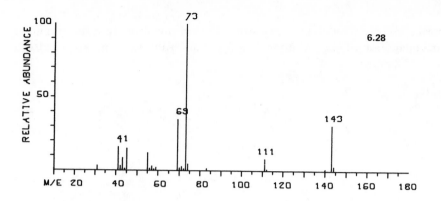

6.7 Thiols and Thioethers

The mass spectra of thiols and thioethers resemble those of the corresponding alcohols and ethers. The spectrum of isopropyl *n*-pentyl sulfide, (Figure 6-21) can be compared to that of isopropyl *n*-pentyl ether (Figure

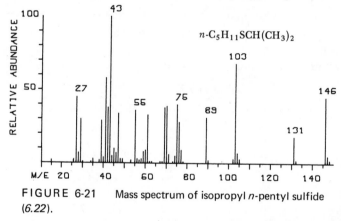

FIGURE 6-21   Mass spectrum of isopropyl *n*-pentyl sulfide (*6.22*).

6-18). A number of the most significant differences arise from the low ionization potentials of sulfur compounds, which are approximately 1 eV below those of the corresponding oxygen compounds. This makes possible the formation of much lower-energy molecular ions, substantially increasing $[M^+]$. Sigma bond ionization can occur, leading to the C–S bond cleavage with charge retention on sulfur (reaction 4-2). Ions such as HS^+, H_2S^+, H_3S^+, and CHS^+ are of sufficient stability to give an ion series useful for characterization; note that few other types of compound give peaks at *m/e* 33, 34, and 35.

THIOLS.   Alpha cleavage (see reaction 4-3) yields the largest $C_nH_{2n+1}S^+$ peak (ion series 47, 61, 75, $\cdots$), but cleavage at other chain positions to yield these ions is much more prevalent than in the corresponding alcohols. In straight-chain mercaptans $[89^+] > [75^+]$ or $[103^+]$, indicating a favorable displacement reaction (4-29) for the formation of $C_4H_8SH^+$. The hydrocarbon ion series 27, 41, 55, $\cdots$ and 15, 29, 43, $\cdots$ are characteristically large, with $C_nH_{2n-1}^+ > C_nH_{2n+1}^+$. $(M - SH)^+$ is significant in secondary thiols, in contrast to $(M - OH)^+$ in alcohols. In primary thiols the $(M - SH)^+$ peak is superseded by $(M - SH_2)^+$; this and the prevalent peaks for $(M - SH_2 - C_nH_{2n})^+$, where $n \geqslant 2$, appear in the $C_nH_{2n}^+$ (28, 42, 56, $\cdots$) ion series (reaction 4-26).

Aromatic thiols undergo fragmentations similar to those expected for phenol, the main exceptions being the formation of $(M - S)^+$, $(M - SH)^+$, and $(M - C_2H_2)^+$ peaks.

Unknowns 6.29 and 6.30 will illustrate these fragmentations.

Unknown 6.29

m/e	Relative abundance	m/e	Relative abundance	m/e	Relative abundance
27	2.1	65	5.5	97	3.1
29	1.3	66	1.5	98	0.31
30	0.49	67	0.21	103	0.42
31	4.2	67.5	0.22	104	1.0
37	1.6	68	3.5	105	3.3
38	1.9	68.5	0.49	106	0.8
39	6.3	69	11.	107	1.3
40	0.20	70	1.1	108	46.
41	0.49	71	1.1	109	21.
42	0.40	72	0.13	110	3.8
43	2.5	73	0.78	111	0.79
44	3.6	74	2.2	120	0.23
45	6.2	75	1.8	121	0.31
46	0.59	76	2.8	122	1.8
49	0.60	77	3.9	123	0.14
50	4.7	78	0.90	124	0.01
51	3.9	79	0.67	135	0.82
52	1.1	80	1.8	136	100.
52.5	0.29	81	2.2	137	10.
53	2.9	82	5.4	138	5.0
54	5.0	83	0.89	139	0.51
54.5	0.74	84	0.78	151	1.6
55	0.66	90	0.65	152	1.1
57	1.0	91	1.1	153	2.8
58	3.0	92	3.9	154	20.
59	0.35	93	1.2	155	1.8
62	1.8	94	0.25	156	1.0
63	4.7	95	0.78	157	0.08
64	1.8	96	1.3		

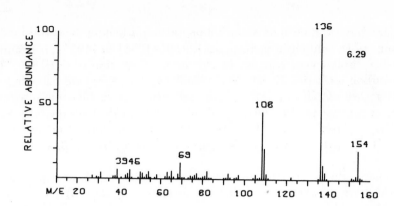

Unknown 6.30

m/e	Relative abundance	m/e	Relative abundance	m/e	Relative abundance	m/e	Relative abundance
15	9.2	46	3.6	67	4.9	88	0.74
26	1.3	47	29.	68	18.	89	11.
27	24.	48	1.6	69	59.	90	0.58
28	6.1	53	4.7	70	70.	91	0.51
29	32.	54	5.7	71	15.	97	4.3
30	0.86	55	74.	72	0.83	98	0.36
33	0.49	56	100.	73	0.98	103	0.93
34	1.1	57	38.	74	0.64	104	0.04
36	0.05	58	2.9	75	1.1	112	23.
39	19.	59	3.0	82	11.	113	2.0
40	4.0	60	4.9	83	46.	114	0.10
41	76.	61	18.	84	51.	145	1.7
42	47.	62	1.6	85	4.9	146	37.
43	74.	63	0.87	86	0.28	147	3.7
44	3.3	65	1.4	87	1.0	148	1.8
45	8.2	66	1.2				

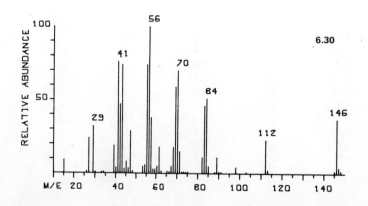

Thioethers.   As can be seen in the spectrum of isopropyl *n*-pentyl sulfide (Figure 6-21), peaks in the $C_nH_{2n+1}S^+$ ion series can now also arise from σ-ionization; this accounts for the presence of $C_5H_{11}S^+$ (*m/e* 103) and, in part, $C_3H_7S^+$ (*m/e* 75). Analogous to the behavior of isopropyl *n*-pentyl ether (Figure 6.18 and scheme 6-41), α-cleavage yields $(CH_3)_2C\overset{+}{H}\overset{+}{S}=CH_2$ (*m/e* 89) and $CH_3CH=\overset{+}{S}C_5H_{11}$ (*m/e* 131) ions, whose decompositions by hydrogen rearrangement reaction 4-36 should produce $H\overset{+}{S}=CH_2$ (*m/e* 47) and $CH_3CH=\overset{+}{S}H$ (*m/e* 61). Decomposition of $CH_3CH=\overset{+}{S}C_5H_{11}$ by reaction 4-35 is an alternative mode for formation of the *m/e* 75 peak.

In contrast to isopropyl *n*-pentyl ether, this sulfide's mass spectrum shows characteristic OE^+ ions at *m/e* 76, $(CH_3)_2CHSH^+$, and *m/e* 70, $C_5H_{10}^+$ (plus *m/e* 42, $C_3H_6^+$) corresponding to the competing products of reaction 4-21 (formation of this charge-retained ion is a dominant pathway for disulfides). Ions resulting from the rearrangement of two hydrogen atoms, such as *m/e* 77 (probably $C_3H_7SH_2^+$), can also be formed in smaller abundance. On the other hand, the charge site product $C_5H_{11}^+$ (reaction 4-9), which is significant in the spectrum of the ether, is very small (possibly owing to the competition of 4-21), although the companion product $C_3H_7^+$ is still the base peak.

Phenyl alkyl sulfides undergo reactions typical of their counterpart ethers but show additional skeletal rearrangements that complicate structure elucidation. Elimination of SH is common in compounds whose usual cleavage pathways are less facile. Aromatic disulfides often undergo additional losses of S_2 and/or HS_2.

Unknown 6.31 is known to contain a hydroxyl group. Could you have deduced this fact from the mass spectrum?

Unknown 6.31

m/e	Relative abundance	m/e	Relative abundance
27	6.0	98	10.
28	1.7	99	2.3
29	5.8	100	0.36
39	8.0	108	2.3
47	1.7	109	0.21
51	2.7	110	0.12
52	1.0	121	2.1
53	11.	122	0.17
61	1.9	123	0.10
63	4.8	125	13.
64	2.3	126	52.
65	5.2	127	4.5
69	7.2	128	2.6
69.5	0.14	129	0.21
70	4.2	137	1.2
71	3.2	139	32.
77	2.6	140	2.7
82	3.0	141	1.6
84	5.2	142	0.16
91	4.0	153	0.80
92	1.5	154	100.
93	2.0	155	9.8
94	5.2	156	5.1
95	8.7	157	0.46
96	3.9	158	0.02
97	40.		

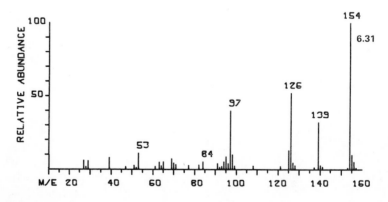

6.8 Amines

Aliphatic amines exhibit very low ionization potentials; despite this, the amine group provides such a powerful driving force for reaction initiation that molecular ions are of low or negligible abundance. Fortunately, aliphatic amines have a strong tendency to undergo protonation at moderately high sample pressures to yield the characteristic $(M + H)^+$ peak (*3.6*). Salts of amine bases will not vaporize in the mass spectrometer; however, they often decompose on heating in the instrument to release the free amine and the acid. The presence of abundant peaks corresponding to HCl (m/e 36 and 38) or HBr (m/e 80 and 82) strongly indicates such a salt, as these ions are not formed in abundance as products of electron-impact-induced reactions.

Studies on indole alkaloid derivatives indicate that quaternary nitrogen compounds (R $\neq$ H) decompose thermally on heating in the mass spectrometer by two principal paths leading to different tertiary amines (*6.23*). In the case of the bromide or iodide salts, dealkylation with formation of the amine and the alkyl halide is favored (reaction 6-44). For the fluoride salt, a thermal Hofmann degradation involving abstraction of a hydrogen atom β to the quaternary nitrogen is favored (reaction 6-45).

$$\underset{\substack{\mid \\ CH_2-CH_2}}{R_3-\overset{\overset{\displaystyle R_2}{\mid}}{\underset{\mid}{N}}-R_1} \; X^- \quad \overset{\Delta}{\longrightarrow} \quad \underset{\substack{\mid \\ CH_2-CH_2}}{R_3-\overset{\overset{\displaystyle R_2}{\mid}}{N:}} \;+\; R_1X \qquad (6\text{-}44)$$

$$\underset{\substack{\mid \\ CH-CH_2 \\ \mid \\ H \quad X^-}}{R_3-\overset{\overset{\displaystyle R_2}{\mid}}{\underset{\mid}{\overset{+}{N}}}-R_1} \quad \overset{\Delta}{\longrightarrow} \quad \underset{\substack{\mid \\ CH=CH_2}}{R_3-\overset{\overset{\displaystyle R_2}{\mid}}{N}-R_1} \;+\; HX \qquad (6\text{-}45)$$

ALIPHATIC AMINES.   The mass spectra of 1-aminodecane (Figure 4.2) and a number of $C_4H_{11}N$ isomeric amines (Unknowns 4.2 to 4.7) have been given and features of their spectra discussed in Section 4.5. The mass spectra of N-methyl-N-isopropyl-N-n-butylamine (Unknown 4.15; see Chapter 9) (*6.24*) and *bis*(3-methylbutyl)amine are given in Figures 6-22 and 6-23.

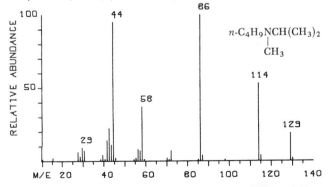

FIGURE 6-22   Mass spectrum of N-methyl-N-isopropyl-N-n-butylamine. (Relative abundance of the m/e 130 peak increases with increasing sample pressure.)

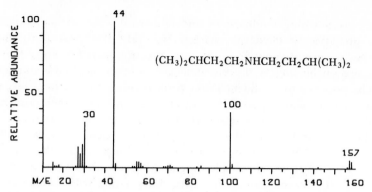

FIGURE 6-23   Mass spectrum of *bis*(3-methylbutyl)amine. (Relative abundance of the *m/e* 158 peak increases with increasing sample pressure.)

Alpha cleavage is a dominant reaction of amines, generally producing the base peak in *n*-alkylamines and α-substituted primary amines, with loss of the largest alkyl group favored (equation 4-8). This cleavage accounts for the *m/e* 30 base peak in Figure 4.1, the *m/e* 86 base peak and *m/e* 114 in Figure 6-22, and the *m/e* 100 in Figure 6-23. Peaks in this $C_n H_{2n+2} N^+$ ion series can be formed by other pathways also, however. In primary *n*-alkylamines displacement reactions (6-46; also see 4-27) account for relatively small peaks with

$$\underset{m/e\ 86}{\includegraphics{}} \qquad (6\text{-}46)$$

the most favored at *m/e* 86. For higher primary *n*-alkyl amines the peaks at *m/e* 44 (β-cleavage), and to a lesser extent *m/e* 58 and 72 (γ- and δ-cleavage), become increasingly important (*m/e* 44 = 40% in the spectrum of *n*-$C_{16} H_{33} NH_2$). For higher-molecular-weight amines the hydrocarbon-type peaks also increase; in the spectrum of $[C_6 H_{13} CH(CH_3)]_2 NH$ the alkyl ion resulting from α-cleavage (*m/e* 85) shows 34% abundance while the immonium ion from α-cleavage (*m/e* 156) has an abundance of only 15%.

A number of secondary rearrangement decompositions of the primary immonium ion can produce other $C_n H_{2n+2} N^+$ ions. The most common such reaction (6-47; also see 4-36) yields the important *m/e* 44 and 58 ions in

$$(6\text{-}47)$$

Figure 6-22, and the less important m/e 30 peak in Figure 6-23. (Although it is not apparent in equations 4-36 and 6-47, for longer-chain compounds deuterium labeling (*6.24*) indicates that the position from which the hydrogen atom is rearranged is relatively nonspecific.) Another possible rearrangement (6-48; see equation 4-35) appears to account for the base peak at m/e 44 in the spectrum of *bis*(3-methylbutyl)amine (note that the hydrogen is transferred from a tertiary carbon atom). Labeling studies (*6.24*) indicate that 65%

$$(CH_3)_2 CHCH_2CH_2 \overset{+\cdot}{N}H-CH_2-C_4H_9 \xrightarrow{\alpha} \underset{m/e\ 100}{\left[\begin{array}{c} H \\ CH_2 \\ NH \\ + \end{array}\right]} \xrightarrow{rH} \left[\begin{array}{c} \\ \end{array}\right] + \underset{m/e\ 44}{\overset{HCH_2}{\underset{+}{NH}}} \quad (6\text{-}48)$$

of the m/e 72 in Figure 6-22 arises through such a mechanism. The remaining EE^+ rearrangements, equations 4-34 and 4-37, do not appear to be important in the aliphatic amine spectra that have been examined, although mechanism 4-34 may increase in importance for large alkyl groups (*6.25*). The loss of NH_3 or a neutral amine molecule (equation 4-26) is not important except in the spectra of certain polyfunctional compounds (for example, loss of NH_3 in α-amino acids and diamines).

Unknowns 6.32 to 6.35 contain the most significant peaks in the spectra of four of the six possible secondary amines of the general formula $C_5H_{13}N$. What are their structures?

Unknowns 6.32-6.35

	Relative abundance			
m/e	6.32	6.33	6.34	6.35
30	52.	4.1	15.	3.8
44	11.	100.	6.2	100.
57	1.0	2.1	7.3	1.4
58	100.	1.8	100.	3.7
72	10.	2.4	20.	0.26
86	4.8	1.2	3.2	1.0
87	16.	10.	4.8	12.

CYCLOALKYLAMINES (*1.17*).   A thoroughly studied example of such spectra is that of *N*-ethylcyclopentylamine, Figure 6-24 (*6.26*). Alpha cleavage in the alkyl group leads to the $(M - CH_3)^+$ peak of moderate intensity. However, α-cleavage at the secondary carbon in the ring should be favored; this leads to an isolated radical site whose further reaction (equation 6-49)

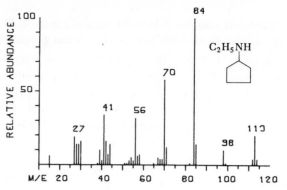

FIGURE 6-24 Mass spectrum of *N*-ethylcyclopentylamine.

accounts for the *m/e* 84 base peak. Homologous even-electron ions at *m/e* 70 and 56 can be formed by a variety of pathways, as was discussed in the case of

$$(6\text{-}49)$$

aliphatic alcohol spectra. Thus, although the *m/e* 56, 70, 84, and 98 ion series is indicative of this general type of structure, the individual peaks, especially those of lower mass, are less characteristic of specific structural features. The *m/e* 85 peak appears to be formed mainly by C_2H_4 loss from the ethyl group (see Reactions 4-21 and 4-22).

In the spectrum of des-*N*-methyl-α-obscurine, a similar mechanism can explain the loss of the $-CH_2-CH(CH_3)-CH_2-$ bridge plus a hydrogen atom to form the $(M-57)^+$ ion *(6.27)* (6-50). The $(M-C_4H_8)^+$ is of much lower

$$(6\text{-}50)$$

abundance than the $(M-C_4H_9)^+$. (The mass spectrum of the complex cyclic amine strychnine is shown in Figure 3.1.)

Other types of reaction that are possible for cyclic amines include the incipient radical site reactions 6.51 (see 4-41) and 6-52. The product from the latter retro-Diels-Alder reaction can also be rationalized by reaction 6-53.

$$(6\text{-}51)$$

$$(6\text{-}52)$$

$$(6\text{-}53)$$

Unknown 6.36 is an androstane derivative, whose basic skeleton is shown. Above *m/e* 60 the spectrum shows only a small peak at *m/e* 331 and a base peak at *m/e* 72. What structure is consistent with these data?

AMINES CONTAINING OTHER FUNCTIONAL GROUPS.   The amine group shows an unusual tendency to undergo new reactions in combination with other functional groups, such as reaction 4-31 and reactions similar to 6-37.

Unknown 6.37 is the spectrum of a compound found in the postrace examination of a urine sample from a thoroughbred. The drug ephedrine, $C_6H_5CH(OH)CH(CH_3)NHCH_3$, is suspected; is the spectrum consistent with this structure?

Unknown 6.37

m/e	Relative abundance	m/e	Relative abundance	m/e	Relative abundance
15	0.41	58	100.	92	0.12
27	0.66	59	3.8	105	2.9
29	1.1	60	0.05	106	1.2
30	4.7	63	0.67	107	0.86
31	0.44	64	0.22	108	0.11
36	4.6	65	0.64	115	0.67
37	0.12	66	0.20	116	0.40
38	1.6	70	0.21	117	1.5
39	1.0	71	1.1	118	0.67
40	0.19	72	0.18	119	0.11
41	0.90	74	0.40	130	0.33
42	2.7	75	0.21	131	0.54
43	1.5	76	0.46	132	0.89
44	1.0	77	5.5	133	0.20
50	0.83	78	1.3	134	0.16
51	2.5	79	2.4	145	0.20
52	0.70	80	0.15	146	1.2
53	0.45	87	0.13	147	0.33
54	0.41	88	0.20	148	0.18
55	0.55	89	0.42	165	0.14
56	3.9	90	0.26	166	1.8[a]
57	2.2	91	1.3	167	0.20[a]

[a] Relative abundance increases with increasing sample pressure.

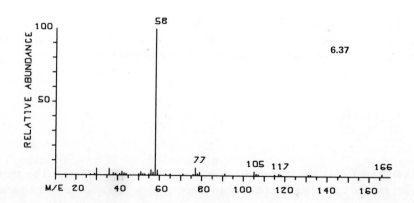

Unknown 6.38 is a derivative of a substance which is essential for nutrition.

Unknown 6.38

m/e	Relative abundance	m/e	Relative abundance	m/e	Relative abundance
27	3.1	63	5.3	103	12.
29	4.6	64	2.6	104	1.8
30	15.	65	12.	117	2.2
31	3.6	66	0.67	118	7.3
39	8.9	76	1.0	119	4.0
40	1.4	77	7.1	120	77.
41	4.2	78	2.0	121	7.1
42	6.9	79	2.6	122	0.26
43	5.0	85	1.2	130	0.34
44	1.9	86	7.9	131	0.88
45	1.8	87	1.8	132	0.08
50	1.7	88	100.	146	0.29
51	7.9	89	3.9	147	0.50
52	1.5	90	1.4	148	0.62
53	0.82	91	30.	149	0.07
54	0.89	92	5.9	179	1.3
60	14.	93	0.50	180	1.4[a]
61	2.0	102	1.7	181	0.14[a]
62	1.9				

[a] Relative abundance increases with increasing sample pressure.

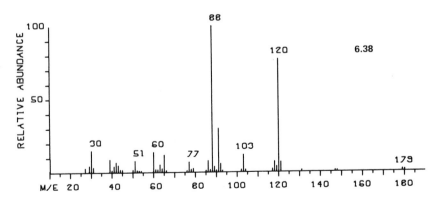

6.9   Amides

The mass spectral behavior of primary amides, such as *n*-octadecanoamide (Figure 6-25), closely resembles that of the corresponding acid and methyl ester (Figures 6-16 and 5-3). The behavior of secondary (such as *sec*-butyl acetamide, Figure 6-26) and tertiary amides parallels that of esters of higher

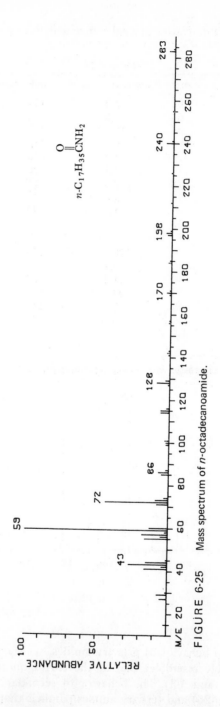

FIGURE 6-25 Mass spectrum of *n*-octadecanoamide.

alcohols, although here in those reactions initiated by the saturated hetero-atom the more powerful directing force of nitrogen is clearly evident. Amides give molecular ion peaks that are generally more distinctive than their ester counterparts and have a strong tendency to form $(M + 1)^+$ ions by ion-molecule reactions (*3.6*).

The resemblance of the spectra of *n*-octadecanoic acid and its amide (Figures 6-16 and 6-25) is so striking that little additional mechanistic interpretation is necessary. The nitrogen-containing peaks are shifted to lower masses by one unit; the β-cleavage–hydrogen rearrangement peak will fall in the series m/e 59, 73, 87, $\cdots$. Alkyl losses produce the ion series 44, (58), 72,

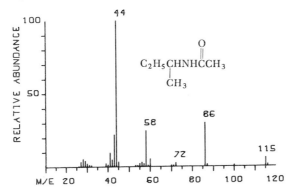

FIGURE 6-26   Mass spectrum of *sec*-butyl acetamide.

86, $\cdots$; note in Figure 6-25 that maxima again appear at intervals corres-ponding to $(CH_2)_4 - m/e$ 72, 128, 184, and 240–although the effect is less pronounced. The numerous hydrocarbon peaks such as $C_n H_{2n+1}^+$ and $C_n H_{2n-1}^+$ are less abundant, as expected, than in the spectra of the analogous acids.

The spectra of secondary and tertiary amides show the additional expected reactions, such as β-cleavage at the N–R bond with rearrangement (reaction 4-39) of one or, especially, two hydrogen atoms (m/e 60 in Figure 6-26). In tertiary amides multiple rearrangement decompositions like reactions 4-19 and 4-39 are possible from both chains on nitrogen as well as from the acid moiety; thus *N,N*-diethylhexanoamide exhibits prominent peaks for $(M - C_4 H_8)^+$, $(M - C_4 H_8 - C_2 H_3)^+$, $(M - C_4 H_8 - C_2 H_4)^+$, and $(M - C_4 H_8 - C_2 H_3 - C_2 H_4)^+$ (m/e 115, 88, 87, and 60, respectively). The decompositions of secondary and tertiary amides also reflect the strong reaction-initiating tendency of nitrogen. Alpha cleavage induced by it gives the $(M - C_2 H_5)^+$ and, partly, the $(M - CH_3)^+$ ions of Figure 6-26; further hydrogen rearrangement decomposition of these ions by reaction 4-36 yields $H_2 \overset{+}{N}=CHCH_3$ and $H_2 \overset{+}{N}=CHC_2 H_5$. Cleavage beta to the nitrogen atom is appreciable (a possible explanation is displacement, reaction 4-29, effected by the carbonyl oxygen); this EE^+ product ion also apparently undergoes the hydrogen rearrangement reaction 4-36. Some amides (for example, diethyl-acetamide) undergo direct ketene loss (reaction 4-22), paralleling the behavior of unsaturated acetates; this provides a very characteristic peak in the spectra of *N*-aryl amides. Hydrogen rearrangement with charge migration away from the amide functionality (either reaction 4-25 or 4-26) occurs only if the result-ing ion $(M - RCONHR)^{\ddagger}$ is substantially stabilized and the R groups are small. The tendency for charge retention is much greater than in esters because of the greatly reduced ionization potentials of amides; however, acetamides of more complex molecules, such as steroids, usually exhibit characteristic $(M - CH_3 CONH_2)^{\ddagger}$ peaks.

Unknown 6.39

m/e	Relative abundance	m/e	Relative abundance
14	0.21	56	1.7
15	0.97	57	11.
16	0.39	58	1.1
27	6.4	59	100.
28	2.1	60	2.6
29	9.8	61	0.23
30	0.83	69	3.7
31	0.69	70	0.21
32	0.11	72	0.54
39	7.1	73	3.4
40	1.0	74	0.05
41	17.	85	1.7
42	6.4	86	11.
43	20.	87	0.54
44	31.	88	0.03
45	1.3	100	1.3
46	0.90	101	1.7
55	1.4	102	0.10

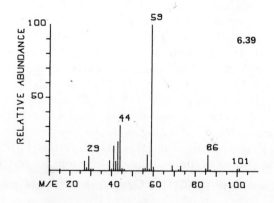

6.10   Cyanides

The ionization potentials of aliphatic nitriles are unusually high, and this is reflected in the unusual degree to which these compounds undergo skeletal rearrangement on electron impact. The basic rules of ion decomposition (Chapter 4) appear to be less applicable to cyanides than to any other simple compound class. Further, the principal nitrogen-containing ion series found for nitriles, $C_nH_{2n-1}N^+$ and $C_nH_{2n-2}N^+$, are isobaric with the common hydrocarbon series $C_nH_{2n-1}^+$ (27, 41, 55, $\cdots$) and $C_nH_{2n-2}^+$ (26, 40, 54, $\cdots$); differentiation of these from isotopic abundances is not usually possible, so that spectral interpretation is further complicated without high resolution data.

Molecular ion peaks are weak or negligible in aliphatic nitriles, although they are usually strong in aromatic compounds. Fortunately, aliphatic nitriles have a substantial tendency to form an $(M + 1)^+$ peak by ion–molecule reactions (3.6); $(M + 2)^+$ peaks have been reported for some cyanoacetates (6.28).

The mass spectrum of n-decyl cyanide is given in Figure 6-27. Its overall

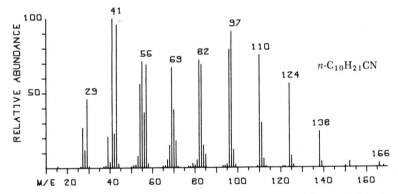

FIGURE 6-27   Mass spectrum of n-decyl cyanide. (The relative abundance of m/e 167 is 0.4%; the relative abundance of the m/e 168 peak increases with increasing sample pressure.)

appearance is unusual by mass spectral standards; it resembles an n-alkane spectrum (Figures 5.1 and 5.2) in its lack of specificity, but its most abundant peaks are at higher masses, and it has pairs of significant peaks separated by only one mass unit. The $(CH_2)_nCN^+$ series (40), 54, 68, 82, $\cdots$ dominates the upper portion of the spectrum; the hydrogen rearrangement series nominally corresponding to $C_nH_{2n-1}N^+$ (41, 55, 69, 83, $\cdots$) is of comparable importance for $n \sim 3$ to 6. A further unusual feature of the spectra of alkyl cyanides is that $[(M - 1)^+] > [M^+]$. This hydrogen loss can come from the α- and other positions (6.29). Note that α-cleavage is unfavorable, requiring formation of a quadruple bond, $C\equiv\overset{+}{N}$, to stabilize the charge on nitrogen.

In Figure 6-27 abundances of the $(CH_2)_n CN^+$ ions increase going down this series in mass from $(M-1)^+$ until the maximum is reached for $(CH_2)_5 CN^+$. Formation of these ions could involve the cyclization–displacement reaction (4-29), with a seven-membered ring ($n = 5$) being the most stable form of the cyclic product ion involving the sp-hybridized $-C\equiv\overset{+}{N}-CH_2-$ bond. Chain branching does increase the abundances of the appropriate ions in the series, but such data must be used with caution for structure determination. The CN group strongly resembles Cl and Br in this reaction (4-29), except that a five-membered ring is favored for the halogens.

Significant OE^{+} ion peaks usually arise from specific processes, so that the formation of an odd-electron ion *series* is unusual in mass spectra. However, the $C_n H_{2n-1} N^{+}$ series in Figure 6-27 shows a regular change in abundance with increasing values of n in the same fashion as the EE^+ series $C_n H_{2n} CN^+$ or $C_n H_{2n+1}^{+}$. For n-decylcyanide, the expected specific process, β-cleavage with hydrogen rearrangement (reaction 4-16) to give $\cdot CH_2 C\equiv\overset{+}{N}H$, is one of the smallest peaks in this series (high resolution measurement shows that 82% of the m/e 41 peak is $C_3 H_5^{+}$), although this process appears to be of higher relative importance for smaller molecules. For the formation of the higher-mass $C_n H_{2n-1} N^{+}$ ions the most logical mechanism again appears to involve cyclization, with loss of a $C_n H_{2n}$ molecule. Rol has shown for 4-methylpenta-nonitrile that the abundant $C_3 H_5 N^{+}$ ion arises from δ-hydrogen migration followed by γ-cleavage (6.29).

This back-donation of electrons by the cyano group may also account for the absence of $(M-CN)^+$ formation, which contrasts with the behavior of electron-withdrawing groups such as chlorine and bromine (reaction 4-10); the behavior of CN actually resembles that of fluorine much more closely in these regards. Only the lower-mass hydrocarbon ions are formed in abundance, reminiscent of the spectra of alkanes; the $C_n H_{2n-1}^{+}$ ions could arise through loss of $C_n H_{2n+1} \cdot$ followed by loss of HCN (reaction 4-42), again analogous to the behavior of halogens.

Unsaturated and aromatic nitriles have much more abundant molecular ions, and those with no α-hydrogen show no significant $(M-H)^+$. Again, many cases with rather unusual breakdown pathways in their spectra have been cited. This behavior is illustrated in the spectrum of Unknown 6.40, a cytotoxic substance isolated from *Viburnum opulous* (6.30); high resolution data showed the molecular formula to be $C_{10} H_8 N_2$. What structures do you think are probable? Originally the investigators thought that three ring-position isomers were the most probable. Unfortunately, *none* of the spectra of the synthesized isomers agreed with that of Unknown 6.40 within experimental error; the mass spectrum of the para isomer is shown as

Unknown 6.41. Can you explain these data? (The compounds can be differentiated by proton magnetic resonance spectroscopy, but not by infrared.)

Unknowns 6.40 and 6.41

m/e	Relative abundance 6.40	Relative abundance 6.41	m/e	Relative abundance 6.40	Relative abundance 6.41
26	1.2	1.3	99	0.63	0.42
27	2.8	3.5	100	1.0	1.0
37	1.5	1.7	101	3.3	2.0
38	2.9	2.8	102	4.6	2.3
39	7.5	8.9	103	2.7	1.6
50	6.7	5.7	104	0.56	0.22
51	8.8	6.3	114	0.87	0.77
52	3.1	2.8	115	0.61	0.50
61	1.5	1.4	116	100.	100.
62	3.9	3.2	117	9.4	9.2
63	8.1	8.0	118	0.39	0.36
64	4.0	4.3	127	1.6	1.1
65	2.0	1.9	128	4.1	1.7
74	2.1	1.9	129	5.3	1.4
75	4.1	4.5	130	1.6	0.12
76	4.1	4.3	141	0.17	0.10
77	5.2	2.6	153	0.28	0.17
78	2.0	1.1	154	0.33	0.21
87	1.5	1.3	155	2.6	1.0
88	2.3	2.3	156	23.	18.
89	8.8	16.	157	2.7	2.1
90	2.1	4.4	158	0.13	0.09
91	0.48	0.65			

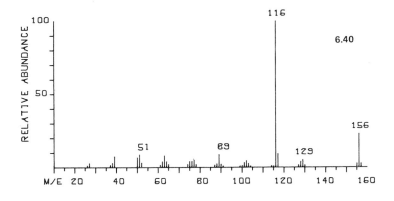

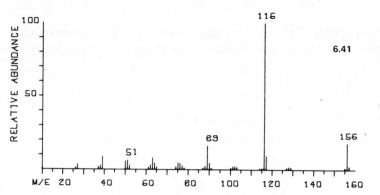

Useful information can be obtained from the mass spectra of nitriles, however; try Unknown 6.42.

Unknown 6.42

m/e	Relative abundance	m/e	Relative abundance
14	1.6	53	0.73
15	4.8	54	76.
16	0.21	55	14.
17	0.17	56	1.3
18	0.75	57	13.
19	1.2	58	1.0
27	23.	59	57.
28	18.	60	2.1
29	39.	61	0.14
30	1.6	68	1.7
31	100.	69	0.39
32	1.5	70	3.0
33	0.23	71	1.0
39	1.2	72	2.0
40	2.5	73	0.10
41	13.	84	9.5
42	5.9	85	0.50
43	6.1	86	0.02
44	1.5	98	3.5
45	13.	99	0.53
46	0.32	100	0.04
52	3.5		

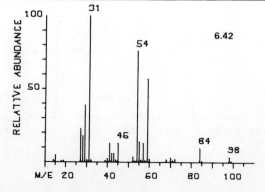

6.11   Aliphatic Halides

The following mass spectra of halogenated compounds are illustrative: HCl, Unknown 2.1; CH_3F, 1.8; CH_3Br, 2.2; CCl_4, 3.7; C_2H_3Cl, 2.4; 1,2-$C_2H_2Cl_2$, 3.4; C_2H_3Cl, 2.14; C_2ClF_5, 3.5; CF_3CN, 5.6; 1-bromohexane, 5.8; and 1-phenoxy-2-chloroethane, 5.11. Figures 6-28 to 6-30 show the mass spectra of 1-chlorodecane, 3-chlorodecane, and 3-bromodecane.

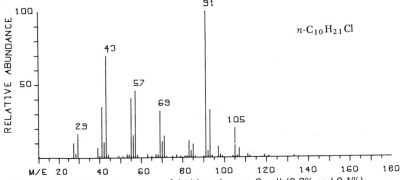

FIGURE 6-28 Mass spectrum of 1-chlorodecane. Small (0.3% and 0.1%) molecular ion peaks are present at *m/e* 176 and 178.

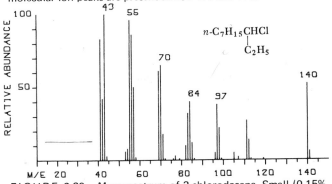

FIGURE 6.29   Mass spectrum of 3-chlorodecane. Small (0.15% and 0.05%) molecular ion peaks are present at *m/e* 176 and 178 (*4.4*).

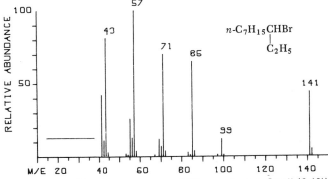

FIGURE 6.30   Mass spectrum of 3-bromodecane. Small (0.1%) molecular ion peaks are present at *m/e* 220 and 222 (*4.4*).

Measurable molecular ions are obtainable from alkyl halides (except fluorides) of moderately high molecular weights or with some chain branching; M^+ is often negligible for perhalogenated compounds unless they are unsaturated. The presence and number of chlorine or bromine atoms in an ion is usually recognizable from its characteristic "isotopic cluster" (Section 2.2 and Table A-2).

The halogens have a relatively small influence on mass spectral reactions. Iodine is the most influential because of the unusually low strength of the carbon–iodine bond. Also affecting carbon–halogen bond cleavage, but in the opposite order (F > Cl > Br > I), is the inductive withdrawal of electrons by the halogen atom. However, the tendency for back-donation of electrons, which strengthens this bond, shows the same order (fluorine greatest), substantially compensating for this effect.

There are two main sources of $C_nH_{2n}X^+$ ions in the spectra of alkyl halides. One source is α-cleavage to form the $R_2C=\overset{+}{X}$ ion, which follows the expected order of electron-donating ability F > Cl > Br > I. For bromine and iodine this reaction is negligible for all but low-molecular-weight compounds, and for chlorine this reaction is of importance mainly for tertiary chlorides. Alpha cleavage does give unusually abundant $(M - H)^+$ ions for lower-molecular-weight fluorides, paralleling the behavior of alkyl cyanides. The weak $C_nH_{2n}X^+$ ion series found for many alkyl halides is quite characteristic and thus useful for general identification.

The second source of $C_nH_{2n}X^+$ ions is the cyclization–displacement reaction 4-29. This leads to an unusually abundant $C_4H_8Cl^+$ or $C_4H_8Br^+$ ion in the spectra of *n*-alkyl chlorides or bromides containing more than five carbon atoms (Figure 6-28 and Unknown 5.8). The abundances of these ions are greatly lowered by chain branching and are negligible for fluorides and iodides.

There are substantial differences in alkyl halide spectra in regard to the proportions of $(M - HX)^+$ and $(M - X)^+$ ions formed by C–X cleavage; the former is accompanied by secondary ions characteristic of an olefin, while the $(M - X)^+$ ions characteristically decompose further by losses of C_nH_{2n}. A prominent OE^+ ion from the loss of HX is observed for fluorides and primary (lower for *n*-alkyl) and secondary chlorides (Figure 6-28 and 6-29); apparently the high C–X stability can be overcome only when the tendency for donation of the unpaired electron on X is neutralized by hydrogen transfer (4-27). Formation of $(M - HX)^+$, in contrast to that of $(M - X)^+$, can be strongly influenced by the presence of other functionalities.

For tertiary and activated (for example, allylic) chlorides and for bromides and iodides (Figure 6.30) the formation of $(M - X)^+$ and lower $C_nH_{2n+1}^+$ ions generally is dominant. (Electron bombardment can also produce R^+ ions of unusually low appearance potential by "ion pair" processes: $R–X \rightarrow R^+ + X^-$.) Although $C_nH_{2n-1}^+$ ions are of significant abundance for low-molecular-weight ions of this type, they commonly arise by loss of HX from $C_nH_{2n}X^+$ ions (reactions 4-42 and 4-44).

Perhalogenated compounds resemble hydrocarbons in their mass spectral behavior, including a high tendency for rearrangement. The smallest perhaloalkyl ions are usually the most stable; for example, CF_3^+ (m/e 69) is the most abundant ion in perfluoroalkane spectra.

Exact mass measurement shows that m/e 171 in the spectrum of Unknown 6.43 has the composition $C_{11}H_{23}O$ (*4.4*).

Unknown 6.43

m/e	Relative abundance	m/e	Relative abundance
41	36.	83	59.
42	4.7	84	3.8
43	8.2	85	0.13
44	1.0	97	23.
45	23.	98	1.9
46	0.51	99	0.06
55	45.	109	7.7
56	3.9	110	0.70
57	15.	111	0.03
58	0.61	139	9.2
67	9.1	140	1.7
68	1.2	141	3.4
69	33.	142	0.35
70	2.7	171	32.
71	15.	172	3.8
72	3.2	173	0.29
73	100.	269	5.1
74	4.5	270	0.52
75	0.29	271	0.03
81	3.5	298	0.88
82	1.3	299	0.10

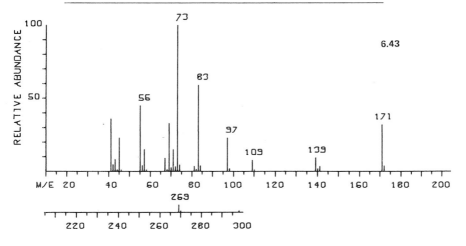

Unknown 6.44

m/e	Relative abundance	m/e	Relative abundance
15	0.17	72	0.15
27	7.0	77	0.99
28	1.5	78	0.09
29	10.	79	0.31
30	0.22	83	4.2
36	0.43	84	0.83
38	0.27	85	0.22
39	5.4	90	0.23
40	0.78	91	0.55
41	21.	92	0.10
42	3.6	93	0.18
43	21.	98	8.4
44	0.70	99	22.
53	2.6	100	1.6
54	0.92	101	0.05
55	19.	105	0.22
56	6.5	107	0.08
57	100.	112	0.24
58	4.4	113	0.02
59	0.07	119	4.7
63	1.1	120	0.31
64	0.16	121	1.5
65	0.57	122	0.11
69	3.3	148	0.12
70	3.9	150	0.03
71	1.7		

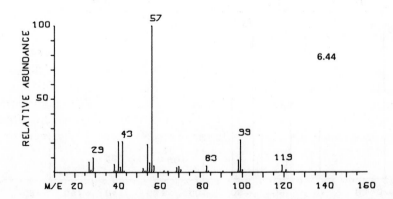

Unknown 6.45

m/e	Relative abundance	m/e	Relative abundance	m/e	Relative abundance	m/e	Relative abundance
31	75.	65.5	0.81	87	3.3	118	1.5
32	0.84	66	3.4	88	0.03	119	0.05
35	9.1	67	0.08	93	13.	128	0.06
36	1.0	68	1.1	94	0.42	131	100.
37	2.8	69	74.	97	3.3	132	3.3
43	2.9	70	0.83	98	0.06	133	0.05
47	4.8	73.5	0.60	99	1.0	147	15.
48	0.05	74	4.1	100	0.84	148	0.49
49	1.5	75	0.16	109	0.41	149	4.7
50	6.9	78	1.1	111	0.12	150	0.16
51	0.10	81	10.	112	4.0	166	10.
55	2.4	82	0.27	113	0.14	167	0.37
62	5.1	85	10.	116	4.8	168	3.1
63	0.13	86	0.10	117	0.06	169	0.12

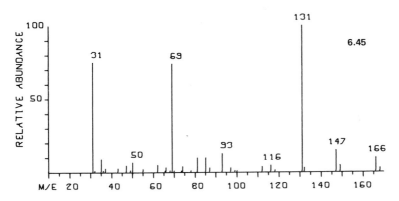

6.12   Other Types of Compounds

In addition to the comprehensive references of Budzikiewicz, Djerassi, and Williams (*1.3, 1.4*), a number of recent reviews give valuable details on the fragmentation behavior of other classes of compounds and applications in particular research areas. In the following list the page number follows immediately after the reference. Several compilations of references to the original literature are also recommended (*1.18–1.21*).

COMPOUND CLASSES
   Terpenes and terpenoids: *1.4*-II, 121; *1.15*, 175; *1.16*, 351.
   Carotenoids: *1.13*, 272.
   Steroids: *1.4*-II, 5; *1.14*, 333; *1.15*, 172; *1.16*, 251.

Bile acids: *1.16*, 291.
Carbohydrates: *1.4*-II, 203; *1.15*, 164; *1.16*, 313.
Lactones, pyrones: *1.3, 205; 1.17*, 139.
Quinones, tropones: *1.3, 527; 1.13*, 279.
Fatty acids, lipids: *1.13*, 256; *1.14*, 342; *1.16*, 211, 229.
Carbonates: *1.3*, 484.
Carbamates, ureas: *1.3*, 500.
Trimethylsilyl ethers: *1.3*, 471.
N-Oxides, nitrosamines: *1.3*, 328.
Amino acids: *1.16*, 387.
Peptides: *1.4*-II, 183; *1.13*, 286; *1.14*, 289; *1.16*, 405.
Lactams, oximes, hydrazones: *1.3*, 353.
Barbiturates: *1.3*, 509.
Isocyanides, isocyanates: *1.3*, 418.
Nitro, nitroso, azoxy compounds, nitrites: *1.3*, 512.
Sulfoxides, sulfones, etc.: *1.3*, 552; *1.17*, 288.
Alkaloids: *1.4*-I; *1.16*, 655.
Nucleic acids: *1.13*, 315; *1.15*, 161; *1.16*, 429.
Nitrogen heterocyclics: *1.3*, 566-612; *1.16*, 591; *1.17*, 325–398.
Porphyrins: *1.13*, 320.
Oxygen heterocyclics: *1.3*, 615; *1.4*-II, 254.
Sulfur heterocyclics: *1.3*, 625; *1.17*, 225.
Mixed heterocyclics: *1.3*, 634; *1.17*, 510.
Organophosphorous compounds: *1.3*, 645.
Organometallic compounds: *1.3*, 654; *1.14*, 330; *1.15*, 182.

APPLICATIONS
Metabolism: *1.4*-II; *1.14*, 217, 327; *1.16*, 573.
Drugs: *1.3*, 509; *1.14, 332; 1.16*, 573.
Antibiotics: *1.16*, 449.
Vitamins and cofactors: *1.16*, 499.
Hormones: *1.16*, 537.
Clinical uses: *1.16*, 601.
Flavor components: *1.13*, 327; *1.16*, 701.
Pesticides and insecticides: *1.14*, 358; *1.16,* 623.
Pheromones (semiochemicals): *1.16*, 723.
Organic geochemistry: *1.13*, 369.
Extraplanetary life: *1.16*, 789.

6.13   Additional Unknowns

Unknown 6.46

m/e	Relative abundance	m/e	Relative abundance
15	6.2	53	13.
26	5.8	54	2.2
27	43.	55	100.
28	7.4	56	5.7
29	46.	57	0.51
30	1.1	58	0.84
31	1.0	59	0.22
36.8 m	0.87	67	1.5
37	3.2	68	0.32
38	7.2	69	0.30
39	42.	70.3 m	1.5
40	5.2	82	1.3
41	13.	83	97.
42	6.8	84	5.4
43	90.	85	0.33
44	2.2	97	0.04
45	0.41	98	51.
51.1 m	0.29	99	3.5
52	2.4	100	0.20

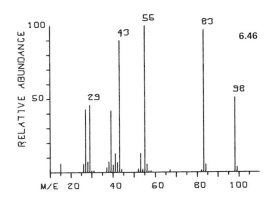

Other methods show that Unknown 6.47 *contains a hydroxyl group.*

Unknown 6.47

m/e	Relative abundance	m/e	Relative abundance
15	2.9	59	0.11
28	12.	70	21.
29	3.8	71	2.2
30	100.	72	16.
31	3.4	73	0.73
39	4.6	74	0.01
41	13.	88	24.
42	14.	89	1.1
43	18.	90	0.07
44	20.	102	2.5
45	5.7	103	4.1
56	4.5	104	0.24
57	1.3	105	0.01
58	3.1		

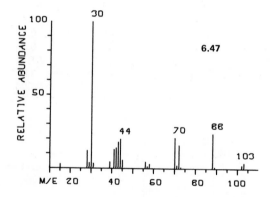

Unknown 6.48

m/e	Relative abundance	m/e	Relative abundance	m/e	Relative abundance	m/e	Relative abundance
15	2.1	52	0.38	91	3.2	121	0.61
28	2.7	63	2.3	92	12.0	122	1.0
30	1.4	64	2.1	93	1.0	123	0.16
38	1.2	65	1.6	94	0.04	150	100.
39	1.3	66	0.30	104	32.	151	8.3
43	26.	74	4.0	105	2.4	152	0.90
44	0.64	75	6.0	106	0.15	165	18.
45	0.05	76	12.	119	1.1	166	1.6
50	9.0	77	3.8	120	6.5	167	0.18
51	2.9	78	0.48				

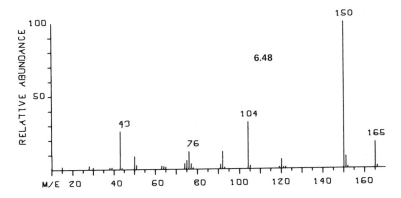

Unknowns 6.49 through 6.53 all have the same elemental composition and all contain a carbonyl group. Although the molecules are fairly simple, considerable difficulty is usually encountered in assigning structures to these, primarily because of the overlapping possibilities of the elemental compositions of particular peaks. (Of course high resolution information would simplify this.) The frequency of maximum absorption in the carbonyl region of the infrared spectrum is given at the end of the table to illustrate how a small amount of information from another source can often make interpretation of the mass spectrum much easier. Mass spectral data below m/e 24 have been omitted.

	Unknowns 6.49–6.53				
	Relative abundance				
m/e	6.49	6.50	6.51	6.52	6.53
26	3.8	5.5	5.7	11.	4.0
27	13.	40.	18.	37.	16.
28	4.1	6.3	12.	16.	8.1
29	25.	8.8	100.	100.	14.
30	1.3	0.25	1.3	4.0	1.5
31	1.7	1.3	2.6	7.2	2.3
32	0.08	0.09	0.22	0.32	1.3
33	—	0.06	—	1.1	0.06
37	—	1.7	1.7	0.26	0.52
37.1 m	—	—	—	0.04	—
38	—	2.9	2.4	0.26	0.53
39	—	15.	20.	0.79	1.6
40	0.08	2.4	3.9	0.24	0.67
41	0.66	42.	36.	3.1	3.0
42	5.9	11.	25.	3.1	3.0
43	100.	100.	58.	1.9	95.
44	2.8	3.8	91.	0.57	4.6
45	13.	13.	28.	5.0	100.
46	0.33	0.47	0.99	0.13	2.4
47	0.03	0.69	1.2	0.01	0.25
53	—	0.56	3.1	0.55	0.72
54	—	0.12	0.55	0.13	0.35
55	0.07	3.8	3.5	3.4	1.9
56	—	0.35	0.50	2.4	0.45
57	0.04	0.20	1.8	75.	0.66
58	0.04	0.09	0.70	2.7	0.33
59	0.09	0.41	0.98	25.	0.38
60	0.61	2.1	1.9	0.95	2.6
61	9.9	0.62	2.8	0.26	0.12
62	0.22	—	0.30	—	—
63	0.04	—	0.62	—	—
67	—	—	3.0	—	0.11
68	—	0.07	2.1	—	0.03
70	4.7	0.38	33.	—	1.9
71	0.21	1.6	16.	0.07	0.41
72	0.02	0.15	1.4	—	2.3
73	3.0	21.	1.9	0.13	2.3
74	0.13	0.77	0.15	—	0.08
75	—	0.10	0.06	—	—
87	0.22	0.66	3.0	1.6	0.54
88	4.0	6.2	1.0	21.	6.9
89	0.19	0.30	0.05	1.0	0.34
90	0.02	0.05	—	0.12	0.05
Infrared $(cm^{-1})^a$					
	1745	1705	1660	1730	1705

[a] Functional groups possible include: <1675 cm^{-1}, strong hydrogen bonding; $\sim$1700 cm^{-1}, saturated carboxylic acids and ketones; $\sim$1725 cm^{-1}, aldehydes; 1730–1750 cm^{-1}, esters.

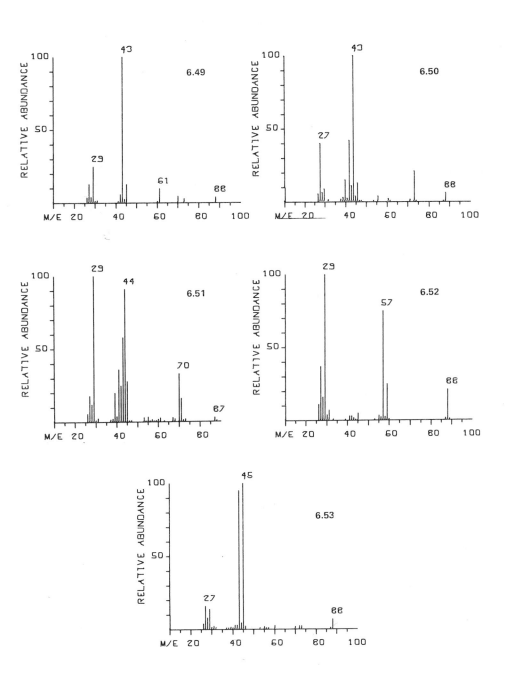

Unknown 6.54 is an α-amino acid isolated from a natural source as the ethyl ester.

Unknown 6.54

m/e	Relative abundance	m/e	Relative abundance	m/e	Relative abundance	m/e	Relative abundance
29	22.	54	2.4	85	0.71	129	6.1
30	11.	55	2.7	86	0.52	130	0.42
31	0.82	56	48.	87	2.2	131	6.3
39	1.8	57	5.1	88	3.5	132	0.36
40	0.41	58	1.2	100	5.6	133	0.28
41	2.3	59	1.8	101	0.62	148	3.2
42	6.7	60	0.82	102	5.4	149	0.20
43	7.9	61	100.	103	1.8	150	0.15
44	2.1	62	3.0	104	48.	160	0.63
45	6.2	63	4.3	105	2.6	161	0.05
46	4.9	74	12.	106	2.3	162	0.16
47	5.3	75	8.0	114	1.1	177	12.
48	1.6	76	0.59	116	3.9	178	1.2
49	1.3	83	2.1	117	0.22	179	0.66

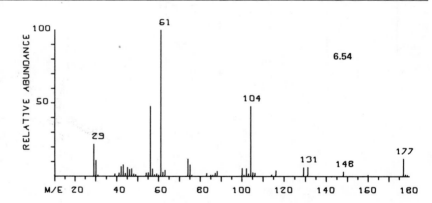

Unknown 6.55.   Exact mass data indicate that *m/e* 44 and 74 are $C_2H_4O^+$ and $C_3H_6O_2^+$.

Unknown 6.55

m/e	Relative abundance	m/e	Relative abundance
17	9.8	42	11.
18	32.	43	89.
19	9.2	44	53.
20	0.09	45	9.9
26	4.1	46	0.50
27	11.	59	1.0
28	9.0	60	10.
29	38.	61	100.
30	5.3	62	5.2
30.4 m*	0.34	63	0.60
31	56.	73	0.65
32	2.9	74	1.3
33	2.4	75	0.88
41	1.9	76	0.04

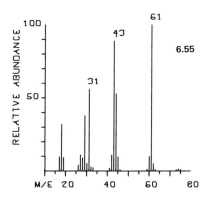

m/e	Relative abundance
15	3.7
26	5.5
27	41.
28	8.5
29	36.
30	0.80
35	4.0
36	5.9
37	2.4
38	6.1
39	42.
40	6.5
41	83.
42	22.
43	76.
44	2.8
54	2.5
55	89.
56	6.6
57	2.0
62	2.2
63	9.4
64	0.49
65	3.2
69	3.7
70	23.
71	75.
72	4.2
73	0.09
76	58.
77	100.
78	21.
79	31.
80	1.0
90	1.6
91	17.
92	1.4
93	5.5
94	0.26

Unknown 6.56

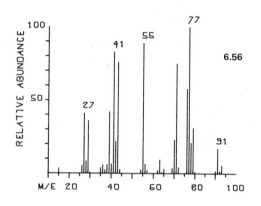

Unknown 6.57	
m/e	Relative abundance
15	0.59
26	1.9
27	2.5
28	1.9
29	0.11
37	1.9
38	3.6
39	11.
40	5.1
41	2.5
42	1.7
45.5	0.69
46	0.85
46.5	2.4
50	5.0
51	10.
52	6.1
53	3.8
54	1.5
63	3.8
64	2.4
65	13.
66	37.
67	7.3
68	0.31
76	0.49
77	0.21
78	15.
79	0.90
80	0.03
91	1.2
92	21.
93	100.
94	7.1
95	0.21

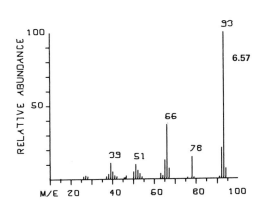

Unknown 6.58

m/e	Relative abundance	m/e	Relative abundance
27	15.	72	60
28	21.	773	2.3
29	40.	74	0.35
30	1.3	77	0.37
31	1.3	78	20.
32	1.0	79 0.47	0.47
33	2.6	96	1.4
41	2.4	97	17.
42	3.9	98	0.40
43	3.4	99	0.03
44	36.	113	0.64
45	3.3	114	4.5
46	2.6	115	0.13
47	4.0	126	100.
50	2.9	127	3.6
51	2.7	128	0.26
56	2.7	140	7.0
69	60.	141	70.
70	4.7	142	3.4
71	0.57	143	0.20

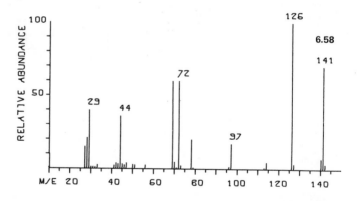

Unknowns 6.59 to 6.63.   A compound isolated from coffee aroma gave the mass spectrum shown as Unknown 6.59. Compounds *a* through *e* were suspected structures; these were synthesized, and the additional spectra are shown as Unknowns 6.60 through 6.63.

Assign the spectra to the proper structures. Do not be discouraged if the "most logical" mechanism for a particular structure does not give an abundant ion in any of the unknown spectra; several structural features are present in these molecules that can influence the decomposition pathways in a variety of ways. Of course, this will also be true of many real unknowns.

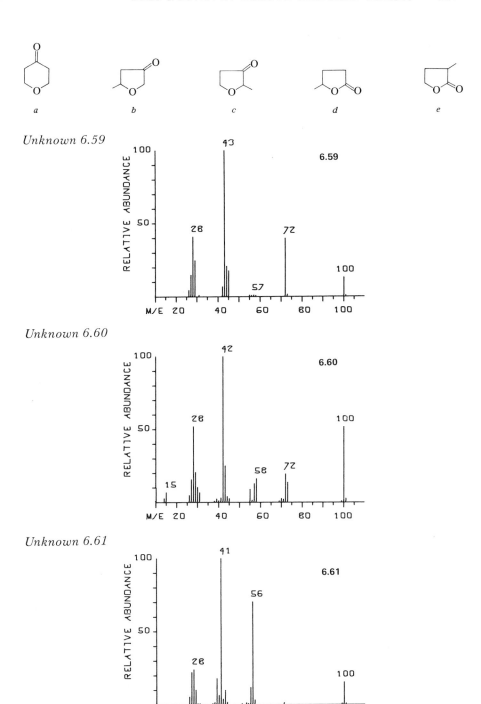

a   *b*   *c*   *d*   *e*

Unknown 6.59

Unknown 6.60

Unknown 6.61

Unknown 6.62

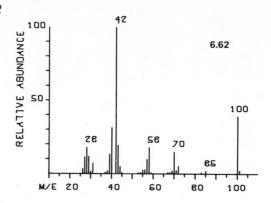

Unknown 6.63

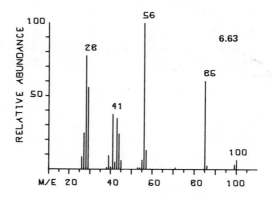

7

AUXILIARY TECHNIQUES

When the normal mass spectrum (70-eV electron impact ionization, unit mass resolution, etc.) does not supply all the needed structural information, there are other types of mass spectral data that may be useful. A complete description of these is beyond the scope of this book, but you should have some familiarity with the auxiliary techniques which are available.

7.1   Metastable Ion Decompositions

With careful examination of the base line of Figure 7-1 you will note several low abundance peaks (for example, m/e 16.2, 18.7, and 24.1) that exhibit shapes more diffuse than those of the normal ions. These arise from the decomposition of metastable ions in the field-free drift region ahead of the magnetic field, and have come to be called "metastable peaks" or just "metastables" by mass spectrometrists (although this terminology is inexact). These ions have decomposed *after* leaving the ion source (ion lifetimes of approximately 10^{-5} sec), so generally they result from decompositions of *lower* internal energy ions than those producing the normal product ions in the spectrum. The mass of a metastable peak, m*, is dependent on both the mass of the precursor (m_1) and the mass of the product (m_2) ions of the reaction, as ion acceleration involves m_1 and magnetic deflection involves m_2. This means that metastables give an extra dimension of information; we shall see that this is valuable in a variety of ways.

The formula $m^* = m_2^2/m_1$ is used to determine the reaction giving rise to the metastable m*. This is best solved by trial and error, using the major normal ions of the spectrum as possible assignments for m_1 and m_2, and logical mass differences (Table A-5) for the neutrals lost. *Note that more than one answer may be possible* (m* = 10.0 can arise from m/e 40 → m/e 20, m/e 90 → m/e 30, etc.). Such trials can be done rapidly with a slide rule. (Set the

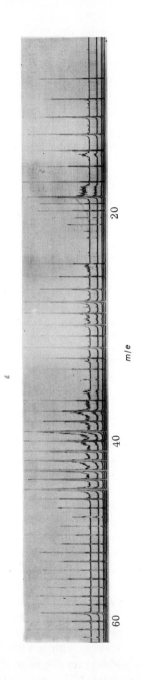

FIGURE 7-1   Mass spectrum of isopropyl alcohol.

proper index of the B scale opposite the m* value on the A scale. Then, setting the slide on the B scale at the suspected m_1 value will give the corresponding m_2 mass under the slide on the D scale.) You can also use the nomograph in Table A-8. For example, for m* = 32.3 in Figure 7.1, placing a ruler at this value in the m* column can yield such unlikely combinations as m/e 45 → m/e 38, but m/e 60 → m/e 44, corresponding to $C_3H_8O^+$ → $C_2H_4O^+ + CH_4$, is the only logical reaction for which $m_2^2/m_1 \sim 32.3$.

A simple alternative method can be used for spectrometers in which the mass scan has an exponential function; in this case m_2 will be equidistant between m_1 and m*.

Unknown 7.1.   Identify the remaining metastable peaks in Figure 7-1 and assign appropriate reactions.

Peaks at nonintegral masses can also arise from doubly (masses ending in .5) and, occasionally, triply (masses ending in .33 and .67) charged ions; metastable peaks are readily distinguishable from these by their width. A variety of other methods for the study of metastable decompositions have been devised which give much higher sensitivities, offer more accurate determinations of m_1 and m_2, and allow variation of ion lifetimes. For example, in the Barber-Elliott "defocusing" technique metastable decomposition product ions formed in the field-free drift region just ahead of the electrostatic analyzer (ESA) can be selected by changing the relative ESA potential to correspond to the relative kinetic energy remaining in the product ion after the decomposition (m_2/m_1). For further reading an excellent recent review by Jennings is recommended (*7.1*).

REACTION PATHWAYS.   The most common use of metastables is in the elucidation of ion decomposition pathways. Identification of a particular reaction pathway can provide valuable evidence as to the arrangement of atoms in a molecule. For example, in a hypothetical spectrum the presence of ions corresponding in mass to AB and ABC could indicate either of the molecular structure possibilities A-B-C-B-A or A-B-B-C-A. However, a metastable decomposition of ABC → AB would be possible, barring rearrangements, only for the structure A-B-C-B-A. In the mass spectrum of *N*-methyl-*N*-isopropyl-*N*-*n*-butylamine (Figure 6-22) α-cleavages give the prominent ions at

$$(7\text{-}1)$$

m/e 86 and 114, and their further rearrangement decompositions yield, respectively, other abundant ions at *m/e* 44 and 58 (6-47). If this were the spectrum of an unknown, the compound *N*-methyl-*N*-ethyl-*N*-2-pentylamine would also have to be considered, as it should also give rise to these peaks (7-1). However, the observation of a metastable corresponding to *m/e* 114 → *m/e* 58 would eliminate the latter compound from consideration; its spectrum should show *m/e* 114 → *m/e* 44.

ELEMENTAL COMPOSITIONS.   Metastable decompositions can give useful evidence of elemental compositions also. Valeraldehyde oxime (*7.2*) exhibits very abundant ions at *m/e* 41 and 59 (7-2); a metastable corresponding to *m/e* 59 → *m/e* 41 indicates the presence of oxygen in *m/e* 59, as such a mass difference almost always is due to the loss of H_2O (Table A-5).

$$(7-2)$$

m/e 59 m/e 41

Note, however, that this is not strong evidence for the presence of the hydroxyl group (*vide infra*). An analogous use in molecular ion identification was given in Section 3.6; see also Unknown 6.11.

Unknown 7.2. The presence of which particular metastable in Figure 7-1 eliminates CH_3COOH as the molecule giving this spectrum?

MIXTURE ANALYSIS.   Metastables can also be useful if the presence of an impurity is suspected. For example, a peak 18 mass units below the M^+ peak could be due to *thermal* dehydration of the sample; the presence of a metastable corresponding to $M^+ \to (M-18)^+$ shows that *at least part* of the $(M-18)^+$ peak is due to ion decomposition.

Metastables can also aid in structure determinations of two or more components in a mixture by indicating which peaks arise from the same component. For example, in the mass spectrum of a peptide mixture (*7.3*) peaks were found corresponding in exact mass to ions containing (order of components in ion unknown): (Ac, Gly)$^+$, (Ac, Gly, Ala)$^+$, (Ac, Gly, Ala, Leu, OMe)$^+$, (Ac, Val)$^+$, (Ac, Gly, Val)$^+$, and (Ac, Gly, Gly, Val, OMe)$^+$. The first three peaks give a positive identification of the tripeptide AcGlyAla-LeuOMe. The last two peaks could arise from the peptides AcGlyValGly-OMe *and/or* AcValGlyGlyOMe; (the masses of their molecular ions, as well as those of AcGlyVal$^+$ and AcValGly$^+$, of course are indistinguishable). Metastables were found corresponding in mass to the transitions (Ac, Gly, Gly, Val, OCH$_3$)$^+$ → (Ac, Val)$^+$ and (Ac, Gly, Val)$^+$ → (Ac, Val)$^+$, positively identifying AcValGlyGlyOAc as a component. A similar approach can be used for the quantitative analysis of mixtures (*7.4*).

Metastables can be used similarly in the determination of isotopic purity(*7.5*) to avoid interferences caused by the presence of $(M-H)^+$ peaks.

For a sample of toluene-d_1 ($M^+ = m/e$ 93) the electrostatic analyzer (ESA) potential of a double-focusing mass spectrometer is set to allow the passage only of ions that have lost approximately 1/93 of their mass. From the M^+ ions $C_7H_8{}^+$, $C_7H_7D^+$, and $C_7H_6D_2{}^+$ only the metastable product ions $C_7H_7^+$, $C_7H_6D^+$, and $C_7H_5D_2^+$, respectively, will then reach the magnetic field, so that a magnetic scan will give peaks reflecting the abundances of these metastable ions. These in turn will reflect the abundance of the molecular species if the isotope effects in their metastable decompositions are identical.

IDENTIFYING REARRANGEMENTS.   As will be discussed in Chapter 8, abundant metastable decompositions of a particular precursor ion arise mainly from its reactions of lowest activation energy, which are commonly the "tight-complex" reactions such as rearrangements. Thus in a spectrum containing an abundant ion formed by a rearrangement and an abundant ion from a simple cleavage ("loose complex") reaction, it is found generally that the metastable corresponding to the rearrangement formation is at least one hundred times as abundant (7.6). In the spectrum of isopropanol (Figure 7-1) there is no metastable corresponding to the formation of m/e 45, the base peak in the spectrum. Yet the metastable transition m/e 60 → m/e 44 is observable, even though the abundance of m/e 44 is only a few percent of that of m/e 45. This indicates that the rearrangement loss of the CH_4 molecule requires a lower activation energy than the simple cleavage loss of the CH_3 radical. However, simple cleavage reactions can give significant metastables if there are no competing reactions of substantially lower activation energy.

Metastable decompositions sometimes represent unusual rearrangements which are not commonly observed in normal mass spectra, and so should be used with caution in structure interpretation. Ions containing carbonyl groups sometimes exhibit appreciable metastables corresponding to loss of H_2O; thus m* (59 → 41$^+$) in valeraldehyde oxime (7-2) is not a reliable indication of the presence of the OH group.

COLLISIONAL ACTIVATION.   The usefulness of unimolecular metastable decompositions is seriously handicapped by the fact that they cannot be observed for many important reactions; the precursor ions which are sufficiently excited to undergo these reactions have already decomposed before leaving the ion source. To cause such reactions to occur in the drift region, energy must be *added* to an ion during its passage through this region. A convenient way to do this is through "collisional activation" (7.1, 7.7, 7.8): if the ion collides with a neutral atom or molecule present in the drift region, it is possible for part of the ion's translational energy to be converted into internal energy. A recommended technique (7.8) is to raise the drift-region pressure with helium until the precursor ion abundance drops (because of scattering) to 10% of its value (approximately 10^{-4} torr); this can even be done (7.7) by *carefully* loosening a drift-region vacuum flange which has been encased in a helium-filled bag. The decompositions resulting from collisional activation can be measured by the same methods used for unimolecular metastables. The decomposition reactions produced from a particular precursor appear to be those expected from the applicable $k(E)$ functions (see Chapter 8) in accordance with the quasi-equilibrium theory. Thus all the major possible decomposition pathways of an ion can be identified by collisional activation using defocusing or other sensitive detection methods for metastables.

ION STRUCTURE CHARACTERIZATION. An ion's decomposition behavior in the field-free drift region can also be used to characterize its structure. For example (7.9), $C_2H_5O^+$ ions of structures $CH_3O=CH_2^+$ and $CH_3CH=OH^+$ (produced from compounds of the type CH_3OCH_2-R and $CH_3CH(OH)-R$, respectively) both give a unimolecular metastable corresponding to $C_2H_5O^+ \rightarrow CHO^+$ (m* = m/e 18.7), but the latter is "flat-topped" (see Figure 7-1) owing to a release of 0.5 eV of energy during ion decomposition (for a thorough discussion of metastable peak shapes see ref. 7.1). Thus this "metastable ion characteristic" (7.9) can be used to distinguish these isomeric ion structures. In this case the abundances of the metastable ions are also characteristic of the precursor ion structure; $[m*(45^+ \rightarrow 19^+)]/[m*(45^+ \rightarrow 29)] = 2$ for $C_2H_5O^+$ ions from all $CH_3CH(OH)-R$ compounds studied, while for those from CH_3OCH_2-R compounds the m*(45 → 19$^+$) was too small to be observed (7.9). This demands that the abundance of $C_2H_5O^+$ ions of the internal energy required for one decomposition relative to that required for the other be *independent of the identity of the molecule* ionized. If these required energy ranges (see the "metastable window" in Figure 8-1) are substantially different, then appropriate changes in the $P(E)$ function will affect the relative metastable abundances, making such characteristics ambiguous (7.10).

Fortunately, collisional activation of higher-energy decomposition processes appears to be virtually independent of the $P(E)$ of the precursor, so that these product ion abundances provide reliable and useful characteristics of ion structure (7.8).

7.2 The Shift Technique

In many cases the addition of a small functional group to a large molecule such as an alkaloid changes the spectrum by merely increasing the mass of the particular ion fragments which contain this functional group, but without changing the relative abundances of these ions to a great extent. Of course, this will not be true if the group added strongly affects the stability of a particular bond or bonds in the molecular ion. An obvious case is isotopic substitution; deuterium labeling of a compound increases the mass of each ion by one for each deuterium atom incorporated, but isotope effects on ion

Text continued on p. 196

Unknown 7.3.   The spectrum of this unknown indole alkaloid (middle) is compared to the spectra of two known structures (*7.11*). (The abundance of *m/e* 124 is greater than that shown by × 3 in the first spectrum and by × 4 in the latter two spectra.) What functional groups does the unknown contain? Where are they most probably located on the molecular skeleton?

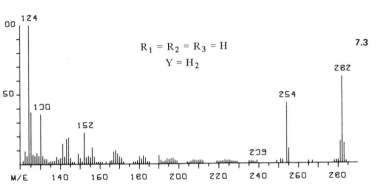

$R_1 = R_2 = R_3 = H$
$Y = H_2$

7.3

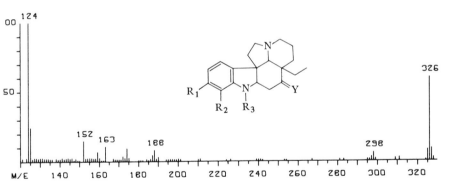

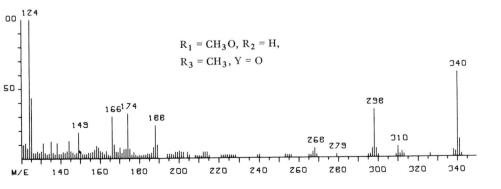

$R_1 = CH_3O$, $R_2 = H$,
$R_3 = CH_3$, $Y = O$

relative abundances are generally small. Substitution of a hydrogen by a group of low influence (such as methyl, methoxyl, or chlorine) at an unreactive position (for example, a ring, especially an aromatic ring) often gives ion abundances similar to those of the original spectrum. This has obvious utility in determining the nature and position of a substituent added to a molecule whose mass spectral behavior is already well understood. This has been termed the "shift technique" by Biemann (*7.11*), who demonstrated its great utility for the indole alkaloids. These stable ring structures contain functional groups that strongly influence the decomposition, minimizing the effect on the spectrum of molecular substitution. The method is less useful for molecules containing less influential groups, such as terpenes or steroidal alcohols.

7.3 Chemical Derivatives

Chemical conversion of a compound to an appropriate derivative can sometimes improve the resulting mass spectral data, either by increasing the compound's vapor pressure or by making its spectrum more easily interpretable. A derivative that decreases the polarity of ionic groups in the molecule generally increases the vapor pressure; for example, oligopeptides of relatively high molecular weight (containing ten amino acids) can be made sufficiently volatile by subjecting them to acetylation of the terminal amino groups followed by permethylation of the carboxyl and amide functionalities (7-3). Trimethylsilylation is probably the most widely used technique

$$H_2N(CHR_i-CO-\overset{\overset{\displaystyle H}{|}}{N})_nCHR_j-COOH \xrightarrow{\text{acetylation}} \xrightarrow{\text{permethylation}}$$

$$CH_3CON(CHR_i-CO-\overset{\overset{\displaystyle CH_3}{|}}{N})_{\overline{n}}CHR_j-CO-OCH_3 \qquad (7\text{-}3)$$

for increasing sample volatility; formation of the trimethylsilyl ether of an alcohol also has a beneficial effect on its fragmentation (for example, the large $(M - 15)^+$ peak is indicative of the molecular weight). Condensation of a 1,2-diol with acetone to yield the acetonide can provide a more useful volatile derivative. Chemical modification can also increase the thermal stability of samples.

Derivatives have been used to provide a surprising variety of changes in the mass spectrum of a compound. Williams (*3.5*) suggests a way to stabilize a molecule whose mass spectrum does not contain a molecular ion; the addition of a functional group that lowers the ionization potential (for example, an aromatic group) sufficiently could make possible the formation of molecular ions of internal energies below the decomposition threshold. In early low-resolution studies of peptide derivatives, Lederer and co-workers found that acylation of the *N*-terminal amino group with a large fatty acid (for example,

n-$C_{19}H_{39}COOH$) gave N-terminal sequence peaks at masses much higher than those from other less-definitive fragmentation pathways, greatly simplifying the interpretation of these sequence peaks (*7.12*). Isotopic labels can serve a similar purpose; if the N-terminal acyl group of the peptide contains a bromine atom, its pair of equal isotopic peaks will serve as an identifying marker (*7.13*).

Introduction of a functional group which will strongly direct the fragmentation (for example, amino, ethylene ketal) will substantially change the mass spectral information; several examples are given in Chapter 6. This could be used, for example, to cause fragmentation in part of a steroid molecule about which the original mass spectrum gave little information.

Derivatization can be used as a chemical test of particular structural features of the unknown molecule, with the mass spectrum of the subsequent product used to determine the results. This technique is especially effective if the reaction at the chemically active site involves the replacement of one or more atoms with their isotopic counterparts, as the concomitant spectral change can usually be predicted accurately. Thus the number of enolizable hydrogen atoms in a molecule can be readily determined from the mass spectrum after exchange with deuterium; the exchange need not be complete, as it is only the mass (not the relative abundance) of product formed with the largest number of deuterium atoms that needs to be determined. As a further example, a variety of reactions have been proposed to introduce isotopic or functional group labels at double bonds (such as those in a fatty acid), as the mass spectrum of the derivative is much more indicative of the original double bond position than is the spectrum of the olefin itself.

More complete descriptions of useful chemical derivatives are available in a number of excellent references (*7.14*).

7.4 Other Ionization Conditions

A wide variety of instrumental techniques are also available for obtaining additional mass spectral data; metastable ions (Section 7.1) and high resolution (Section 7.5) are discussed separately.

LOW-TEMPERATURE IONIZATION.   Spiteller (*7.15*) has shown that lowering the sample and ion source temperature can sometimes reduce the degree of fragmentation markedly. The molecular ion internal energy distribution, $P(E)$, is determined by the energy added on ionization and the initial thermal energy of the molecule; the latter is lowered by reducing the temperature, thus reducing the *minimum* (as well as the average) internal energy of $M^{\ddagger}$. For example, the average internal energy of 1,2-diphenylethane is lowered 0.4 eV in changing the temperature from 200° to 75°C. The effect of temperature on internal energy increases with increasing molecular size; unfortunately, reduction of the sample temperature for larger molecules is restricted by sample vapor pressure requirements. Changing the temperature of a chemical ionization source causes dramatic changes in the fragmentation pattern as all the ions are at thermal energies.

LOW-ENERGY IONIZATION.   Lowering the energy of the bombarding electrons will also lower the average (but *not the minimum*) internal energy of the molecular ions. For structure elucidation it is sometimes useful to take a second mass spectrum at a lower electron energy (*ca.* 15 eV), as this will eliminate higher-energy reactions giving secondary product ions which are much less representative of the original structure (although these do provide "ion series" information—Section 5.2). However, lower electron energies increase the relative abundance of primary rearrangement reactions, in the same manner that these increase in metastable ion decomposition (Chapter 8). Further, lowering the electron energy decreases the *absolute* abundance of all ions; although the *relative* abundance of the molecular ion increases, it nevertheless is more difficult to detect at lower electron energies (unless it has been obscured by fragment ions from a higher-molecular-weight impurity— Section 3.6).

OTHER IONIZATION METHODS (*7.16*).   It was pointed out in Section 3.6 that chemical ionization and field ionization are particularly valuable when the electron impact spectrum shows no molecular ion. Although fragmentation is usually reduced by these ionization methods, additional useful structure information can sometimes be obtained from the fragment ion data (*3.7, 3.8*). Negative ion spectra (*7.16, 7.17*) generally suffer from a much lower sensitivity, although special techniques of M. von Ardenne and of R. C. Dougherty appear to alleviate this problem; recent applications of Bowie (*7.18*) are especially promising. Ion cyclotron resonance spectroscopy, like chemical ionization, utilizes ion–molecule reactions. However, this instrument operates at relatively low pressures (*ca.* 10^{-4} torr) and long ion lifetimes (milliseconds), and its double resonance feature makes it possible to identify both the precursor and the products of such reactions (*7.19*). This technique appears to be especially useful in determining ion structures and energetics (*7.19*) and is promising for molecular structure elucidation (*7.20*).

7.5   High Resolution

The most common use of the high-resolution mass spectrometer (*1.16, 7.21*) is the direct *determination of elemental compositions* through exact mass measurement. This generally utilizes a double-focusing mass spectrometer, although satisfactory results can often be achieved with modern single-focusing instruments.

Measurement of the mass of an ion *with sufficient accuracy* provides an unequivocal identification of its elemental (and isotopic) composition. The monoisotopic atomic weights of the nuclides are not exact whole numbers on the basis of mass (^{12}C) = 12.00000 (Table 7-1); this "mass defect" is uniquely characteristic of the isotope, so that the mass of the ion (which shows the total mass defect) identifies its isotopic and elemental composition. Thus an ion of mass 43.0184 must be $C_2H_3O^+$ (for example, acetyl), not $C_3H_7^+$, $C_2H_5N^+$, CH_3N_2, $CHNO^+$, or C_2F^+; to distinguish this requires a mass measuring accuracy of 500 ppm.

TABLE 7-1   *Exact Nuclidic Masses*

Isotope	Atomic weight	Isotope	Atomic weight
^1H	1.00782522	^{19}F	18.9984046
^2H	2.01410222	^{28}Si	27.9769286
^{12}C	12.00000000	^{31}P	30.9737633
^{13}C	13.00335508	^{32}S	31.9720728
^{14}N	14.00307440	^{35}Cl	34.96885359
^{16}O	15.99491502	^{79}Br	78.9183320
^{18}O	17.99915996	^{127}I	126.9044755

From A. H. Wapstra and N. B. Gove, *J. Nuclear Data*, **9**, 267 (1972).

The usefulness of elemental composition information increases exponentially with increasing mass. Figure 7-2 shows the exact mass of a variety of possible ions of molecular weight 310 containing carbon, hydrogen, not more than three nitrogen atoms, and not more than four oxygen atoms. Note, however, that identifying a number of these requires a mass measuring accuracy of *2 ppm*, which is near the limit attainable with all but the most expensive instruments.

Such determinations are made by comparing the focus position of the unknown peak with that of a reference peak whose composition, and thus exact mass, is known. Manual "peak-matching" can give ppm accuracy, but is time-consuming (2 to 10 minutes per peak).

The mass accuracy attainable is usually 10 to 100 times the resolving power that can be achieved. Fortunately, the latter is not usually the critical factor in determining elemental composition. For a pure compound there is only a small probability that two different ions will have a nominal mass of 310 so that they must be separated at high resolution by the instrument. Although the chances are much larger at *m/e* 43, the *relative* mass differences are much greater, allowing a much lower resolving power to be used. High resolving power can be useful, however, in the determination of isotopic purity. Ordinarily the abundance of a peak corresponding to a particular ion (for example, $C_7H_8^+$) must be corrected for the contribution from the higher isotopic peak which has lost a hydrogen atom through fragmentation (for example, $C_7H_6D^+$ or $^{13}CC_6H_7^+$). The latter ions differ from $C_7H_8^+$ by 1.5 and

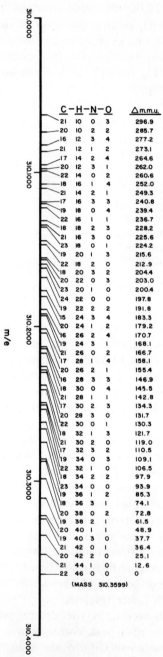

C – H – N – O				Δm.m.u.
21	10	0	3	296.9
20	10	2	2	285.7
16	12	3	4	277.2
21	12	1	2	273.1
17	14	2	4	264.6
20	12	3	1	262.0
22	14	0	2	260.6
18	16	1	4	252.0
21	14	2	1	249.3
17	16	3	3	240.8
19	18	0	4	239.4
22	16	1	1	236.7
18	18	2	3	228.2
21	16	3	0	225.6
23	18	0	1	224.2
19	20	1	3	215.6
22	18	2	0	212.9
18	20	3	2	204.4
20	22	0	3	203.0
23	20	1	0	200.4
24	22	0	0	197.8
19	22	2	2	191.8
15	24	3	4	183.3
20	24	1	2	179.2
16	26	2	4	170.7
19	24	3	1	168.1
21	26	0	2	166.7
17	28	1	4	158.1
20	26	2	1	155.4
16	28	3	3	146.9
18	30	0	4	145.5
21	28	1	1	142.8
17	30	2	3	134.3
20	28	3	0	131.7
22	30	0	1	130.3
18	32	1	3	121.7
21	30	2	0	119.0
17	32	3	2	110.5
19	34	0	3	109.1
22	32	1	0	106.5
18	34	2	2	97.9
23	34	0	0	93.9
19	36	1	2	85.3
18	36	3	1	74.1
20	38	0	2	72.8
19	38	2	1	61.5
20	40	1	1	48.9
19	40	3	0	37.7
21	42	0	1	36.4
20	42	2	0	25.1
21	44	1	0	12.6
22	46	0	0	0

(MASS 310.3599)

m/e

310.0000
310.1000
310.2000
310.3000
310.4000

FIGURE 7-2   Exact masses of possible ions of molecular weight 310 containing carbon, hydrogen, not more than 3 nitrogen atoms, and not more than 4 oxygen atoms.

4.5 mmu; thus they could be separated to allow individual measurement of the $C_7H_8^+$ peak using resolving powers of 60,000 and 20,000, respectively.

ELEMENT MAPS.   Biemann (*7.21*) has pointed out that spectral interpretation is simplified in important ways if the elemental compositions of *all* but the smallest peaks are determined. These compositions are displayed as columns of ions with increasing numbers of carbon and hydrogen atoms, using a separate column for each combination of hetero atoms. Such an "element map" helps to visualize the possible relationships between the molecular fragments.

7.6   Computer Techniques

Possibly the most important reason to expect an even more rapid increase in the use of mass spectrometry in the future is that more and more of its time-consuming, tedious tasks of data acquisition, data reduction, and even interpretation can now be done by computers (*1.16, 7.21–7.29*). Of particular promise is the use of the dedicated on-line computer whose hardware and software have been designed specifically to serve the mass spectrometer. A major drawback to the use of gas chromatography/mass spectrometry has been the problem of obtaining spectra of dozens to hundreds of peaks in a single gas chromatogram. Modern on-line computer systems are actually capable of recording and storing low-resolution spectra taken at frequent intervals (for example, a few seconds) *over each GC peak* for such a chromatogram (*1.16, 7.21, 7.23*).

High-resolution mass spectral data for element maps virtually requires computer processing. Modern on-line systems acquire the data describing each peak, calculate the centroid (in time) and area (and thus abundance) for each, locate the internal reference peaks, interpolate between these to determine the exact masses of the unknown peaks, and find which possible elemental compositions are within the allowed mass error of each peak. The exact masses of as many as 600 peaks can be determined in spectra taken at 2-minute intervals, which is valuable for the direct probe introduction of mixtures to achieve fractional vaporization (*7.3*).

REFERENCE FILE SEARCHING.   A wide variety of systems have been developed to match an unknown mass spectrum against a file of reference spectra (*7.24*). Location of closely similar spectra in the file is a relatively straightforward task; the capabilities of the systems differ, however, in their selectivity between different reference compounds giving similar spectra, tolerance of quantitative differences in ion abundances (the corresponding reference compound often has been run under different instrumental conditions), tolerance of impurities (in either the reference or unknown), search speed, and ability for the chemist to utilize his mass spectral knowledge also in the matching.

SPECTRAL INTERPRETATION.   For obvious reasons we have left to the last the discussion of the ability of the computer (*7.25–7.29*) to do many of the interpretation tasks that you have now learned how to do by studying this book. Elemental compositions can be calculated from isotopic abundances (Chapter 2), and real or hypothetical peaks can be examined as molecular ion possibilities (Chapter 3) by the computer. The total ion abundance can be summed for all designated ion series, and the neutral losses can be identified (Chapter 5). For particular compound classes (for example, aliphatic ketones, esters, amines) the computer has been programmed to follow the logic of the human interpreter in applying the known fragmentation mechanisms (Chapter 6) to deduce the structure (*7.27*); the Artificial Intelligence system (*7.28*) is an elegant example of this approach. The task of extending this capability to a substantial proportion of applicable compound classes appears overwhelming at this time, however, mainly because such spectral correlations have not been worked out in sufficient detail.

A promising alternative suggestion of Isenhour and Jurs (*7.29*) is to have the computer itself develop useful spectra–structure correlations from reference data using "learning machine" methods. The computer "trains" itself to answer a series of yes–no structural questions such as Does the compound contain oxygen? For each question it develops iteratively a mathematical comparison of the spectral data which will distinguish all the "yes" from the "no" reference spectra (that is, classify them so that they are in distinguishable areas in mathematical hyperspace). The computer's ability to give the correct answer on a spectrum not in the reference set increases as the size of the reference set used in training increases; unfortunately, this causes an exponential increase in computer training time. Of course the number of yes–no questions necessary for the complete description of a complex molecule is very large.

We have developed a Self-Training Interpretive and Retrieval System (*7.26*) which attempts to combine the mass spectrometrist's knowledge of the structural significance of mass spectral data with a "learning machine" type of examination of the spectral reference file for similarities in these data. For each of several different types of mass spectral data of the unknown (ion series, neutral losses, characteristic ions) in several mass ranges (a total of ten categories) the computer locates the ten spectra in the reference file which, *on that basis*, most closely match the unknown spectrum. For example, if most of the compounds selected to match the ion series data are pyridines, and most of those selected for the primary neutral loss data are primary alcohols, these are generally found as structural features of the unknown.

8

UNIMOLECULAR ION DECOMPOSITION
REACTIONS

For a thorough understanding of the capabilities, and especially of the limitations, of mass spectrometry for structure elucidation it is necessary to be cognizant of the theoretical aspects of unimolecular ion decompositions. Presentation of this has been delayed until this point because the mechanistic approach already presented has been found in practice to be much more useful in the actual determination of structures. Although quantitative calculations of ion abundances is far beyond the scope of present theory, a knowledge of the theoretical principles has served as a very valuable guide for mechanistic interpretations and the development of auxiliary techniques such as applications of metastable ions.

8.1   Quasi-Equilibrium Theory

The quasi-equilibrium theory (QET) (*8.1*) provides a physical description of mass spectral behavior which is now generally accepted. Ionization of the molecule, which takes place in approximately 10^{-15} sec, initially yields the excited molecular ion without change in bond length (a Franck–Condon process). Except for the smallest molecules, transitions between all the possible energy states of this ion are sufficiently rapid so that a "quasi-equilibrium" among these energy states is established before ion decomposition takes place. Thus the probabilities for the various possible decompositions of an ion are dependent only on its structure and internal energy, and not on the method used for the initial ionization, on the structure of its precursor, or on the mechanistic pathway for the formation of the ion undergoing decomposition (thus an ion's decomposition is said to be "independent of initial preparation"). The effect of the internal energy, E, of the precursor ion on the rate constant, k, for a particular ion decomposition reaction defines the function $k(E)$, illustrated in the lower half of Figure 8-1, for the hypothetical molecular ion M^+ which can decompose to give daughter ions AB^+ and AD^+. (For further details and key references see 8.2.) (In this laboratory Figure 8-1 is referred to as the Wahrhaftig diagram, as it was first described to the author by Professor Austin Wahrhaftig, University of Utah.)

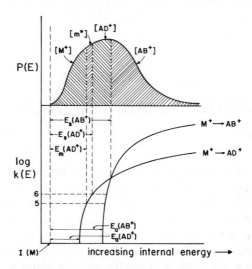

FIGURE 8-1   The Wahrhaftig diagram: relationship of $P(E)$ and $k(E)$ for unimolecular ion decompositions in the mass spectrometer. See text for definitions.

Ions, even those of a particular structure, when formed by 70-eV electron bombardment exhibit a wide range of values of internal energy; this distribution is described by the probability function $P(E)$. For the hypothetical case of Figure 8-1, impact of electrons with M molecules produces M^+ ions with a variety of internal energy values. The probability that an ion will be formed with a particular value of E is shown by the distribution $P(E)$; the relative abundances of M^+, AD^+, and AB^+ ions formed are thus determined by the functions $P(E)$, $k(E)_{M^+ \to AD^+}$, and $k(E)_{M^+ \to AB^+}$.

The thermochemical appearance potential, $A_t(AD^+)$, is the minimum energy necessary to produce AD^+ from the ground-state neutral molecule. The activation energy, $E_a(AD^+)$, is the minimum internal energy of M^+ required for the decomposition to yield AD^+, and thus $A_t(AD^+) = I(M) + E_a(AD^+)$. (These and other relationships to be discussed later are shown in Figure 8-2.) Molecular ions containing internal energy $<E_a$ cannot decompose, regardless of the amount of time allowed for decomposition. However, the probability that M^+ ions of internal energy $>E_a$ will produce AD^+ in the ion source depends on the rate constant, k; $\ln [M^+]_0/[M^+] = kt$. The dependence of k on internal energy is shown by the $k(E)$ function, as illustrated in Figure 8-1. For conventional mass spectrometers, ions whose half-life corresponds to the ion source residence time decompose with rate constants of approximately 10^6 sec^{-1}. We shall define $E_s(AD^+)$ as the

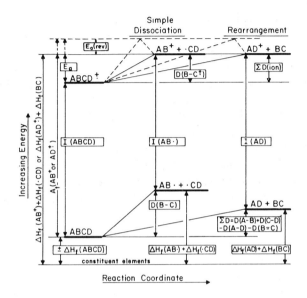

FIGURE 8-2   Thermochemical energy relationships for unimolecular ion decompositions in the mass spectrometer.

internal energy of precursor ions which have an equal probability of leaving the ion source as $M^{\ddagger}$ or AD^+. This causes the measured appearance potential to be higher than the thermochemical value by approximately $E_s - E_a$, which is known as the "kinetic shift"; although this is often <0.01 eV, it can be as large as 2 eV.

For fragment ions other than the one of lowest appearance potential, such as AB^+ in Figure 8-1, an additional kinetic factor which we shall call the "competitive shift" also increases the measured appearance potential with reference to $E_a(AB^+)$. Most $M^{\ddagger}$ ions whose energy corresponds to that required for $k = 10^6$ sec^{-1} for $M^{\ddagger} \rightarrow AB^+$ will decompose instead to produce AD^+, as k for this reaction is much larger. The internal energy of $M^{\ddagger}$ must be $E_s(AB^+)$ as shown in Figure 8-1 to yield equal rates of formation for AB^+ and AD^+. Note that $M^{\ddagger}$ ions of energy $>E_s(AB^+)$ have a greater probability of decomposition to produce AB^+, despite the lower activation energy of the competing reaction which yields product AD^+.

ION ABUNDANCES.   If $P(E)$ for the molecular ion is known, note that the lowest of the E_s values for the M^+ decomposition reactions determines $[M^+]$ directly. Thus in Figure 8-1 the ratio of $[M^+]$ to the total abundance of product ions is approximately determined by the area under the $P(E)$ curve to the left of the $E_m (AD^+)$ line relative to the area to the right of the $E_s(AD^+)$ line. If a structural change in M lowers this E_s value without changing $P(E)$, $[M^+]$ will be reduced; if a structural change lowers $I(M)$ without changing the shape of $P(E)$ or any appearance potentials (which thus will *increase* the E_s values), $[M^+]$ will be increased.

The mass spectral abundances of the *initially formed* product ions follow directly from the data of Figure 8-1; however, further decompositions may be possible which will reduce the abundances of the primary products. The final abundance, $[AD^+]$, will thus be determined also by the $P(E)$ function which describes the internal energy values with which the AD^+ ions have been formed, and the $k(E)$ functions of all the possible decomposition reactions of AD^+. In the further discussion, except where noted, we shall assume that the primary product ion abundance is not decreased appreciably by secondary decompositions; this can be approached experimentally by lowering the energy of the bombarding electrons, or by choosing a system producing stable product ions.

METASTABLES.   Ions formed by metastable decompositions in a field-free drift region of the spectrometer can give very valuable information because the region defines a relatively narrow range of decomposition times for a particular precursor ion, and thus represents a similarly narrow range of rate constants of approximately 10^5 to 10^6 sec^{-1}. Metastable ions formed by the reaction $M^+ \rightarrow AD^+$, which will be designated as m*$(M^+ \rightarrow AD^+)$, thus arise with highest probability from M^+ ions of energies between $E_m (AD^+)$ and $E_s(AD^+)$, and their abundance is represented by the area of the corresponding narrow window in the $P(E)$ curve. In the same manner the metastable ions m*$(M^+ \rightarrow AB^+)$ must arise from M^+ of energies corresponding to k between 10^5 and 10^6, but the probability of such ions decomposing instead of the ion source by $M^+ \rightarrow AD^+$ is much higher (see Figure 8-1), so that $[m*(M^+ \rightarrow AB^+)]$ will be only a small fraction of the abundance indicated by the relative area of the corresponding window in the $P(E)$ curve of M^+.

8.2   Determination of P(E) Functions

Most methods for approximating $P(E)$ of a molecular ion involve measurement of the energy transferred in producing M^+ from M, to which must be added the internal energy of M before ionization. Because ionization involves a vertical transition, the energy necessary to produce M^+ is dependent on the energy level in the neutral molecule of the electron which is expelled. Thus the effect of a structural feature on the energy of a molecular state can be reflected in the internal energy of M^+ produced by ionization from this state. The representation of the $P(E)$ function of M^+, such as in Figure 8-1, results from plotting E for each state against the relative transition probability (Franck–Condon factor) for the state, convoluted with the internal energy of the neutral molecule.

A number of experimental methods for the derivation of $P(E)$ functions for molecular ions have been used. A crude approximation of the amount of energy transferred in producing M^+ can be obtained from the second derivative of the ionization efficiency curve, which is a plot of the increase in total ion abundance with increasing energy of the bombarding electrons. It appears to be possible to obtain a much more detailed description of the energy states in the $P(E)$ function from the photoelectron spectrum, although the indicated populations of these states may be inaccurate.

Useful information on the effect of structure on the $P(E)$ function of molecular ions can be obtained by studying the corresponding photoelectron spectra (a useful compilation of these is available in reference *8.3*). The lower energy limit of the $P(E)$ curve is defined by the ionization potential (I). The change in I caused by the addition of the substituent to a molecule such as ABCD in Figure 8-2 is due to the difference in stabilization energy conferred by the substituent on $ABCD^+$ and ABCD (neutral). The ionization potentials of a variety of substituted aromatic compounds show a good correlation with σ^+ constants for para substituents; note these and other I data on Table A-3. Photoelectron spectral data indicate the shapes of $P(E)$ functions above I can also be related to molecular structure. For example, ionization of the lone pair or π-electrons of added substituents can introduce characteristic new low-energy states, and thus enhance the corresponding low-energy portions of the $P(E)$ curve.

The $P(E)$ function for a primary product ion AB^+ will be determined (*8.4*) by (1) $P(E)$ for the molecular ion; (2) $k(E)$ for the reaction forming AB^+; (3) $k(E)$ for other reactions competitive with AB^+ formation ($M^+ \rightarrow AD^+$); and (4) partitioning of the excess energy in M^+ between the AB^+ ion and the neutral lost in its formation (the neutral CD in the hypothetical case of Figure 8-1). For the latter the excess energy is partitioned proportionally to the number of vibrational degrees of freedom in the ion and neutral products; this is in part responsible for the so-called "degrees-of-freedom" effect which relates the metastable ion abundance, [m*], for the further decomposition of a particular fragment ion to the size of the molecular ion from which it is formed. In general for a homologous series of molecular ions a linear relation is found for $\log([m*]/[AB^+])$ versus the reciprocal of the number of vibrational degrees of freedom in the molecular ion yielding AB^+.

8.3   Determination of k(E) Functions

Some of the accessible energy states of an ion can correspond to activated complexes capable of undergoing decompositions; the minimum energy at which such an energy state can be populated corresponds to E_a for the minimum energy reaction. The rate constant for a particular reaction will be a function of the energy state population of its activated complex relative to the population of all other energy states of the decomposing ion. As described by the Rice-Ramsperger-Kassel-Marcus (RRKM) theory (8.5):

$$k(E) = \frac{1}{h} \frac{Z^{\ddagger}}{Z^*} \frac{\Sigma \mathbf{P}^{\ddagger}(E - E_a)}{\rho^*(E)}$$ (8-1)

where h is Planck's constant, Z is the partition function for the adiabatic degrees of freedom, ‡ refers to the activated complex, * refers to the active molecule (which in this case is an ionic species), $\mathbf{P}(E - E_a)$ is the number of states in the energy range $E - E_a$, and $\rho(E)$ is the density of states. Adiabatic, in contrast to active, degrees of freedom cannot contribute their energy freely to the dissociating bond. In the active molecule the nonfixed internal energy, E, is randomly distributed over all degrees of freedom. In the activated complex one degree of freedom has been transformed into the translational coordinate requiring E_a, so that only $E - E_a$ is available for distribution. The partition function includes the symmetry factor, which is the number of identical pathways by which the reaction takes place.

The RRKM form of the theory is preferred because it uses an exact enumeration of states (8.1, 8.5). However, some discussions of mass spectral reactions continue to use the approximate form of the theory:

$$k(E) = \nu \left(\frac{E - E_a}{E} \right)^{n-1}$$ (8-2)

where ν is the frequency factor, E is the internal energy of the reacting ion, and n is the number of vibrational degrees of freedom. (The magnitude of ν is qualitatively related to the "looseness" of the activated complex to be discussed below.) The predictions of this theory are much poorer for lower-energy ion decompositions.

In general the terms in the RRKM theory reflecting the number of energy states are those affected the most by the structural features of the decomposing ion. The probability that energy sufficient to cause reaction, E_a, will reside in the activated complex depends on the number of activated-complex energy states available for energy residence versus the number of energy states elsewhere in the ion to which the internal energy could be distributed. If the excess internal energy, $E - E_a$, is small, k increases rapidly with increasing E

(see Figure 8-1), as an incremental increase in E will increase $\mathbf{P}^{\ddagger}$ proportionately much more than ρ^*. The rate of increase of k with E should decrease as $E - E_a$ becomes larger, approaching a constant value as E_a becomes very small compared to E. The equation predicts further that a change in structure can affect the $k(E)$ function by effects on (1) E_a, (2) $\mathbf{P}^{\ddagger}/\rho^*$, and (3) $Z^{\ddagger}/Z^*$.

(1) E_a. If a structural change increases the activation energy, the excess energy, $E - E_a$, of the activated complex must decrease, so that the number of states found between E_a and E should also decrease. Thus k will exhibit a lower value, as the probability of accumulating the energy E_a in the reaction coordinate will be decreased. The energy states are quantized, so that at $E = E_a$ only the ground state of the activated complex is available; the equation demands that $k = 0$ for $E < E_a$. The minimum rate, k_{min}, will also be reduced

$$k_{min} = \frac{1}{h} \frac{Z^{\ddagger}}{Z^*} \frac{1}{\rho^*(E_a)} \tag{8-3}$$

by an increase in E_a because of the increase in $\rho^*(E_a)$. Note that an increase in E_a will increase both E_s and the kinetic shift, $E_s - E_a$, as the slope of $k(E)$ will decrease.

(2) $\mathbf{P}^{\ddagger}/\rho^*$. A modification of the molecular ion structure which adds or subtracts states, or changes the energy values of states, will change $\mathbf{P}^{\ddagger}/\rho^*$, and will thus also change the $k(E)$ function.

If, while keeping other parameters constant, the number of vibrational degrees of freedom (n) in the reactant ion is increased, $\rho^*(E)$ will increase. This will lower k_{min}, and will thus usually increase the kinetic shift, which is the amount of excess internal energy necessary to reach $k = 10^6$. A major factor in determining $\mathbf{P}^{\ddagger}/\rho^*$ is the nature (energy levels and degeneracies) of the vibrational degrees of freedom, all of which are assumed to be active. It is also possible that the number of *active* rotational states, the so-called "free rotors," can change in going from the active molecule to the activated complex. A reaction is said to have a "loose complex" if the number of active rotational states have increased at the expense of vibrational states; for example, stretching of a C–C bond in the activated complex would allow ___ion of the attached groups while decreasing the vibrational ___ond. A reaction is said to have a "tight complex" if ___edom are frozen out in the transition state. Rearrange- ___mple of this, as the juxtaposition of atoms demanded ___ectively stops rotation about their adjacent bonds. A ___free rotors can have an important effect on the rate ___ of rotational states is much larger than that of ___edicts that reactions with tight complexes will have a ___ k with increase in E (lower slope of $k(E)$ in Figure ___much larger kinetic shift.

(3) $Z^{\ddagger}/Z^*$. The partition function includes the symmetry factor, which takes account of the fact that the total rate will be proportional to the number of identical reaction pathways. $Z^{\ddagger}/Z^*$ also reflects the moments of inertia of the activated complex relative to the active molecule; such values usually fall between 1 and 10.

8.4   Thermochemical Relationships

DETERMINATION OF E_a.   Equation 8-4 is a simple cleavage reaction to form an even-electron ion and a neutral radical. The thermochemical

$$\text{ABCD} \rightarrow \text{ABCD}^{\ddagger} \rightarrow \text{AB}^+ + \cdot\text{CD} \qquad (8\text{-}4)$$

relationships for this reaction are shown in Figure 8-2. $\Delta H_f(\text{ABCD})$ signifies the heat of formation of ABCD from the constituent elements, and $D(\text{B}-\text{C})$ is the dissociation energy of the B—C bond. $A_t(\text{AB}^+)$ is the *thermochemical appearance potential* of AB^+, so that $A_t(\text{AB}^+) - I(\text{ABCD}) = E_a(\text{ABCD}^{\ddagger} \rightarrow \text{AB}^+)$. The activated complex may be of higher energy than the sum of the energies of the products in their ground states; this excess energy is a reflection of the activation energy for the reverse reaction, $E_a(\text{rev})$. For simple cleavage reactions in neutral systems it is usually assumed that $E_a(\text{rev})$ is negligible, as most gas-phase radical-recombination reactions proceed without an activation energy. Similar conclusions have been reached for simple cleavage reactions of ions. However, for rearrangement reactions such as equation 8-5 in which two bonds are cleaved and two are formed to yield an odd-electron ion and a molecule, $E_a(\text{rev})$ often has an appreciable value.

$$\text{ABCD}^{\ddagger} \rightarrow \text{AD}^{\ddagger} + \text{B}=\text{C} \qquad (8\text{-}5)$$

If $E_a(\text{rev})$ is negligible, E_a is equal to the bond dissociation energy of the ion and is predicted directly from several thermochemical relationships (Figure 8-2). For reaction 8-4,

$$E_a(\text{AB}^+) = \Delta H_f(\text{AB}^+) + \Delta H_f(\cdot\text{CD}) - \Delta H_f(\text{ABCD}^{\ddagger}) \qquad (8\text{-}6)$$

$$= \Delta H_f(\text{AB}\cdot) + I(\text{AB}\cdot) + \Delta H_f(\cdot\text{CD}) - \Delta H_f(\text{ABCD}) - I(\text{ABCD}) \qquad (8\text{-}7)$$

$$= I(\text{AB}\cdot) + D(\text{AB}-\text{CD}) - I(\text{ABCD}) \qquad (8\text{-}8)$$

A substantial collection of ionic thermochemical data has been tabulated (*8.6*), most of which is for smaller molecules.

Note that equation 8-8 utilizes bond dissociation energies of *neutral* species, to which the organic chemist's intuition and knowledge of mechanistic principles should be directly applicable. For two competing reactions of the same molecular ion (and thus the same $I(\text{M})$ values) equation 8-8 predicts that ΔE_a

is determined by ΔI of the respective radicals and ΔD of the respective bonds; this substantiates the conclusions of correlation studies, that the relative stabilization of the product ion and the relative bond strengths are important driving forces for mass spectral reactions. The term $I(AB\cdot)$ reflects the electron affinity of the product ion, AB^+. This term, and thus E_a, will decrease with increasing ability of the product ion to stabilize the positive charge. A great deal is known from organic chemistry about the factors governing such stabilization, especially in aromatic systems. The substituted benzyl radicals illustrate this well; the experimental values of $I(YC_7H_6\cdot)$ correlate closely with σ^+ constants (*8.7*). For the compounds YC_7H_6R the remaining term of equation 8-8, $I(M)$, is correlated by σ_p^+ with a smaller positive ρ value.

8.5 Examples of RRKM Calculations

The applicability of equation 8-1, and especially the usefulness of the concept of the "looseness" or "tightness" of the activated complex, are illustrated by a few model calculations which have been carried out for larger molecules (reactions 8-9 to 8-11). The best agreement between the experimental data and the calculated $k(E)$ functions (Figure 8-3) were obtained by

$$C_6H_5CH_2CH_2C_6H_5^{\dagger} \rightarrow C_7H_7^+ \qquad (E_a = 1.3, E_s = 1.8 \text{ eV}) \qquad (8\text{-}9)$$

$$p\text{-}H_2NC_6H_4CH_2CH_2C_6H_5^{\dagger} \rightarrow p\text{-}H_2NC_7H_6^+ \qquad (E_a = 0.7, E_s = 1.4 \text{ eV}) \qquad (8\text{-}10)$$

$$\rightarrow C_7H_7^+ \qquad (E_a = 2.3, E_s = 7 \text{ eV}) \qquad (8\text{-}11)$$

assuming that the activated complex undergoes an increase of one or two free rotors over the ion for equation 8-9, a *reduction* of one free rotor in equation 8-10, and an increase of three to four free rotors in equation 8-11. In equation 8-9 the importance of product ion stability (see Chapter 4) suggests that the activated complex resembles the products more than the precursor. In such a model the central C—C bond will be substantially dissociated, thus lowering the barrier to rotation about this bond, and increasing the number of free rotors in the activated complex.

Quite a different situation is indicated for the decomposition of *p*-amino-1,2-diphenylethane. The presence of the *p*-amino group should lower the ionization potential of the benzyl radical, lowering E_a, and thus lower the

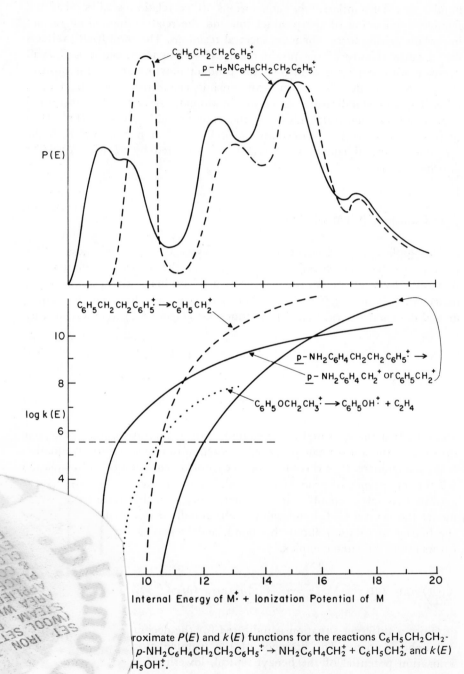

roximate $P(E)$ and $k(E)$ functions for the reactions $C_6H_5CH_2CH_2$-
$p\text{-}NH_2C_6H_4CH_2CH_2C_6H_5^+ \rightarrow NH_2C_6H_4CH_2^+ + C_6H_5CH_2^+$, and $k(E)$
$H_5OH^{+\cdot}$.

kinetic shift. This is not observed, however, suggesting a *substantial reduction in the "looseness" of the activated complex.* The presence of the amino group

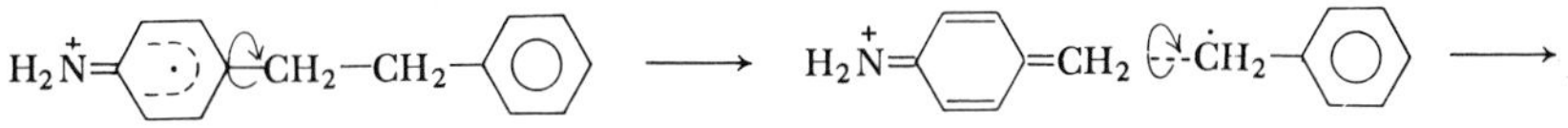

$$H_2NC_7H_6^+ + \cdot C_7H_7$$

will increase the electron density in the N–C bond of the molecular ion; however in the activated complex the partial formation of the resonance-stabilized *p*-aminobenzyl ion should also reduce the free rotation about the C(aryl)–CH$_2$ bond, offsetting the increased rotation about the central C–C bond. This indicates that the configuration of the activated complex for equation 8-10 is substantially "tighter" than that for the active molecule, in direct contrast to the situation in equation 8-9.

The activation energy for equation 8-11 is even higher than that for equation 8-9 because of the lowered value of *I*, and there is an even greater increase in the value of the combined kinetic and competitive shifts. The significant abundance of this product ion in the 70-eV spectrum indicates that $k(E)$ for equation 8-11 must rise much more rapidly than that for equation 8-10. The transition state equation 8-11 must involve an even greater *increase* in free rotors than for equation 8-9, based on the fact that the partial charge on the amino group and the adjacent aromatic ring must now *decrease* in the transition state, lowering the double bond character of the adjacent bonds.

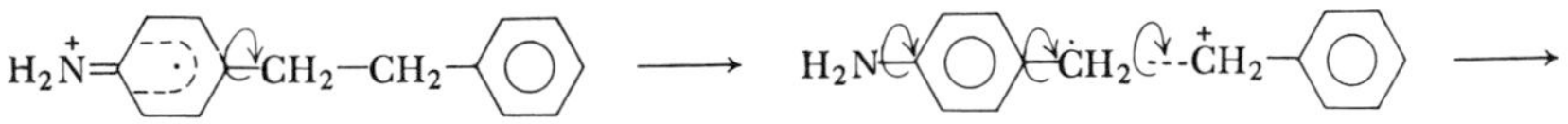

$$H_2NC_7H_6\cdot + C_7H_7^+$$

RRKM calculations have also been made for the major decomposition of the phenyl ethyl ether molecular ion which yields the phenol ion through loss of C$_2$H$_4$. The reaction proceeds through a four-membered ring transition state

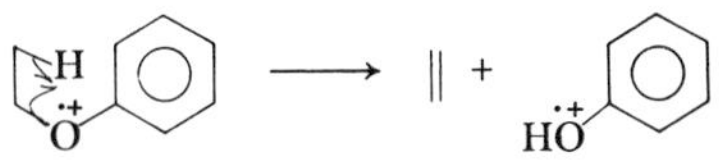

(E_a = 1.0, E_s = 2.5 e V)   (8-12)

supporting this mechanism; calculations assuming the loss of three free rotors in the activated complex give results which are in agreement with the observed product ion abundances (*8.8*). Note in Figure 8-3 that the activation energy, the tightness of the activated complex, and the size of the ion are of major importance in determining the shape of the $k(E)$ curve.

8.6   Possible Complexity of Mass Spectral Reactions

It should be emphasized that a much wider variety of reactions are possible under mass spectral conditions than in usual condensed phase reactions, as evidenced by the presence of literally hundreds of product ion peaks in the mass spectra of complex molecules. This might be compared to running a condensed phase reaction under a wide range of temperatures; for example, the types of products obtained by the pyrolysis of an *n*-alkane change quite dramatically with increasing temperature. Small changes in structure can have a large effect on the mass spectrum if these make possible a new reaction of higher rate constants over an appreciable range of precursor ion internal energies. Thus the dramatic differences between the spectra of *n*-decane and 1-amino-*n*-decane (Figure 4-2) are due primarily to the high rate constants for the new reaction forming the $CH_2=NH_2^+$ ion. Increasing the activation energy of a reaction decreases the slope of the $k(E)$ curve, so that a higher-energy reaction must have a sufficiently looser activated complex in order to be competitive.

Structural effects on the $P(E)$ function of the molecular ion can also affect the mass spectrum, particularly in the abundances of the molecular and metastable ions. Addition of a *m*-amino group to 1,2-diphenylethane only lowers the activation energy for benzylic cleavage by 0.2 eV, but lowers the ionization potential by 1.1 eV; this produces a doubling of the molecular ion abundance. Adding a *p*-nitro group to 1,2-diphenylethane makes no appreciable change in either the I value of the molecule or the A value of the benzyl ion (10.5 ± 0.2 eV). However, the nitro group greatly increases the population of the $P(E)$ curve of M^{+} around 10.5 eV, presumably through ionization at the nitro group, resulting in a several-fold increase in the ion abundance arising from the metastable decomposition $M^{+} \rightarrow C_7H_7^+$; in Figure 8-3 note the low population of $C_6H_5CH_2CH_2C_6H_5^{+}$ ions in the energy region required for this metastable decomposition. In general, the $P(E)$ functions of fragment ions are less sensitive to structural changes. Sharp changes in the $P(E)$ function of a molecular ion (such as the "valley" at 10.5 eV in Figure 8-3) undergo substantial smoothing in the formation of the product ion (this is the so-called "fluctuation effect").

The most favorable ring size of the activated complex appears to be a sensitive function of the activation energy and activated complex geometry. Rearrangements giving abundant ions in the normal mass spectrum more often involve five- and, especially, six-membered ring transition states, probably because the lower E_a associated with these ring sizes more than offsets their less favorable transition state geometry. In α-cleavage reactions the loss of a larger neutral often has a higher activation energy, due to the formation of a less stable ion; the common observation that the loss of the largest neutral is favored in 70-eV spectra is consistent with a greater increase in the number of free rotors in stretching the bond between the α-carbon and the largest group.

8.7   Information from Metastable Ion Data

As was discussed in Section 7-1, metastable ion data can be used as evidence for the relative "looseness" of the activated complex for a particular ion decomposition. These data must be used with caution, however. If an ion can only decompose by simple cleavage reactions, the one of lowest energy could still show an appreciable metastable peak (note, however, that its $k(E)$ function should have a steeper slope, and thus a simple cleavage reaction should give a less abundant metastable peak than a tight-complex reaction). Also if an ion can decompose by two rearrangement processes, the process of higher energy might give no measurable metastable. Further, the precursor ion must be formed with the internal energy required by the metastable decomposition ($k \sim 10^5 \ \text{sec}^{-1}$); the metastable for $C_6H_5CH_2CH_2C_6H_5^+ \rightarrow C_6H_5CH_2^+$ is of low abundance because there is a low probability in the corresponding area of the $P(E)$ function.

8.8   Reaction Initiation by Radical and Charge Sites

The mechanistic concepts presented earlier can also be rationalized in terms of the quasi-equilibrium theory. Indicating the most probable sites for the charged or unpaired electron in an ion is a method of visualizing its important energy states similar to that of writing various contributing canonical forms for a resonance-stabilized structure. The amine group in $n\text{-}C_{10}H_{21}NH_2^+$ (Figure 4-2) appears to be reactive for several reasons. It lowers the ionization potential of the molecule, thus lowering the relative number of ions present with sufficient energy to undergo reactions not involving the NH_2 functionality. Secondly, as mentioned above, it is now possible for new reactions having lower activation energies to compete with the former reactions. Lower E_a reactions occur because structural factors important in stabilizing an odd-electron molecular ion are usually even more effective in the stabilization of an even-electron product ion, again making this group appear as a reactive center in the molecule. Thus the localized radical or charge site formalism provides a way of depicting the most probable reactive center; the QET teaches that it does not matter where ionization actually takes place in the molecule, as there is sufficient time to populate the most probable energy states before decomposition takes place.

9

SOLUTIONS TO UNKNOWNS

(Instructions are given before Unknown 2.1.)

1.1. This is the mass spectrum of water. If any peak in the spectrum corresponds to the mass of the molecule (that is, molecular weight), this peak must be the one of highest mass. This spectrum, therefore, indicates that the sample has a molecular weight of 18. This molecule must contain elements of atomic weight no greater than that of oxygen, such as hydrogen, carbon, nitrogen, or oxygen, which have atomic weights of 1, 12, 14, and 16, respectively. An obvious combination is H_2O. This is confirmed by the peaks at masses 17 and 16 which represent the molecular fragments HO and O, respectively. [Water]

1.2. For this spectrum a molecular weight of 16 is indicated, which could correspond to CH_4. The other peaks in the spectrum support this, each of them corresponding to a carbon atom to which is attached a smaller number of hydrogen atoms. [Methane]

1.3. A molecular weight of 32 corresponds to two or less oxygen atoms. O_2 is ruled out, as its only possible fragment would have a mass of 16. The elemental composition CH_4O is indicated. The only possible arrangement for these is CH_3OH, and the other peaks in the spectrum can all be justified as pieces of such a structure. [Methanol]

1.4. The knowledge that the main gaseous components of *air* are nitrogen, oxygen, and argon identifies the large 28, 32, and 40 peaks as N_2, O_2, and Ar, respectively. Masses 29, 33, and 34 are due to heavy isotopes of nitrogen and oxygen. The significance of such naturally occurring isotopes will be discussed later. Peaks at masses 14, 16, and 20 represent monoatomic and doubly charged species (for example, m/e $Ar^{2+} = \frac{40}{2} = 20$). The ion of mass 44 is discussed in Unknown 1.5. [Nitrogen, oxygen, argon]

1.5. If the isotopic peaks of masses 45 and 46 are ignored, the base (largest) peak in the spectrum indicates a molecular weight of 44. The major peaks at 12 and 16 indicate that the compound contains carbon and oxygen, and m/e 28 corresponds then to CO. Note that there are no peaks at masses 13, 14, and 15 which were indicative of CH_n groups in the spectra of CH_4 and CH_3OH. The formula of carbon dioxide does fit the observed peaks, with the m/e 22 corresponding to CO_2^{2+}. [Carbon dioxide]

1.6.   Ignoring m/e 27 and 28 brings us to an indicated molecular weight of 26. The only apparent logical combination of atoms is $C_2 \cdot H_2$, a fact which can be deduced from the presence of peaks at masses 12 (C_1) and 24 (C_2). Peaks at m/e 13 and 25 correspond to CH and C_2H, respectively, and the remaining small peaks contain heavy isotopes. [Acetylene]

1.7.   [Hydrogen cyanide]

1.8.   [Fluoromethane]

1.9.   [Methanal]

INSTRUCTIONS FOR SOLUTIONS TO THE UNKNOWNS.   As has been emphasized in other parts of this book, the most important way to learn how to interpret mass spectra is by actually working out structures from unknown spectra. Whether this book is used in a formal course or for self-instruction, it is important that the student work through a variety of unknown spectra. In attempting to solve a particular unknown, use the solution here only when you think you know the answer, or when you cannot go further. When you need help, use the solution given here only to get you past your particular difficulty and keep trying to arrive at your own answer. It is suggested that reference spectra *not* be used to solve these unknowns. These unknowns are designed to illustrate principles set forth in the text. Most are common molecules, so that little will be learned in locating them in a reference file of spectra that is properly indexed.

Follow *all* the applicable steps of the outline (Table A-1) which you have covered in the text. The solutions will follow this order, although space limitations prohibit a discussion of every point for each unknown.

The spectra have been taken from the files of this laboratory or from the literature. The data have been corrected for contributions from impurities, ion–molecule reactions, and background, where such corrections appeared to be necessary. The abundance of a peak due to the contribution of natural isotopes is accurate within the larger of the following limits: ±10% relative to the abundance of the peak, or ±0.02% relative to the abundance of the largest peak in the spectrum. Peaks of small abundance that were thought to be inconsequential to the solution of the spectrum have been omitted. This includes unimportant peaks below 1% (relative to the most abundant peak) at the low mass end of a group of peaks of unit mass separation, or at the low mass end of the spectrum. Except where noted otherwise, the spectral data can be found in references 5.3 and/or 5.4.

2.1.   (Be sure to note the instructions that precede this unknown.) This spectrum *could* indicate a molecule of mass 38 which could form an abundant fragment ion by the loss of two hydrogen atoms (m/e 36, $[M-2]^+$). The hints in the text should lead to the observation in Table 2-1 of the 3/1 abundance ratio of the natural chlorine isotopes, masses 35 and 37. Thus, the spectrum is a mixture of $H^{35}Cl$ and $H^{37}Cl$, in proportions corresponding to the isotopic abundances of ^{35}Cl and ^{37}Cl. [Hydrogen chloride]

2.2. The large peaks at masses 94 and 96 should arouse your suspicions, and a check of Table 2-1 reveals that bromine has mass 79 and 81 isotopes of nearly equal abundances. The presence of bromine is supported by the fragment peaks of equal height (abundance) at m/e 79 and 81. Assuming that the masses 94 and 96 represent the molecular ions, by difference the molecule contains 15 mass units in addition to the bromine atom. There is support for this also in the spectrum at m/e 15. The smaller fragment ions at m/e 12–14 indicate the presence of CH_3, as do the ions of m/e 91–95. Note that there is some overlap here because of the bromine isotopes. Mass 94 is mainly CH_3 ^{79}Br, but contains an additional 2% CH ^{81}Br. Peaks at masses 39.5–48 are due to doubly charged ions. [Methyl bromide]

2.3. In answer to the question in the text, if the mass 43 peak were due to $C_2H_3O^+$, the expected m/e 44/43 abundance ratio would be 2.2% from the two ^{13}C atoms present. Thus the observed ratio corresponds more closely to that predicted for three carbon atoms, such as in the ion formula $C_3H_7^+$. However, one should always be aware of the possible contribution from "background" in the instrument, which is much more likely to give a high (*not* low—why?) indication of the number of carbon atoms. On the other hand, if an oxygen atom is present in the m/e 43 ion, there should be a 0.20% contribution to the m/e 45 peak due to C_2H_3 ^{18}O. The 0.05% contribution observed is mainly due to the $C^{13}C_2H_7$ and C_2 $^{13}CH_6D$ ions.

To calculate the number of carbon atoms in the large m/e 58 peak, note that the abundance ratio of masses 59/58 is 4.4%; from this, Table 2-2 indicates four carbon atoms. The calculation for the $(M + 2)^+$ ion is within the experimental error expected for the measurement of the small abundance of m/e 60. Thus, m/e 58 corresponds to C_4H_{10}, and the molecule is butane. The fact that this is the straight-chain isomer is not obvious from the spectrum with your present knowledge. Identities of major ions, such as masses 15 (CH_3^+) and 29 ($C_2H_5^+$), should be obvious. [*n*-Butane]

2.4. Again, no "isotopic cluster" is readily apparent in the molecular ion region. From the [73]/[72] value, Table 2-2 indicates three carbon atoms in the base peak at mass 72; however, for this, the m/e 74/72 ratio should be 0.04% in comparison to the 0.48% found. Check the common isotopes of Table 2-1 for an explanation. The C_3 accounts for only 36 amu of the molecular weight of 72. Both this difference and the m/e 74/72 ratio can be accounted for by assuming the presence of two oxygen atoms. For these there will be twice the probability that one of the oxygens of the molecule is an

^{18}O. Thus, from Table 2-2 the m/e 74/72 ratio should be 0.04% + 2 x 0.20% = 0.44%, checking the 0.48% found. The molecular formula $C_3H_4O_2$ is thus indicated. Similar calculations indicate $C_3H_3O^+$ for m/e 55 (loss of OH). Interferences prevent such calculations on other peaks (m/e 46/45 indicates a maximum of C_7). In interpreting the spectrum, the prominent m/e 27 must be C_2H_3 (it is far too abundant to be mass 54^{+2}). $C_3H_4O_2 - C_2H_3 = CO_2H$, suggesting (although not requiring) a carboxyl group as an assignment for the m/e 45. The only acid molecule of this composition is $CH_2=CHCOOH$. [Acrylic acid]

2.5.   In attempting to determine elemental compositions in this group of peaks, start with the most abundant. Because the most abundant isotopes of all the common elements are the isotopes of lowest mass, the m/e 62 peak must be composed mainly of the most abundant isotopes of the elements. Looking first for "A + 2" elements, we find that the m/e 64 shows a strong indication of sulfur; silicon is not possible from the abundance of the m/e 63 peak. An easy way to check for "A + 1" elements is to use the $[m/e\ 65]/[m/e\ 64]$ ratio, which indicates C_2. Although these peaks are less abundant than m/e 62 and 63, they are nearly free of contributions from ions with less hydrogen containing the heavier sulfur isotopes. This can be seen in the following breakdown of isotope and abundance assignments, which should be prepared for any complex set of overlapping isotopes as a final check of the assignment.

```
m/e      C₂             S
                                C₂          S
                                                   C₂          S
60    9.0          9.0
61    19.   0.2       0.07     18.7
62    100.         0.4   0.4      0.1              99.1
63    3.8    0.01      0.00        0.82  2.2          0.8
64    4.4                   0.02             0.01         4.4
65    0.09                                          0.09
```

Note that the probabilities of the higher carbon and sulfur isotopes must be considered separately; the formula $^{12}C_2{}^{32}S$ (m/e 62) demands that another peak of 2.2% of this abundance be found corresponding to $^{12}C_1{}^{13}C_1{}^{32}S$ and 0.8% of $^{12}C_2{}^{33}S$, although these two ions will have the same nominal mass. Further, the combined possibilities must be considered; the 0.09 abundance of m/e 65 arises from $^{12}C_1{}^{13}C_1{}^{34}S_1$ (to be exact, this also includes 0.0001 of $^{13}C_2{}^{33}S_1$). [C_2H_6S]

2.6.   Again we should start with the most abundant peak. The presence of one or more "A + 2" elements should be immediately obvious. Although the $[m/e\ 132]/[m/e\ 130]$ value of 0.98 strongly suggests Br_1, this is ruled out by the higher mass ratios. Note that the ratios of the series $[129]/[131]/[133]/[135]$ are very similar to those of the series $[130]/[132]/[134]/[136]$, and that these correspond closely with the "isotopic cluster" for Cl_3 in Figure 2-1 and Table A-2. The number of

"A + 1" elements is indicated from the peaks which contain only the ^{37}Cl isotope; this $[m/e\ 137]/[m/e\ 136]$ value of 0.020 indicates C_2. Again, the expected contributions of the proposed formulas C_2Cl_3 should be checked by constructing a table similar to that shown in the solution to Unknown 2.5, starting with the lowest mass ion in the series. $[C_2HCl_3]$

2.7.   The striking feature of the isotopic ratios that you should note in this spectrum is the low $[M + 1^+]/[M^+]$ ratio and similar ion abundance ratios. Because of these ratios the elements carbon, oxygen, silicon, sulfur, and chlorine are all eliminated from consideration. Note that there are abundant peaks at $[M - 19]^+$ and $(M - 2 \times 19)^+$ as well as m/e 19 indicating the presence of fluorine. [Nitrogen trifluoride]

2.8.   The presence of the "A + 2" element chlorine should be obvious from both the m/e 104/106 and 85/87 abundance ratios. The m/e 104/105 abundance ratio indicates approximately one carbon atom, which is substantiated by both m/e 85/86 and 69/70, 50/51, and 31/32. The remaining mass of each of these ions must be provided by an "A" element, and only fluorine appears to be appropriate. [Chlorotrifluoromethane]

2.9.   The $[m/e\ 134]/[m/e\ 132]$ ratio clearly shows that no silicon, sulfur, chlorine, or bromine atoms are present. The $[m/e\ 133]/[m/e\ 132]$ value indicates C_9. This accounts for only 0.44 of the $[m/e\ 134]$ value of 0.65; ^{18}O nicely accounts for the difference. The remainder of the m/e mass value, which must be due to "A" elements, is accounted for by H_8. [C_9H_8O, r + db = 6]

2.10.   The abundance of the m/e 78 peak shows immediately that no "A + 2" elements can be present. For the "A + 1" elements, Table 2-2 tells us that the possibilities are C_3 and C_2N_3; C_3 yields a calculated abundance for m/e 77 and 78 of 2.6 (80% $\times$ 3.3) and 0.03, respectively, and C_2N_3 yields 2.8 [80% $\times$ (2.2 + 3 $\times$ 0.37)] and 0.01. (For reasons discussed in Chapter 3, the m/e 76 molecular ion cannot contain an odd number of nitrogen atoms.) C_3 is correct; a possible combination of "A" elements is H_9P. ($C_3H_2F_2$ could not fragment to yield m/e 73.) [C_3H_9P, r + db = 0]

2.11.   If m/e 86 and 87 are only isotope peaks of m/e 85, then the presence of one silicon atom explains their relative abundances. The absence of m/e 84 actually is evidence that there are no hydrogen atoms in m/e 85. A logical composition for the "A" elements is F_3. [SiF_3, r + db = 0]

2.12.   The most abundant peak, m/e 182, can contain no "A + 2" elements except oxygen; the indicated abundance of the "A + 1" elements is sufficiently great that these must be approximated before a determination for oxygen can be made. The $[m/e\ 183]/[m/e\ 182]$ value of 15.1% indicates C_{13} to C_{15} (the stated error limit of ±10% means that values in the range 13.6 to 16.6% must be considered). The abundance values predicted for m/e 184 for C_{13}, C_{14}, and C_{15} are 0.52, 0.60, and 0.70, respectively, if no oxygen is present, and 0.63, 0.71, and 0.81 if one oxygen atom is present; the experimental accuracy does not allow us to distinguish between $C_{14}O_0$ and $C_{13}O_1$. The m/e 185 peak is due to the presence of three ^{13}C atoms; if an oxygen atom is present, the $^{12}C_{12}{}^{13}C_1{}^{18}O_1$ contribution to this peak would be $8.3 \times 0.20\% = 0.017$, thus predicting an abundance of 0.038 for m/e 185. The validity of this as evidence for the $C_{14}O_0$ assignment is obviously dependent on the accuracy of this abundance measurement. [$C_{14}H_{14}$, r + db $= 8$; $C_{13}H_{10}O$ also possible]

  2.13.   This unknown illustrates the difficulties encountered in sorting out complex isotopic contributions in a group of peaks if ions containing different numbers of hydrogen atoms are present. It happens that in this case no ion of this group contains more hydrogen atoms than the m/e 355; as discussed in Chapter 3, a loss of 11, 12, 13, or 14 mass units from $M^{\ddot{+}}$ is improbable. Starting with the most abundant peak, m/e 355, an "A + 2" element, probably chlorine, is indicated. The [358]/[356] value of 33% suggests the same possibility for m/e 356. The appreciable $(A + 4)^+$ peaks at m/e 359 and 360 must be accounted for; if these are due mainly to a second "A + 2" element, such as silicon, the [359]/[357] ratio should be comparable to that of the [360]/[358] ratio; these are actually 3.3% and 1.1%, respectively, making the presence of any additional "A + 2" element, except oxygen, unlikely, and suggesting that there is a sufficient number of carbon atoms present to show such contributions from peaks containing two ^{13}C atoms. The value of [356]/[355] indicates that approximately twenty-five carbon atoms are present; it is possible that some nitrogen is present also. For more complex cases such as this, it is best to check your postulated compositions by deducing for each peak the possible isotopic compositions and their abundances, and comparing the latter to the experimental values.

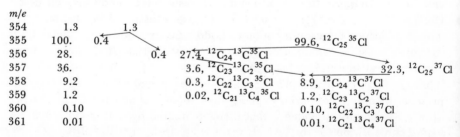

m/e				
354	1.3	1.3		
355	100.	0.4		99.6, $^{12}C_{25}{}^{35}Cl$
356	28.	0.4	27.4, $^{12}C_{24}{}^{13}C{}^{35}Cl$	
357	3.6.		3.6, $^{12}C_{23}{}^{13}C_2{}^{35}Cl$	32.3, $^{12}C_{25}{}^{37}Cl$
358	9.2		0.3, $^{12}C_{22}{}^{13}C_3{}^{35}Cl$	8.9, $^{12}C_{24}{}^{13}C{}^{37}Cl$
359	1.2		0.02, $^{12}C_{21}{}^{13}C_4{}^{35}Cl$	1.2, $^{12}C_{23}{}^{13}C_2{}^{37}Cl$
360	0.10			0.10, $^{12}C_{22}{}^{13}C_3{}^{37}Cl$
361	0.01			0.01, $^{12}C_{21}{}^{13}C_4{}^{37}Cl$

It is important that you understand where each of these contributions arise. For example, m/e 358 is composed of $^{12}C_{22}{}^{13}C_3{}^{35}Cl_1$ and $^{12}C_{24}{}^{13}C_1{}^{37}Cl_1$. The abundance value of 8.9 for the latter can be calculated by multiplying the abundance of the $^{12}C_{24}{}^{13}C_1{}^{35}Cl_1$ ion (27.4) by 32.5%, or the abundance of the $^{12}C_{25}{}^{37}Cl_1$ ion (32.2) by 27.5%. As discussed in Unknown 2.12, the experimental accuracy makes it impossible to determine if one (or more) oxygen atoms replace CH_4 in this formula. [$C_{25}H_{20}Cl$, r + db $= 15\frac{1}{2}$]

2.14. The isotopic cluster of *m/e* 62 and 64 should catch your eye immediately when you look at the bar graph. This signpost for chlorine is repeated again, although less clearly, at other places in the spectrum such as *m/e* 48/50 and 35/37. The balance of the indicated molecular weight of 62 is then 27 (62 − 35). Several indications suggest the C_2H_3 to account for the mass 27 balance such as the mass 59–61 series (presence of at least three hydrogen atoms) and the mass 24–27 series (C_2^+–$C_2H_3^+$). [Vinyl chloride]

2.15. In the molecular ion region the abundance pattern does not fit any "A + 2" element pattern; however, Table 2-2 indicates five carbon atoms in *m/e* 66. Interferences reduce the significance of such calculations for other ions in the spectrum; for example, the mass 41/40 ratio indicates a maximum of four carbon atoms. The assumption of a C_5 formula for *m/e* 66 as the molecular ion can indicate a great deal about the structure of the molecule, however. Thus, the molecular formula must correspond to C_5H_6; 66 − (12 × 5) = 6 × 1. Only a limited number of highly unsaturated hydrocarbons have this formula. A choice cannot be made between these without reference spectra. [Cyclopentadiene]

2.16. The molecular weight is 73. The highest mass peaks give no indication of isotopic clusters, but the possible error in the *m/e* 74 abundance limits any further calculations of elemental composition. However, *m/e* 58 should contain a maximum of three carbon atoms (Table 2-2). Mass 60 supports this and also indicates no oxygen. For the formula of *m/e* 58, there could be up to seven hydrogen atoms associated with the three carbon atoms, accounting for 36 to 43 amu. The common elements (Table 2-1) which can account for the 15 to 22 amu are now limited to hydrogen, nitrogen, and fluorine. The highly unsaturated ion $C_3H_3F^+$ can be discarded in view of the rest of the spectrum (for instance, *m/e* 42 must then be $C_3H_6^+$). This makes $C_3H_8N^+$ the choice for *m/e* 58, and suggests $C_4H_{11}N^+$ for the molecular formula. (The difference of 15 amu is most likely CH_3, as removing an NH group from *m/e* 73 to yield *m/e* 58 would require multiple bond cleavage.) This formula corresponds to a saturated amine, and ways of differentiating these isomers will be discussed later. This is the spectrum of $(CH_3)_3CNH_2$, which one might expect to show a strong tendency for loss of methyl. [*tert*-Butylamine]

3.1. $C_2H_4^+$, *m/e* 28; $C_3H_7O^+$, *m/e* 59; $C_4H_9N^+$, *m/e* 71; $C_4H_8NO^+$, *m/e* 86; $C_7H_5ClBr^+$, *m/e* 203; $C_6H_4OS^+$, *m/e* 124; $C_{29}F_{59}^+$, *m/e* 1469; H_3O^+, *m/e* 19; and $C_3H_9SiO^+$, *m/e* 89.

3.2. $C_{10}H_{15}O^+$ is an even-electron ion, and so cannot be the molecular ion.

3.3. $C_9H_{12}^+$ is an odd-electron ion. The other ions represent losses of H, H_3 (H + H_2, for example), CH_3, $CH_3 + H_2$, and C_2H_5, respectively, all of which are possible losses. *n*-Propylbenzene would exhibit such a spectrum.

3.4. The presence of the large *m/e* 96 and 98 peaks casts doubt on the assignment of m/e 100 as the molecular ion. None of the common isotopes corresponds to this type of isotopic cluster, however. The ions of lower mass give helpful hints for elucidating this. Note particularly the m/e 63/61 ratio, the chlorine signpost. Formation of m/e 61 from m/e 96 involves the loss of 35 amu, a hint for a second chlorine atom in the molecule. This is confirmed by checking the isotopic abundances of masses 96/98/100 against Figure 2-1 or Table A-2. To calculate the carbon content of M^{+} from m/e 97/96, do not forget that the $^{35}Cl^{37}Cl$ isotopic ion of $(M-1)^{+}$ will contribute 65% of the m/e 95 to the 97 peak. $(3.3\% - 0.65 \times 3.0\%)/67\% \times 1.1\% = 1.8$ or $\sim C_2$. This calculation is superfluous, however, as the balance of molecular formula of 26 amu $(M^{+} - Cl_2 = 96 - 70)$ is most logically due to $C_2 H_2$. It is difficult to distinguish between the possible isomers of $C_2 H_2 Cl_2$ without standards. [*trans*-1,2-Dichloroethylene]

3.5. The isotopic cluster at m/e 135–137 indicates one chlorine atom, and m/e 135 contains a maximum of two carbon atoms, $0.52/(1.1\% \times 24) = 2.0$. Similar assignments can be made for the lower mass ions: m/e 119, $C_2 Cl_0$; m/e 100, $C_2 Cl_0$; m/e 85, $C_1 Cl_1$; m/e 69, $C_1 Cl_0$; and m/e 50, $C_1 Cl_0$. The absence of evidence for hydrogen atoms and the differences of 19 amu between several pairs of ions containing the same numbers of chlorine atoms implicate fluorine as the missing element. Thus, the formulas CF^{+}, CF_2^{+}, CF_3^{+}, $CClF_2^{+}$, $C_2 F_4^{+}$, $C_2 F_5^{+}$, and $C_2 ClF_4^{+}$ will correspond in mass to the prominent peaks in the spectrum. You should have already noted that the m/e 135 and 137 peaks failed several of the requirements for a molecular ion. Because there is no indication of ions containing more than two carbon atoms or one chlorine atom, the most probable structure to account for this spectrum is $CClF_2 CF_3$. [Chloropentafluoroethane]

3.6. [Nitromethane]

3.7. [Carbon tetrachloride]

4.1. The first rule emphasizes the importance of product ion stability. The highly stabilized *p*-aminobenzyl ion

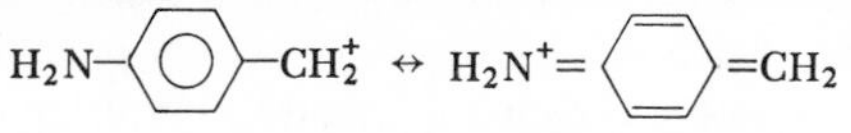

$$H_2N\text{—}\langle O \rangle\text{—}CH_2^{+} \leftrightarrow H_2N^{+}=\langle \rangle=CH_2$$

produces by far the most abundant peak in this spectrum.

4.2. Alpha cleavage can be initiated by the radical site on either the oxygen or the nitrogen atom:

$$H_2NCH_2\text{—}CH_2\text{—}\overset{\cdot\,+}{O}H \xrightarrow{\alpha} H_2NCH_2\cdot + CH_2=\overset{+}{O}H \ (m/e \ 31)$$

$$H_2\overset{+\cdot}{N}\text{—}CH_2\text{—}CH_2OH \xrightarrow{\alpha} H_2\overset{+}{N}=CH_2 \ (m/e \ 30) + \cdot CH_2OH$$

The electron-donating ability of nitrogen is superior to that of oxygen, so that ionization should occur more readily at nitrogen (Table A-3), and the m/e 30 ion should be more stable than m/e 31. Actually $[m/e \ 30] = 57\%$ of total ionization, while $[m/e \ 31] = 2.5\%$.

4.3 through 4.7.   Unknown 2.6 was discussed previously, and diethyl-amine is identified in the text. Although the information is given that these are isomeric C_4-amines, note that determination of the elemental composition of M^+ would be high in several cases using the m/e 74/73 ratio. This is mainly due to the production of $(M + 1)^+$ by an ion–molecule reaction (see Section 3.6).

In answer to the question in the text, loss of an α-methyl group is in competition with the losses of other α-substituents. The probability of α-CH_3 loss is much greater than α-hydrogen loss, but less than α-C_2H_5 loss. This helps to identify Unknown 4.7 as $C_2H_5CH(CH_3)NH_2$. Of the five α-CH_3 amines listed (see text), only $(CH_3)_2CHNHCH_3$ and $CH_3CH_2N(CH_3)_2$ remain unidentified; the first should have a larger $(M - CH_3)^+/M^+$ ratio, and so is Unknown 4.5. The assignment of the latter structure to Unknown 4.6 is borne out by the m/e 44 of this spectrum; it is formed by the elimination of C_2H_4 from the $(M - 1)^+$ ion through a rearrangement similar to the formation of m/e 30 in $C_2H_5NHC_2H_5$ (see Section 4.6).

The remaining possible isomers are $CH_3CH_2CH_2CH_2NH_2$, $(CH_3)_2CHCH_2$-NH_2, and $CH_3CH_2CH_2NHCH_3$. The first two should yield abundant ions of m/e 30, and are thus Unknowns 4.3 and 4.4. These spectra are surprisingly similar, reflecting the dominant effect of the amine function on the cleavage; however, the small absolute differences in the abundances of the alkyl ions are reproducible and significant. The abundances of the $C_3H_7^+$ and $C_4H_9^+$ ions in Unknown 4.4 are several times the corresponding abundances in Unknown 4.3 (only small contributions should be present from $C_2H_5N^+$ and $C_3H_7N^+$), compatible with *n*- and isobutylamine assignments for 4.3 and 4.4, respectively. No spectrum is given for *n*-$C_3H_7NHCH_3$; it should give a base peak at m/e 44, but an insignificant peak at $(M - CH_3)^+$. [2.6, *tert*-Butylamine; 4.2, diethylamine; 4.3, *n*-butylamine; 4.4, isobutyl-amine; 4.5, isopropylmethylamine; 4.6, ethyldimethylamine; and 4.7, *sec*-butylamine]

4.8, 4.9.   For the symmetrical 3-pentanone, α-cleavage can only give the $C_2H_5CO^+$ and $C_2H_5^+$ ions, m/e 57 and 29. On the other hand, 3-methyl-2-butanone should yield CH_3CO^+, $(CH_3)_2CHCO^+$, CH_3^+, and $C_3H_7^+$ ions at m/e 43, 71, 15, and 43, respectively. [4.8, 3-Pentanone; 4.9, 3-methyl-2-butanone]

4.10.   Elemental composition determinations are inaccurate because of interferences and low relative abundances. Mass 130 appears to be a good possibility for the molecular ion, however, and the ion series (Section 5.2) 31, 45, 59, 73, 87, 101, and 115 strongly suggests that the molecular formula is $C_8H_{18}O$. Table A-4 shows that the abundance of M^+ is indicative of an ether, not an alcohol. Facile cleavage of C_α–C_β bonds should yield the most abundant $C_nH_{2n+1}O^+$ ions; the $(M - 43)^+$ is the most abundant of these by far, and thus indicates one or two propyl groups substituted on one or both α-carbon atoms. The abundances of $(M - CH_3)^+$ and $(M - C_2H_5)^+$ are roughly 3% and 10%, respectively, of $(M - C_3H_7)^+$, making the presence of methyl or ethyl substituents on an α-carbon atom unlikely, although comparison with spectra of similar compounds would be necessary to evaluate these effects quantitatively. The other common decomposition of ethers via cleavage of the C–O bond to yield the alkyl ion strongly indicates a butyl ether (m/e 57); of course $C_8H_{18}O$ must then be a dibutyl ether. The formula $C_3H_7CH_2OC_4H_9$ is required; $C_3H_7CH_2OCH(CH_3)C_2H_5$ is less probable because of the abundances of $(M - CH_3)^+$ and $(M - C_2H_5)^+$, as discussed. [Diisobutyl ether]

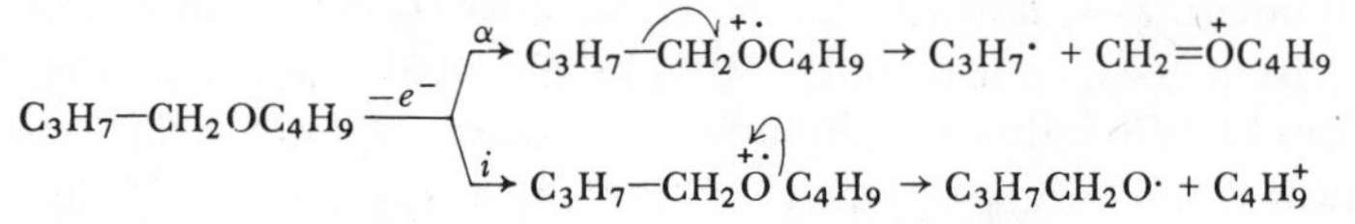

$$C_3H_7-CH_2OC_4H_9 \xrightarrow{-e^-} \begin{array}{l} \xrightarrow{\alpha} C_3H_7-\overset{+\cdot}{CH_2}OC_4H_9 \rightarrow C_3H_7{}^\cdot + CH_2{=}\overset{+}{O}C_4H_9 \\ \xrightarrow{i} C_3H_7-CH_2\overset{+\cdot}{O}C_4H_9 \rightarrow C_3H_7CH_2O^\cdot + C_4H_9^+ \end{array}$$

4.11

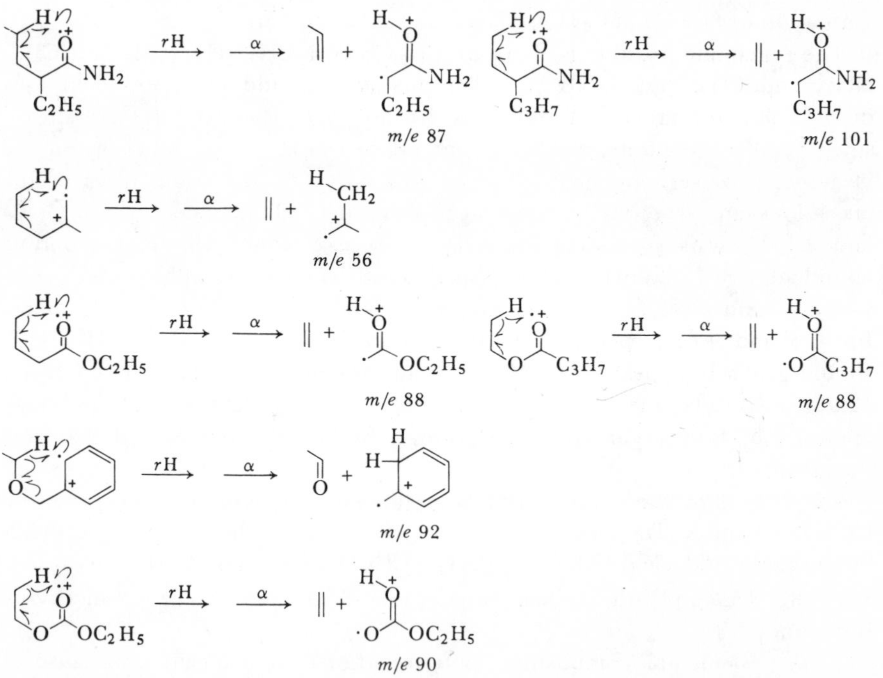

m/e 87 m/e 101

m/e 56

m/e 88 m/e 88

m/e 92

m/e 90

4.12, 4.13

m/e 58   4.13 m/e 72

4.12

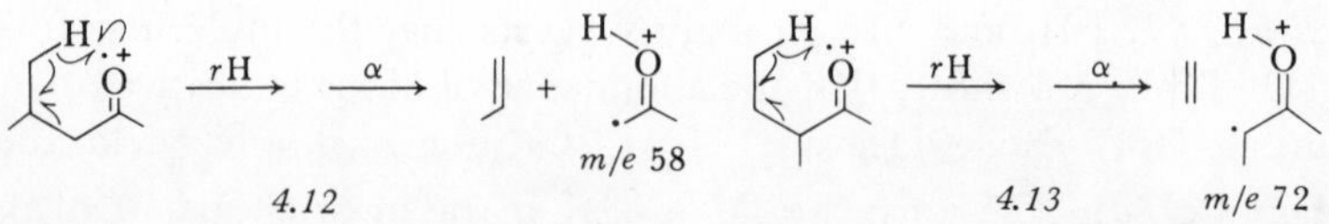

[4.12, 4-Methyl-2-pentanone; 4.13, 3-methyl-2-pentanone]

4.14.   The apparent molecular ion at m/e 134 contains 10 ± 1 carbon atoms and probably no oxygen atoms. Thus $C_{10}H_{14}$ is a favorable postulate, with rings plus double bonds = 4. The odd-electron ion at m/e 92 is especially noteworthy. There is some indication of an alkyl ion series (m/e 15, 29, 43), but the most striking is the aromatic ion series. This is borne out by the rings-plus-double-bonds value and the abundant doubly charged ions. A logical postulate for the unknown is thus a C_4-benzene; the abundant m/e 92 (Table A-7) indicates that the structure is $C_6H_5CH_2-C_3H_7$. The low abundance ratio of m/e 43/29 indicates that the alkyl chain is not branched. [*n*-Butylbenzene]

$$CH_3 \underset{}{\overset{H}{\diagup}}\!\!\bigcirc \quad \xrightarrow{\ rH\ } \quad C_3H_6 + \left[H\underset{}{\overset{H}{\diagdown}}\!\!\bigcirc \right]^{\ddagger}$$

4.15.   Alpha-cleavage reactions can result in the loss of three different groups: $C_3H_7\cdot$, $CH_3\cdot$, and $H\cdot$. These reactions will produce peaks at m/e 86, 114, and 128, with abundances decreasing in this order as predicted by the rule for the loss of the largest alkyl group. Each of these ions can undergo loss of an olefin by cleavage of an N–C bond with hydrogen rearrangement (reactions 4-36 and 4-38). For the m/e 114 ion there is the additional possibility of hydrogen rearrangement through a six-membered ring transition state involving an endocyclic double bond (4-35); this reaction also will produce a peak at m/e 72. See Figure 6-22 for the spectrum of this compound.

$$\overset{\overset{\displaystyle H}{|}}{\underset{\underset{\displaystyle CH_3\ CH_3}{|\ \ |}}{C_3H_7-CH_2-\overset{\cdot+}{N}-\overset{}{C}-CH_3}} \quad m/e\ 129$$

$$\alpha \diagdown \!\!-C_3H_7\cdot \qquad \alpha\!\!\downarrow\!\!-CH_3\cdot \qquad \alpha\diagdown\!\!-H$$

$CH_2=\overset{+}{N}-CH(CH_3)_2$	$C_3H_7CH_2-\overset{+}{N}=CHCH_3$	$C_3H_7CH_2-\overset{+}{N}=C(CH_3)_2$
$\underset{CH_3}{|}$ m/e 86	$\underset{CH_3}{|}$ m/e 114	$\underset{CH_3}{|}$ m/e 128

$$rH\!\!\downarrow\!\!-C_3H_6 \qquad rH\!\!\downarrow\!\!-C_4H_8 \qquad rH\!\!\downarrow\!\!-C_4H_8$$

$CH_2=\overset{+}{N}-H$	$H-\overset{+}{N}=CHCH_3$	$H-\overset{+}{N}=C(CH_3)_2$
$\underset{CH_3}{|}$	$\underset{CH_3}{|}$	$\underset{CH_3}{|}$
m/e 44	m/e 58	m/e 72

$$\underset{m/e\ 114}{\bigcirc\!\!\!\overset{H}{\diagup}} \quad \xrightarrow{\ rH\ } \quad \| + \underset{m/e\ 72}{\searrow\!\!\overset{H}{\diagup}}$$

4.16. Mass 178 can be postulated as the molecular ion, with roughly twelve carbon atoms. Both m/e 105 and 123 appear to contain seven carbon atoms. The m/e 122 is of questionable significance as an odd-electron ion because of the abundant m/e 123 ion; however the mass 56 peak, $(M - 122)^+$, should be noted. A weak alkyl ion series through C_4 is present, as is an aromatic ion series (see Section 5.2). There are weak alkyl loss ions at $(M - 15)^+$, $(M - 29)^+$, and $(M - 43)^+$, but instead of $(M - 57)^+$ there are the major ions at $(M - 55)^+$ and $(M - 56)^{\ddagger}$. From Table A-5 a common loss of 55 is loss of C_4H_7 from esters (double hydrogen rearrangement) and the loss of 56 would be the rearrangement loss of C_4H_8 from carbonyl compounds. The abundant m/e 56 odd-electron ion supports this; Table A-7 indicates a corresponding C_4H_8-RY structure. Two other abundant ions provide the final clues; m/e 77 and 105 should be phenyl and benzoyl, suggesting that the compound is a butyl benzoate. This is probably not *sec-* or *tert*-butyl; for example, $(M - 15)^+$ and $(M - 29)^+$ are less abundant than $(M - 43)^+$. [*n*-Butyl benzoate]

5.1. Although the possible molecular ion at m/e 128 probably has the composition $C_{10}H_8$, a C_9 formula cannot be ruled out on the basis of isotopic abundances. The probable molecular ion is of high stability; there are few fragment peaks of importance, and these resemble the aromatic series (Table A-6). (The large M^{2+} is also typical of aromatics.) The formula $C_{10}H_8$ requires seven rings plus double bonds $(10 - \frac{8}{2} + 1)$. Again reference spectra would be necessary to distinguish between the several isomers possible. [Naphthalene]

5.2. In calculating the elemental composition of m/e 182, correct the abundance of m/e 183 for the $(A + 2)^+$ contribution from the m/e 181 by assuming that this is the same as m/e 184/182; $8.5 - (0.61 \times 8.2)/60 = 8.4$ (thus, the correction is relatively insignificant). Then $8.4/(1.1\% \times 60) = 12.7$ carbon atoms. The error in this figure depends on instrument reproducibility, but the accuracy is usually $\pm 10\%$. Therefore, C_{12}, C_{13}, and C_{14} are possible, suggesting the formulas $C_{12}H_{22}O$, $C_{12}H_6O_2$, $C_{13}H_{26}$, $C_{13}H_{10}O$, and $C_{14}H_{14}$. For these, the m/e 184/182 ratio does not allow a clear-cut decision, but the appearance of the spectrum strongly militates against the formula $C_{13}H_{26}$, and, to a lesser extent, $C_{12}H_{22}O$, both of which should have considerable resemblance to the aliphatic hydrocarbon pattern. Note the abundant peak that is probably the molecular ion, and the simplicity of the spectrum. The molecule should thus be generally stable, with one or a few bonds of much higher lability. Notice that there is a definite resemblance between the spectra of Unknowns 5.1 and 5.2—the peaks such as 39, 51, 63, and 77 suggest aromatic character. The possible formulas $C_{12}H_6O_2$, $C_{13}H_{10}O$, and $C_{14}H_{14}$ would have rings-plus-double-bonds values of 10, 9, and 8, respectively. With four per phenyl ring, the best possibilities for the mass 182 are $C_6H_5COC_6H_5$ and $(C_6H_5)_2C_2H_4$. The 1,1 isomer of the latter should give a large $(M - CH_3)^+$ peak (m/e 167), and the 1,2 isomer a large $C_7H_7^+$ (m/e 91), neither of which is present. [Benzophenone]

5.3.   Mass 86 appears to have the elemental composition $C_4H_6O_2$ (a better check with isotopic abundances than $C_5H_{10}O$), and for m/e 43 the formula $C_2H_3O^+$ is definitely preferable. Mass 15 should be CH_3^+. The appearance of the spectrum (that is, dominated by mass 43 and 15) suggests C_2H_3O and CH_3 groups that are readily lost. If the CH_3 is part of the C_2H_3O, the balance is CO. The absence of other peaks suggests a symmetrical structure, $CH_3CO-COCH_3$. Most other compounds of the formula $C_4H_6O_2$ would be expected to give some other fragments. The $(M - CH_3)^+$ is much smaller than CH_3^+ because of the electronegative groups on the concomitant $-COCOCH_3$ fragment. When the CH_3-CO bond is cleaved, the charge is preferably retained by the CH_3 group. [2,3-Butanedione]

5.4.   The m/e 61 peak is probably due to heavy isotope contributions from m/e 60; m/e 60, however, is too large to be due to isotopic contributions from the common elements, and thus should be suspected as the odd-electron molecular ion. Mass 45 should contain two (or less) carbon atoms, but isotope calculations for m/e 31 are thwarted by its relatively small size and the O_2 background contribution to m/e 32. (The m/e 32 datum was omitted for these reasons.) The most significant ion series of the spectrum is that of masses 31, 45, and 59. (The series 15, 29, 43 and 27, 41 are less indicative as they can arise by losses of small molecules from the 31, 45, 59 series.) Table A-6 suggests $C_nH_{2n+1}O$ from alcohols or ethers for this series; from Table A-4 alcohols would be suspected to have M^+ abundances corresponding to the low abundance of m/e 60. Only two isomers are possible; the sizable $(M - 1)^+$ and $(M - 15)^+$ peaks strongly indicate $(CH_3)_2CHOH$. [Isopropanol]

5.5.   Again the molecular weight is apparently 60, and the formula contains three carbon atoms or less. The spectrum is dominated, however, by m/e 30, which is either an odd-electron ion or contains an odd number of nitrogen atoms. This could also be viewed as part of the series 16, 30, 44, but in either case Table A-6 makes the grouping $-CH_2NH_2$ a prime suspect. The formula for mass 60 should now be $C_2H_8N_2$, for which the isomer $H_2NCH_2CH_2NH_2$ is the best choice because of the appreciable $(M - 1)^+$ and $(M - NH_2)^+$ peaks, and lack of $(M - CH_3)^+$. [1,2-Diaminoethane]

5.6.   There are a number of signs that this compound is quite different from the preceding ones. Masses 76, 69, 50, 31, and 26 have a maximum of two, one, one, one, and one carbon atoms, respectively. Mass 95 is either *not* the molecular ion, or else has an odd number of nitrogen atoms. Similarly, prominent ions of m/e 76, 50, and 26 are either odd-electron fragment ions, or contain an odd number of nitrogen atoms. There are few or no hydrogen atoms present (no groups of peaks in unit mass sequence, as 66, 67, 68, 69). The practiced eye may have found a valuable clue in the ion series of masses 31, 50, and 69 (see Table A-6). The lack of hydrogens even makes the low mass peaks of 12, 14, and 19 serve as clues to the atoms present. Assuming m/e 95 to be the molecular ion gives correspondence between ions at masses 19 and M − 19, and at 26 and M − 26, suggesting the parts F−CF$_2$−CN. [Trifluoroacetonitrile]

5.7.   If m/e 130 is the molecular ion, the number of carbon atoms is quite small (five or less) for this high mass. Therefore m/e 129 is a much better candidate to be the molecular ion, which would mean that the molecule contains an odd number of nitrogen atoms. The abundant ions of even mass such as 102, 98, and 78 could in this way be even-electron ions. The high abundance of this postulated molecular ion would also be consistent with the aromatic-type ion series. (Be sure you do not confuse the doubly charged ions with members of some other low mass ion series.) Again several isomers are possible of the formula C_9H_7N (rings plus double bonds = 7), and reference spectra would give positive identification. [Isoquinoline]

5.8.   A relatively abundant $(M − 2)^+$ ion is unusual in mass spectra, so the 164/166 should be checked out as a possible isotopic cluster. One bromine atom is indicated by a number of such ion pairs. The ion series m/e 15, 29, 43, 57, 71, and 85 indicates alkyl to C_6, or possibly carbonyl to C_5. The bromine-containing ion series m/e 79–81, 93–95, 107–109, 121–123, and 135–137 gives strong support to the presence of the alkyl chain, and to the formula $C_6H_{13}Br$ for the m/e 164–166 ions. Unfortunately, the presence of the CH_2Br^+ ion cannot be taken as proof that this is a 1-bromoalkane, as small amounts of CH_2Br^+ are formed by rearrangement in the spectra of some alkanes in which the bromine atom is not terminally substituted. However, the large m/e 135–137 ions strongly indicate the isomeric identity, as they arise through the displacement reaction 4-29. [1-Bromohexane]

5.9.   The base peak at m/e 101 has isotopic abundances corresponding to $C_5H_9O_2^+$; this peak is also a member of the alkyl acid–ester ion series 87, 101, 115, ⋯ (Table A-6) for which many peaks can be identified. The highest mass of these at m/e 311 corresponds to $(M − CH_3)$ if m/e 326 is the molecular ion, and the latter does fulfill all the requirements for M^+. The large OE^+ ion at m/e 74 confirms that this is the methyl ester of a large aliphatic acid containing no substituents in the 2-position. Comparison with the spectrum of methyl octadecanoate (Figure 5-3) shows substantial differences in the abundances of the ion series peaks, however. The shift of the abundant mass 87 peak to 101 is consistent with a 3-methyl group; the pairs of peaks at masses 143/171 and 213/241 (and the very small peaks at m/e 157 and 227) indicate additional methyl groups at the 7- and 11-positions. (Peaks arising from the loss of CH_3OH from masses 171 and 241 are also indicative of these methyl branches.) There is actually a 15-methyl substituent also, as might be suspected from the polyisoprenoid character of the rest of the molecule; unfortunately, such a terminal isopropyl group usually causes no significant difference in the spectrum in comparison to the straight-chain compound. (These can be differentiated by reduction to the alcohol, whose mass spectra are sensitive to this difference.) [Methyl 3,7,11,15-tetramethyl-hexadecanoate]

5.10.   The base peak at mass 149 has a maximum of nine carbon atoms; the $[151^+]/[149^+]$ value indicates as many as three oxygen atoms, so that $C_8H_5O_3$ (r + db = 6) and $C_9H_9O_2$ (r + db = 5) are the best possibilities. The peak at m/e 222 is a likely candidate for $M^{\ddagger}$ and has approximately twelve carbon atoms. An aromatic compound is indicated by the r + db value and the 39, 50, 51, 64, 65, etc., ion series; the small peaks at masses 29, 31, 43, 45, etc., indicate that some other type of functionality (oxygen-alkyl?) is also present. The small $OE^{\ddagger}$ ion at $(M - 28)^{\ddagger}$ is significant, but the smaller $(M - 27)^+$ ion is even more useful because its presence in nonnitrogen compounds is so unusual (Table A-5). Both of these peaks strongly suggest an ethyl ester; the $(M - 45)^+$ is also consistent with this assignment. The base peak at m/e 149 corresponds to $(M - 45 - 28)^+$, which could be the further loss of C_2H_4 or CO. The latter could be logical for an ester; however, the $149^{\ddagger}$ ion still has a high oxygen content. This ion must be unusually stable as judged both from its high abundance and the low abundance of its fragment ions. The most straightforward solution to this problem involves the identification of this characteristic ion, as discussed in the next section. [Diethyl phthalate]

5.11.   You should have made the following probable assignments: m/e 156, $M^{\ddagger}$, C_8H_9OCl; 107, C_7H_7O, and 94, C_6H_6O, $OE^{\ddagger}$. A phenyl ring is indicated by the aromatic ion series (the high abundance of the m/e 77 is a fairly reliable indication of monosubstitution). The $C_6H_6O^+$ peak indicates that oxygen is attached to the ring. The fact that $(M - CH_2Cl)^+$ is much larger than $(M - Cl)^+$ is indicative of a labile CH_2Cl group; cleavage alpha to the C_6H_5O- would account for this, suggesting $C_6H_5OCH_2CH_2Cl$. A strong peak resulting from hydrogen rearrangement with loss of C_2H_3Cl would be expected for this compound, accounting for the base $OE^{\ddagger}$ ion at m/e 94. [2-Chloroethyl phenyl ether]

5.12, 5.13, 5.14.   These appear to be isobars of molecular weight 120. The possible error in the m/e 121/120 ratio makes it difficult to distinguish between C_9 and C_8, although the m/e 122/120, 107/105, and 106/105 ratios give preference to C_8H_8O for Unknown 5.13 and to C_9H_{12} for the other two. Rings plus double bonds are thus either 5 or 4. There are many other signs in the spectrum that all three compounds are aromatic. *Mass Spectral Correlations (5.2)* suggests that phenyl moiety in compounds giving sizable m/e 77 peaks, benzyl for m/e 91, and either $CH_3C_6H_4CH_2-$, $C_6H_5CH(CH_3)-$, or C_6H_5CO- for m/e 105. The spectrum of Unknown 5.14 can therefore be explained by the structure $C_6H_5CH_2CH_2CH_3-$ the abundance of the $C_7H_7^+$ ion produced by benzylic bond cleavage is not surprising in light of the chemistry of such compounds, and the lower loss of

CH_3 would also be expected. A subtle confirmation is provided by the small, but real, $C_7H_8^{\ddagger}$ ($OE^{\ddagger}$) ion at m/e 92, arising from rearrangement reaction 4-18. For Unknowns 5.12 and 5.13, a number of compounds of molecular weight 120 could give large losses of CH_3: $CH_3C_6H_4CH_2CH_3$, $C_6H_5CH(CH_3)_2$, and $C_6H_5COCH_3$. Even $C_6H_3(CH_3)_3$ cannot safely be eliminated without reference standards. The large m/e 77 indicates the C_6H_5-containing compounds, although the m/e 79 rearrangement ion of Unknown 5.12 gives little confidence in this reasoning for this molecule. The very small losses of hydrogen (masses 119, 118, 104, 103) of Unknown 5.13 compared to the others indicate $C_6H_5COCH_3$ in confirmation of the elemental composition data. The $(M-15)^+/M^+$ ratio of Unknown 5.12 supports the structure $C_6H_5CH(CH_3)_2$ (the structure $CH_3C_6H_4C_2H_5$ has fewer benzylic methyls), but reference spectra would be necessary to establish this firmly. [Isopropylbenzene, acetophenone, and n-propylbenzene]

6.1, 6.2, 6.3.   The $C_nH_{2n+1}^+$ ion series is strongly indicated, and its distribution should suggest the n-alkane $C_{16}H_{34}$ as the compound yielding spectrum 6.1. (You also saw this spectrum as Figure 5-1.) Several of the prominent $C_nH_{2n+1}^+$ ions of Unknowns 6.2 and 6.3 appear paired with a $C_nH_{2n}^+$ ion; loss of (R + H) is also a common decomposition reaction for a compound with an R alkyl branch. Thus in Unknown 6.2 the ions of m/e 211, 168–169, 140–141 (weak), and 84–85 indicate chain branchings corresponding to C_1-C_{15}, C_4-C_{12}, C_6-C_{10}, and $C_{10}-C_6$. The grouping n-C_4H_9—$CH(CH_3)$— will explain these data. The compound is actually $CH_3(CH_2)_3CH(CH_3)(CH_2)_9CH_3$,   although   the   compound CH_3-$(CH_2)_3CH(CH_3)(CH_2)_4CH(CH_3)(CH_2)_3CH_3$ also should give similar prominent alkyl ions. For Unknown 6.3 the ions of m/e 182–183, 140–141, and 85 are abundant in comparison to the spectrum of n-$C_{16}H_{34}$, indicating branches corresponding to C_3-C_{13}, C_6-C_{10}, and $C_{10}-C_6$. A first postulate to fit these data might be the C_3H_7—$CH(C_2H_5)$— group, but this is made improbable by the low abundance of $(M-C_2H_5)^+$; that is, the *negative* information that there is no appreciable loss of C_1, C_2, C_4, or C_5 is very valuable. The data can be fitted by $CH_3(CH_2)_5CH(n\text{-}C_3H_7)(CH_2)_5CH_3$. [$n$-Hexadecane, 5-methylpentadecane, and 7-n-propyltridecane]

6.4.   Isotopic abundances give calculations of $C_{7.5}$, $C_{6.8}$, and C_4 for m/e 112, 97, and 57, respectively; the molecular formula is probably C_8H_{16}. Table A-6 and the low mass ion series are consistent with this. The ion $C_4H_9^+$ dominates the alkyl ion series; a *sec*- or *tert*-butyl group is possible. The $[(M-CH_3)^+] > [(M-C_3H_7)^+] \gg [(M-C_2H_5)^+]$, so that the *sec*-butyl group is unlikely. A C_8H_{16} molecule containing a C_4H_9 group should also contain an olefinic, cyclobutyl, or methylcyclopropyl group. Even if this group activated the cleavage C_4H_7—C_4H_9 (for example, an allylic cleavage), the large $C_4H_9^+/C_4H_7^+$ ratio indicates that the C_4H_9 is highly stabilized; that is, it is *tert*-butyl. However, it is dangerous to carry the interpretation too far without comparison with spectra of close isomers, because of the ubiquitous random rearrangements of hydrocarbons. (The m/e 56/55 ratio can be used as evidence for a 2-methylalkene. The reaction shown should be much less favored for the 1-methyl isomer.) [2,4,4-Trimethyl-1-pentene]

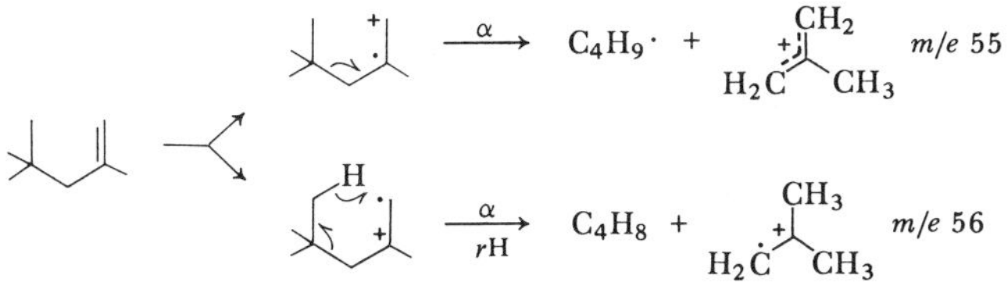

6.5, 6.6. The retro-Diels-Alder reactions expected for these isomers are shown here. The low abundance of m/e 164 in the second spectrum is due to the competition of the loss of CH_3 by a displacement reaction (see reaction 6-27). [6.5, α-Ionone; 6.6, β-ionone]

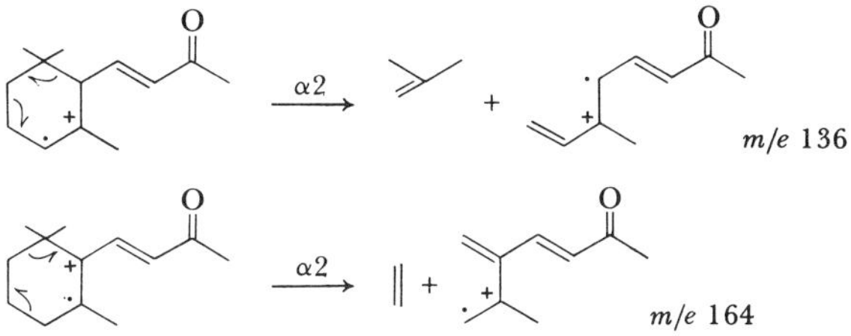

6.7, 6.8, 6.9. Note that alkylphenols are among the few common types of molecules which would account for the ions formed at lower molecular weights. To elucidate the nature of the alkyl substitution, only the $(M - C_n H_{2n+1})^+$ ions need be considered. For Unknown 6.7, $(M - CH_3)^+$ dominates this series. This can only mean that there are many more benzylic methyl groups than any other such substituent; the compound is actually the di-*tert*-butyl isomer, although the *tert*-butyltetramethyl isomer could behave similarly. The $(M - alkyl)^+$ ion series of Unknown 6.8 is dominated by the $(M - C_2 H_5)^+$ ion, suggesting a number of structures with multiple ethyl substitution on a carbon atom adjacent to the benzene ring. The small amount of $(M - CH_3)^+$ peak is actually significant in this case, however, as benzylic loss of $C_2 H_5$ is heavily favored over the benzylic loss of the smaller CH_3. The compound is actually the di-*sec*-butyl isomer. (The loss of $C_2 H_5$ is much more abundant than loss of CH_3 even in *sec*-butyl-*tert*-butylphenol.) Finally, Unknown 6.9 indicates almost no alkyl loss smaller than $C_5 H_{11}$, which loss yields the largest peak found in the spectrum. This peak indicates HO—phenyl—C—$C_5 H_{11}$, to which must be added two methyl groups. The structure is actually $HO-C_6 H_4-C(CH_3)_2-CH_2 C(CH_3)_3$, so that the 0.21% $(M - CH_3)^+$ ion represents the benzylic methyl cleavage of two CH_3 groups in competition with the large $C_5 H_{11}$ group. Note the *absence* of the corresponding OE‡ rearrangement ion at m/e 136, $(M - C_5H_{10})^{\ddagger}$. This is a strong indication of no γ-hydrogen, consistent with the side-chain arrangement $C-CH_2C(CH_3)_3$. The significant m/e 107 gives indication of the α,α-dimethyl substitution, as loss of C_2H_4 is expected from the ion $Y-phenyl-C(CH_3)_2^{+}$ (reaction 6-13). The preponderance of $C_4H_9^+$ among the alkyl ions of the spectrum is consistent with the terminal *tert*-butyl group. For these compounds, changing the position of substitution on the benzene ring makes relatively small changes in the spectra. [di-*tert*-Butylphenol, di-*sec*-butylphenol, 1,1,3,3-tetramethylbutylphenol]

6.10. The indicated molecular ion, m/e 178, could have a variety of compositions of thirteen to fifteen carbon atoms. The huge $M^{\ddagger}$ peak and the large M^{2+} peak are consistent with the indication of aromatic character given by the series of ions m/e 39, 50, 51, 52, 63, and so on. Loss of C_2H_2 is typical of aromatic molecules. Several isomers of $C_{14}H_{10}$ (rings plus double bonds = 10) are possible, and again reference spectra are necessary to distinguish between the isomers. The higher-energy processes involved in the decompositions of such molecules make rearrangements much more probable. [Diphenylacetylene]

6.11. Masses 45, 73, and 87 probably have two, four (?), and five carbon atoms each, and thus contain one oxygen atom each. The rings-plus-double-bonds value of each of these and of the m/e 129 ions should thus equal 1/2, so that they are saturated ions. $C_8H_{17}O^+$ cannot be the molecular ion; it is an even-electron ion. The m/e 112 ion is an odd-electron ion. Mass 130 might be $M^{\ddagger}$, but its abundance is within experimental error of that expected for the heavy isotope contribution from m/e 129. The ion series m/e 31, 45, 59, 73, 87 suggests (Table A-6) that an alcohol or ether function is a dominant feature of the molecule; the lack of $M^{\ddagger}$ indicates (Table A-4) that this is not a straight-chain ether. A key clue is the metastable ion of m/e 96.5 (see Section 7.1); for the transition m/e 130 → 112 a metastable would be expected at m/e 96.4 (m/e 129 → 112 would appear at m/e 97.0, but would involve the unlikely loss of 17 amu). This suggests that m/e 130 is the molecular ion, and that m/e 112 is the $(M - 18)^{\ddagger}$ formed by loss of H_2O from an alcohol. (The mass 130 could also be an odd-electron *fragment* ion, but this would predict a second functional group in the molecule, for which there appears to be no evidence in any of the peaks.) The abundant $(M - 43)^+$ and $(M - 57)^+$ ions indicate the identity of the octyl alcohol as $C_4H_9-CHOH-C_3H_7$; the lack of $(M - 15)^+$ and $(M - 29)^+$ ions indicate that there is no chain branching. The other ions then present a consistent picture. [4-Octanol]

6.12. This was a "trick" question; the compound is not phenolic, which you might have assumed if you incorrectly identified the mass 172 OE‡ peak as $(M - CO)$. Its elemental composition is C_6H_5OBr, while that of the probable $M^{\ddagger}$ ion at m/e 200 is C_8H_9OBr. Don't skip the steps in Table A-1! The rearrangement loss of C_2H_4 cannot occur if the C_2H_4 moiety is directly attached to the ring; it is likely, however, if it is attached to another atom (such as oxygen) which is attached to the ring. [*p*-Bromophenyl ethyl ether]

6.13, 6.14, 6.15,   All these molecules appear to have the molecular formula C_3H_6O, and thus contain one ring or double bond. One approach that is often valuable is to record all likely isomers and predict their spectra (this approach can be applicable for complex molecules when other information has eliminated many structural possibilities.) For C_3H_6O the following molecules are possible:

$$\underset{\text{(I)}}{CH_3CH_2\overset{\overset{\displaystyle O}{\|}}{C}H} \qquad \underset{\text{(II)}}{CH_3\overset{\overset{\displaystyle O}{\|}}{C}CH_3} \qquad \underset{\text{(III)}}{H_2C\overset{\displaystyle O}{\triangle}CH-CH_3}$$

$$\underset{\text{(IV)}}{H_2C\overset{\displaystyle O}{\triangle}CH_2-CH_2} \qquad \underset{\text{(V)}}{CH_2=CH-CH_2OH} \qquad \underset{\text{(VI)}}{CH_2=CHOCH_3}$$

In compound I a large m/e 29 peak should result from α-cleavage, no matter which fragment retains the charge; α-cleavage should give $(M - H)^+$ in less abundance. These are the predominant features of Unknown 6.13. The m/e 28 is probably formed by the rearrangement loss of formaldehyde. Unknown 6.14 is dominated by the $(M - 1)^+$ ion; this indicates strong activation of a hydrogen atom and that there is no other labile group in the molecule. Compound IV has four α-hydrogen atoms, but the formation of the $(M - 18)^+$ from IV would require considerable rearrangement. In V the α-hydrogen is activated by both the —OH and —CH=CH$_2$ groups; the m/e 31 would be expected by cleavage of the $C_\alpha-C_\beta$ adjacent to the —OH group. Unknown 6.15 shows a strong tendency for loss of methyl; only compounds II and III are consistent with this. Without a knowledge of the spectra of cyclic compounds it is difficult to eliminate III *a priori*; actually, the largest peak in the spectrum of III is at m/e 28. [Propionaldehyde, allyl alcohol, acetone]

6.16.   The molecular weight is the same as that of β-ionone, 192, so that a double bond has been formed in opening the ring. Allylic cleavage would account for the high abundance of the m/e 69 peak, suggesting either of the structures *a* or *b*, but not *c*. Formation of the abundant m/e 109, $(M - 83)^+$,

is much more difficult to rationalize, however, through an allylic cleavage involving the double bonds of the conjugated dienone system; a possible explanation would involve the displacement reaction 6-27 with structure *a* to give the aromatic oxonium ion *d*. Further support for structure *a* comes from the OE$^+$ ion at m/e 124, (M − 68)$^+$. Its formation can be rationalized through the 4-hydrogen rearrangement (reaction 4-16), possibly following isomerization of the double bond (reactions 6-5, 6-26), or through two hydrogen rearrangements. [Pseudoionone, *a*]

6.17. The molecular composition of the m/e 248 peak could be $C_{13}H_6OCl_2$ from the isotopic abundances. This corresponds to the replacement of the elements of CH_2Cl_2 in DDE by an oxygen atom, and an increase in the rings-plus-double-bonds value from 9 to 10. The m/e 248 peak passes the tests for the molecular ion; there are no other peaks containing more than two chlorine atoms. Strong additional evidence for the presence of oxygen is provided by the abundant OE$^+$ ion at m/e 220; this should represent the loss of CO, as C_2H_4 loss would be unlikely from a highly aromatic molecule. Note that the probable elemental composition of the OE$^+$ ion of m/e 150 is $C_{12}H_6$; it can contain no chlorine *or oxygen*, so it must be (M − Cl$_2$ − CO)$^+$. This is also evidence that the OE$^+$ ion of m/e 220 is (M − CO)$^+$, not (M − C$_2$H$_4$)$^+$. A large CO loss peak suggests a phenol or endocyclic carbonyl group; the latter would be consistent with the chemically logical molecule. [3,6-Dichlorofluorenone]

6.18. The mass 122 ion appears to have seven carbon atoms and two oxygen atoms, so it could be $C_7H_6O_2$, rings-plus-double-bonds value = 5. The m/e 104 ion possibly has seven carbon atoms, and it should be noted as an odd-electron ion along with masses 94 and 76. Mass 122 seems to be a prime candidate for the molecular ion, and its abundance indicates a highly stable molecule. In the low mass region the predominant ion series indicates an aromatic hydrocarbon, so that the rings-plus-double-bonds value of 5 corresponds to a phenyl ring plus an additional ring or double bond. The striking $(M-1)^+$ peak indicates the presence of a labile hydrogen atom, and $(M-18)^{\ddagger}$ indicates a ready loss of H_2O (Table A-5 suggests that this is due to a hydroxyl group). The $(M-28)^{\ddagger}$ and $(M-29)^+$ ions are probably $C_6H_6O^{\ddagger}$ and $C_6H_5O^+$, respectively, due to loss of CO, and COH, as losses of C_2H_4 and C_2H_5 would yield unusually unsaturated structures. The $(M-29)^+$ suggests that the $-CHO$ group is present, which would account for the extra double bond predicted by the rings-plus-double-bonds calculation above. From these indications of a labile hydrogen, phenyl, $-OH$, and $-CHO$ an obvious structure postulation is $HO-C_6H_4-CHO$, a structure which also is consistent with the m/e 76 ion, $C_6H_4^{\ddagger}$. The odd-electron ion m/e 104 indicates that this is the ortho isomer; an $(M-CO)^{\ddagger}$ peak is also commonly found in the spectra of phenols. [Salicylaldehyde]

6.19.   Isotopic abundances indicate that the m/e 186 ion is approximately C_{12}; identification of m/e 141 as $C_9H_{17}O$ and m/e 129 as $C_7H_{13}O_2$ indicates that m/e 186 is $C_{11}H_{22}O_2$, r + db = 1. This absence of unsaturation, other than in the ester carbonyl, is confirmed by the low mass ion series, and m/e 186 passes the molecular ion tests. The $(M-27)^+$, $(M-28)^{\ddagger}$, and $(M-C_2H_5O)^+$ peaks show that this is an ethyl ester; the large OE‡ mass 88 peak thus is strong evidence (reaction 6-30) that the α-carbon is unsubstituted $(R-CH_2COOC_2H_5)$. The base m/e 101 peak indicates that the β-carbon is also unsubstituted; this peak would then arise from the reciprocal hydrogen-rearrangement reaction 6-31, and from the direct loss of $C_6H_{13}^+$. The large m/e 129 $(M-C_4H_9)^+$, ion indicates a methyl branch on the next carbon $(R'-CH(CH_3)CH_2CH_2COOC_2H_5$ (reactions 4-1, 4-29, or 6-32). The appreciable $(M-C_2H_5)^+$ is evidence for another methyl branch on the next carbon, but the $C_4H_9^+$ is rather low for this assignment. [Ethyl 4-methyloctanoate]

6.20.   The m/e 303 peak corresponds in mass and isotopic abundances to the $M^{\ddagger}$ of cocaine, and the relative abundance of this peak is consistent with the stability of this cyclic molecule. There is an aromatic ion series; the prominent (68), 82, and 96 ions are consistent with an EE$^+$ bicycloalkylamine series (Table A-6) and/or an OE$\overset{+}{\cdot}$ cycloalkyl series (Table A-7); these are also supported by the abundances of m/e 42, 55, 83, and 97. The intense high mass peaks at $(M - 31)^+$, $(M - 105)^+$, and $(M - 121)^+$ give strong evidence for the presence of the methyl ester, benzoyl, and benzoyloxy groups, respectively. The corresponding ions at m/e 59, 105, and 122 (OE$\overset{+}{\cdot}$, reaction 4-16) provide additional evidence for the methoxycarbonyl, benzoyl, and benzoyloxy groups, respectively. High-resolution information on elemental compositions would make all this evidence more positive, however; for example, the large m/e 122 peak may also be due to the loss of benzoyloxy and acetic acid to give the stable EE$^+$ ion, $C_8H_{12}N^+$. The m/e 94 could correspond to the loss of C_2H_4 from this ion (reaction 4-7). [Cocaine]

                                  m/e 122 m/e 94

6.21.   A significant m/e 57 peak could arise from d, but m/e 43 should be weak because of the low stability of $R\overset{+}{O}$ ions. The important peaks fit well with the expected α- and i-cleavage of c; a large m/e 41 peak usually accompanies an abundant $C_4H_9^+$ ion. [Methyl *tert*-butyl ketone]

6.22.   The large $(M - 31)^+$ peak suggests a methyl ester; the large 41$^+$ and $(M - 41)^+$ suggest C_3H_5—CO—OCH$_3$. [Methyl methacrylate]

6.23.   The base peak at m/e 43 is consistent with the presence of CH_3CO. The m/e 61 could result from the 2H rearrangement (reaction 4-39) of an acetate ester, CH_3CO—O—C_3H_5; the $(M - 42)\overset{+}{\cdot}$ OE$\overset{+}{\cdot}$ ion also indicates an unsaturated acetate. [Allyl acetate]

6.24.   Calculations on isotopic abundances suggest elemental compositions of $C_8H_6O_4$ and $C_8H_5O_3$ for the peaks at m/e 166, and 149, respectively (rings-plus-double-bonds value for each equals 6). The OE$\overset{+}{\cdot}$ m/e 166 ion is a logical candidate for the molecular ion. There are characteristic low mass aromatic ions, and the intense peaks at m/e 149 $[(M - 17)^+]$, m/e 121 $[(M - 17 - 28)^+]$, and m/e 45 (CHO_2^+), provide strong evidence for a carboxyl group. These C_6H_5— and —COOH moieties leave only CO_2 unaccounted for in the molecular formula, so that a benzenedicarboxylic acid is a logical postulate. Although the intensity of the peak at m/e 122 is slightly greater than that expected from the isotopic contributions, in this case an "ortho effect" would give an m/e 122 peak of much higher abundance. [Terephthalic acid]

6.25.   Isotopic abundances point to $C_7H_6O_3^+$ and $C_7H_4O_2^+$ for the m/e 138 and 120 peaks; these suggest the assignment $C_9H_8O_4^+$ for the mass 180 peak, which passes the molecular ion tests. The former peaks correspond to losses of C_2H_2O ($CH_2=C=O$, reaction 4-18), and $C_2H_4O_2$ (CH_3COOH?), both of which could arise from an acetoxy group attached to an unsaturated functionality (Table A-5) (an aromatic low mass ion series is present). Both m/e 43 and 15 also support the presence of an acetyl group. The CHO_2^+ ion, m/e 45, indicates that the other two oxygen atoms are in a carboxyl group; if this is ortho to the acetoxy group it could supply the labile hydrogen atom for the rearrangement loss of CH_3COOH which gives the base peak. Note that reactions initiated by the carboxyl group, such as those producing $(M - OH)^+$ and $(M - COOH)^+$, are completely suppressed. [Acetylsalicylic acid]

6.26.   You may find that the solution of this spectrum is difficult. Check to see if you have assigned the formulas $C_3H_7O_2$ to m/e 75 and C_2H_5O to m/e 45. If not, rework the problem assuming these data were supplied by high-resolution mass spectrometry.

This spectrum is difficult because of the variety of isobaric formulas which can be applied to each major ion, and because of the absence of a molecular ion. Yet many students are able to arrive at the correct structure in a relatively short time, mainly because the data fit this structure so well. Without reference spectra it is difficult to eliminate many other possible structures unequivocally. However, such a "best guess" can often be very valuable.

The m/e 75 ion has no more than three carbon and two oxygen atoms; m/e 45 has no more than two carbon atoms. Despite its low abundance, the presence of any m/e 61 is strong evidence that m/e 75 is not the molecular ion. Additionally, molecular formulas such as C_3H_9NO and $C_2H_5NO_2$ necessary to fit an ion of m/e 75 are difficult to envision as giving the other ions found, such as m/e 31. Thus there appears to be no $M^{\ddagger}$. For such low-molecular-weight compounds the lack of $M^{\ddagger}$ suggests a saturated structure (Table A-4), so that CH_3O^+, $C_2H_5O^{\ddagger}$, and $C_3H_7O_2^+$ are the most favorable postulates for the abundant m/e 31, 45, and 75 ions, respectively. Thus m/e 75 must contain two functional groups; there is no odd-electron $(M - 18)^{\ddagger}$ ion to indicate that either is a hydroxy group. The abundant CH_3^+ suggests a CH_3O moiety; relative ion stabilities predict a low abundance for CH_3^+ unless it is attached to an electron-attracting group. The CH_3O group is probably attached to $-CH_2-$, as it cannot be part of a $CH_3OCH(CH_3)-$ or $CH_3OC(CH_3)_2-$ group. If these groups were present the abundance of the m/e 59 or 73 ions, respectively, would be much greater than is observed. (To reiterate, never neglect the large amount of *negative* information present in every mass spectrum—it can be very valuable.) The few abundant ions in the spectrum suggest a simple molecular structure, so that there is a strong possibility that one of the two oxygen-containing functional groups in the m/e 75 ion is the same as the one in the m/e 45 ion. If there is no hydroxyl group, the most logical structure for the m/e 75 ion is $(CH_3O)_2CH-$ (see ref. *5.2*), and for the molecule it is $CH_3OCH_2OCH_3$. It should be reemphasized that this was not a rigorous proof of structure by mass spectrometry, but rather a way to hypothesize a probable structure which can then be checked against reference spectra or other techniques. [Methylal]

$$\text{CH}_3\text{O}\overset{H}{\underset{}{\text{C}}}\overset{H}{\underset{}{}}\text{OCH}_3 \quad \xrightarrow{\alpha} \quad H\cdot \; + \quad \text{CH}_3\text{O}\overset{H}{\underset{}{\text{C}}}\text{OCH}_3 \qquad m/e\ 75$$

$$\text{CH}_3\text{O}\overset{H}{\underset{}{\text{C}}}\overset{H}{\underset{}{}}\text{OCH}_3 \quad \xrightarrow{\alpha} \quad \text{CH}_3\text{O}\cdot + \text{H}_2\text{C}\overset{+}{\underset{\text{OCH}_3}{}} \qquad m/e\ 45$$

6.27. Alpha cleavage of the 12-isomer leads to two possible radical

species, neither of which can abstract a hydrogen to give m/e 99 ($C_5H_7O_2^+$) by mechanisms similar to reaction 6-43. For the 17-keto derivative, however, α-cleavage of the weakest bond leads to m/e 99.

6.28. Isotopic abundances indicate $C_9H_{19}O^+$ as the composition of the m/e 143 peak, suggesting $C_{11}H_{24}O^+$ for the mass 172 peak (r + db = 0), although $C_{10}H_{20}O_2^+$ cannot be ruled out. The characteristics of m/e 172 are consistent with those of M^+; its finite abundance and the presence of the saturated oxygen ion series (m/e 31, 45, 59, 73) indicate that the compound is an aliphatic ether. The two largest peaks in this series, m/e 73 and 129, should represent the α-cleavage loss of C_2H_5 and C_7H_{15} from $R_1CH_2OCHR_2R_3$; thus $C_2H_5CH_2OCH_2C_7H_{15}$ and $CH_3OCH(C_2H_5)C_7H_{15}$ are the most probable candidate structures. The $(M - 32)^+$ peak is consistent with a methyl ether structure (reaction 4-26), as is the $(M - 29 - 32)^+$ (reaction 4-42, 4-44). Decomposition of either m/e 73 or 143 through reaction 4-37 would yield m/e 45. The insignificance of other alkyl loss peaks or of alkyl peaks suggests that the alkyl chain is unbranched. [3-Methoxydecane]

6.29.   The peak at m/e 154, which passes the molecular ion tests, appears to contain sulfur (or possibly silicon) and approximately seven carbon atoms. Isotopic abundances of m/e 136 agree with $C_7H_4OS^{\ddagger}$, so that the molecular formula may be $C_7H_6O_2S$. An aromatic molecule is suggested by the abundant aromatic ion series, doubly charged ions, and high mass ions. Important peaks for $(M - H_2O)^{\ddagger}$ $(OE^{\ddagger})$, $(M - HCO_2)^+$, and $(M - H_2CO_2)^{\ddagger}$ $(OE^{\ddagger})$ indicate an ortho-substituted aromatic acid. By difference the o-substituted group is —SH, which is also consistent with the small $(M - S)^{\ddagger}$ and $(M - HS)^+$ ions (Table A-5). Note that significant ions at m/e 69, 81, 82, 96, and 97 probably arise from a sulfur-containing aromatic ion series. [Thiosalicylic acid]

6.30.   The mass 146–148 appearance should suggest an isotopic cluster. The most probable suspects of Table 2-1 are silicon and sulfur. One atom of sulfur fits the mass 148/146 ratio better, and this postulation leaves a residual at m/e 147 indicating eight or nine carbon atoms (correspondingly, Si_1 would indicate approximately C_5). Sulfur (or silicon) is also indicated in m/e 89, but not in masses 112, 98, or 84. Assuming that m/e 146 is the molecular ion and contains no nitrogen atoms, a series of abundant *odd-electron* ions is apparent; masses 42, 56, 70, 84, 98, and 112. Table A-7 suggests an olefin ion series; the abundant $(M - 34)^{\ddagger}$ and $(M - 62)^{\ddagger}$ indicate a thiol. This is supported by the alkyl ion series and by the m/e 47, 61, 75, 89, 103 ion series. Mass 89, the most abundant ion of these, corresponds to the cyclic ion formed in n-alkyl mercaptans. For a dramatic confirmation of this evidence, compare this spectrum to that of 1-octanol, Figure 5-5. [n-Octyl mercaptan]

m/e 89

6.31.   The isotopic abundances of the m/e 154 indicate the composition $C_8H_{10}OS$, r + db = 4; this peak passes the $M^{\ddagger}$ tests also. There is an aromatic ion series, and the peaks at 69, 82, 95-7, and 108 are evidence for sulfur attached to an aromatic ring (Table A-6), although a thiophene substituted with an unsaturated or cyclic group is also possible. The m/e 47 and 61 peaks indicate that an alkyl moiety is also attached to sulfur. The $OE^{\ddagger}$ m/e 126 peak has the composition C_6H_6OS (don't forget that the m/e 125 isotopes contribute to the m/e 127 peak), or $(M - C_2H_4)^{\ddagger}$; possible mechanisms for its formation include reaction 4-18 or 4-21 with $a - d$, and reaction 4-7 with e. The presence of a hydroxyl group, possibly in an ortho position, is

a   *b*   *c*   *d*   *e*

indicated by the peak at m/e 121, $(M - CH_3 - H_2O)^+$. The m/e 98 and, presumably, 97 peaks still contain sulfur, and thus apparently are $(M - C_2H_4 - CO)^{\ddagger}$ and $(M - C_2H_4 - CHO)^+$, consistent with a phenolic-type hydroxyl group. [Ethyl *o*-hydroxyphenyl sulfide]

6.32 through 6.35. Prominent ions are expected from α-cleavage (4-8); these ions may decompose further by rearrangement reaction 4-36. This predicts prominent peaks for the six isomers as follows:

$$C_3H_7\!-\!CH_2\overset{+\cdot}{N}HCH_3 \xrightarrow{\ \alpha\ } CH_2\!=\!\overset{+}{N}HCH_3$$

$$(CH_3)_2CH\!-\!CH_2\overset{+\cdot}{N}HCH_3 \xrightarrow{\ \alpha\ } CH_2\!=\!\overset{+}{N}HCH_3$$

$$\begin{array}{l} C_2H_5 \\ \diagdown \\ CH\!-\!\overset{+\cdot}{N}HCH_3 \\ \diagup \\ CH_3 \end{array} \quad \begin{array}{l} \xrightarrow{\ \alpha\ } CH_3CH\!=\!\overset{+}{N}HCH_3 \\[4pt] \xrightarrow{\ \alpha\ } C_2H_5CH\!=\!\overset{+}{N}HCH_3 \end{array}$$

$$(CH_3)_3C\!-\!\overset{+\cdot}{N}HCH_3 \xrightarrow{\ \alpha\ } (CH_3)_2C\!=\!\overset{+}{N}HCH_3$$

$$C_2H_5CH_2NHCH_2CH_3 \quad \begin{array}{l} \xrightarrow{\ \alpha\ } CH_2\!=\!\overset{+}{N}HCH_2CH_2 \xrightarrow{\ rH\ } CH_2\!=\!\overset{+}{N}H_2 \\[4pt] \xrightarrow{\ \alpha\ } C_2H_5CH_2\overset{+}{N}H\!=\!CH_2 \xrightarrow{\ rH\ } H_2\overset{+}{N}\!=\!CH_2 \end{array}$$

$$(CH_3)_2CHNHCH_2CH_3 \quad \begin{array}{l} \xrightarrow{\ \alpha\ } CH_3CH\!=\!\overset{+}{N}HCH_2CH_3 \xrightarrow{\ rH\ } CH_3CH\!=\!\overset{+}{N}H_2 \\[4pt] \xrightarrow{\ \alpha\ } (CH_3)_2CH\overset{+}{N}H\!=\!CH_2 \xrightarrow{\ rH\ } H_2\overset{+}{N}\!=\!CH_2 \end{array}$$

Spectra 6.33 and 6.35 are the only ones giving prominent m/e 44 peaks and so must be from the *n*- or isobutylmethylamines; the larger $(M - CH_3)^+$ for 6.33 suggests that this is the iso isomer. Methyl-*sec*-butyl- and ethylpropyl-amine should give a large m/e 58 and a smaller m/e 72 peak, as shown by 6.32 and 6.34; the larger m/e 30 of 6.32 indicates that this is ethylpropylamine. [6.32, *N*-ethyl-*N*-propylamine; 6.33, *N*-methyl-*N*-isobutylamine; 6.34, *N*-methyl-*N*-*sec*-butylamine; 6.35, *N*-methyl-*N*-*n*-butylamine]

6.36. Since the androstanyl skeleton has a mass of 259, the peak at 331 is a good candidate for the molecular ion if R has a mass of 72. This odd-mass molecular ion indicates an odd number of nitrogen atoms, which is consistent with an isotopic composition of $C_4H_{10}N$ for the intense m/e 72 peak. This should result from an aliphatic amine undergoing α-cleavage loss of the largest substituent, namely the androstanyl moiety. R should thus have the structure $-CR_1R_2NR_3R_4$, where $R_1 + R_2 + R_3 + R_4 = C_3H_{10}$. [R = $-CH(CH_3)N(CH_3)_2$]

6.37. The pressure-sensitive peak at $(M + 1)^+$ is expected for amines; the 3/1 abundances of the m/e 36, 38 pair indicates that the sample was introduced as the hydrochloride. Alpha cleavage explains the base peak, $CH_3CH\!=\!\overset{+}{N}HCH_3$; this will not undergo rearrangement reaction 4-38, accounting for the relatively low abundance of the m/e 30 peak. The effectiveness of a hydroxyl group for reaction initiation is much lower than that of an amine; this is reflected in the low abundance of m/e 107, $C_6H_5CH\!=\!\overset{+}{O}H$. Also weak

$(M - OH)^+$ and $(M - H_2O)^{\ddagger}$ peaks are present. Some anomalous peaks remain; m/e 146 might be $C_6H_5CH=C(CH_3)-\overset{+}{N}H=CH_2$, and m/e 118 might be

[Ephedrine]

6.38.   The pressure-dependent m/e 180 peak is probably the $(M + 1)^+$ ion and is approximately C_{11}; M^+ (m/e 179) then contains an odd number of nitrogen atoms. The m/e 120 and 88 peaks have values of 8 and 3, respectively, for their maximum number of carbon atoms. Low mass peaks indicate the presence of aromatic and saturated amine (m/e 30) and oxygenated (m/e 31, 45) functionalities. A methyl ester, $-CO-OCH_3$, is a probable cause (Table A-5) of the peaks representing $(M - 31)^+$, $(M - 32)^{\ddagger}$, and $(M - 59)^+$. Two of the largest peaks in the spectrum, m/e 88 and 91, could arise from cleavage of the same bond ($88 + 91 = 179$); the m/e 91 could be $C_6H_5CH_2^+$. The greater charge retention by the m/e 88 suggests stabilization by the amine moiety; $-CH(=\overset{+}{N}H_2)COOCH_3$ appears to be the only possible group containing the carboxymethyl functionality; this also is consistent with the high abundance of m/e 120. [Phenylalanine methyl ester]

6.39.   If mass 101 is the molecular ion, it must contain an odd number of nitrogen atoms. The $(M - CH_3)^+$ ion appears to have no more than four carbon atoms, and m/e 59 to have two carbon atoms and no more than one oxygen atom. Any even-electron ion series of Table A-6 that includes m/e 59 is ruled out by the isotopic abundances. In fact, the identity of this ion fragment is a major key to the identity of Unknown 6.39. With a maximum of C_2 and O_1, and with the indicated presence of nitrogen, the formula C_2H_5NO is a logical postulate for m/e 59, and is an *odd-electron ion*, $(M - 42)^{\ddagger}$. Table A-7 suggests H_2NCOCH_2-Z-H or $HON=CHCH_2-Z-H$; for Z, 42 amu, Table A-5 suggests C_3H_6 or CH_2CO. Corresponding to these, the prominent $(M - 15)^+$ and m/e 43 peaks suggest either $-CH(CH_3)_2$ or $-COCH_3$ as terminal groups. The former is indicated by the mass 88/86 ratio, but the accuracy of this is doubtful. Differentiation between the possible amide and oxime structures also requires study of reference spectra of similar compounds. [3-Methylbutyramide]

6.40, 6.41.   The m/e 116 peaks of these compounds contain no more than eight carbon atoms and no oxygen; C_8H_6N appears to be a logical formula. This suggests $C_{10}H_8N_2$ ($r + db = 8$) as the best formula for m/e 156, which passes the M^{+} tests. The low mass ion series indicates an aromatic molecule; the base peak is consistent with $-CH_2CN$ loss to give a very stable ion. A bicyclic structure for this ion such as [indole structure with N–H] would not appear to be particularly stable, but $NC-C_6H_4-CH_2^{+}$ should be stable. One of the unknowns is thus likely a ring isomer of $NC-C_6H_4-CH_2CH_2CN$; it is stated, however, that the other unknown cannot be a second ring-position isomer. Unknown 6.40 is actually an α,α'-dicyanoxylene; remember that xylene gives $(M-CH_3)^{+}$ as its base peak, probably because the molecular ion isomerizes to methylcycloheptatriene. The suprising similarity in the spectra of 6.40 and 6.41 makes differentiation difficult; the larger $(M-26)^{+}$ peak of 6.40 could be due to the preferential loss of the benzylic cyano group. [6.40, 1,4-bis-(cyanomethyl)benzene; 6.41, 1-(p-cyanophenyl)-2-cyanoethane]

6.42.   The m/e 99/98 ratio is suspiciously large for m/e 98 to be the molecular ion; the m/e 84 makes m/e 99 a much more likely candidate. This suggests that the molecule contains an odd number of nitrogen atoms and makes difficult the identification of the odd-electron ions of the spectrum. The m/e 59, 45, and 31 ions appear to contain three, two, and one carbon atom, respectively. If we assume that the m/e 84 ion contains one nitrogen atom, the 85/84 ratio indicates four carbon atoms. The significant mass 31, 45, and 59 ions suggest (Table A-6) an alcohol or ether functionality, but the possibility of nitrogen demands consideration of C_2H_5NO (Table A-7) for m/e 59. This dilemma can be resolved if the nitrogen functionality can be pinpointed, and the anomalous m/e 54 gives a strong indication of this. Table A-6 suggests $-C_2H_4CN$, and the presence of a nitrile group would also explain the unusual $(M-1)^{+}$ and $(M-27)^{+}$ ions. The m/e 59 ion is most likely $HOC(CH_3)_2-$, $CH_3OCH(CH_3)-$, or $C_2H_5OCH_2-$, in light of $(M-15)^{+} \gg (M-29)^{+}$. The only one of these compatible with the base peak at mass 31 is $C_2H_5OCH_2-$. (This is a difficult unknown because of the two functional groups and the isobaric possibilities for a number of the ions. Obviously some additional information would greatly simplify the solution, for example, the infrared spectrum defining the presence of a nitrile group.) [β-Cyanoethyl ethyl ether]

$$CH_3\overset{+\cdot}{CH_2}OCH_2CH_2CN \xrightarrow{\alpha} CH_3\cdot + CH_2=\overset{+}{O}CH_2CH_2CN \ (m/e\ 84)$$

$$CH_3CH_2\overset{+\cdot}{O}CH_2CH_2CN \xrightarrow{i} CH_3CH_2O\cdot + \overset{+}{C}H_2CH_2CN \ (m/e\ 54)$$

$$CH_3CH_2\overset{+\cdot}{O}CH_2CH_2CN \xrightarrow[\alpha]{-\cdot CH_2CN} \underset{CH_2CH_2}{H\rangle\ \overset{+}{O}=CH_2} \xrightarrow{rH} C_2H_4 + H\overset{+}{O}=CH_2$$

$$(m/e\ 59) \qquad\qquad (m/e\ 31)$$

6.43.   Possible elemental compositions are: m/e 298, $C_{10} - C_{12}$; 269, C_9, O_{0-2}; 171, $C_{11}H_{23}O$ (given); 141, $C_9H_{17}O$ or $C_{10}H_{21}$; 109, C_8H_{13}; 97, C_7H_{13}; 83, C_6H_{11}; and 73, C_4H_9O. The peak at m/e 298 passes the M^{+} tests. The abundant $(M - 127)^{+}$ ion apparently is formed with no appreciable loss of "A + 1" or "A + 2" elements, and thus must correspond to the loss of iodine, so that M^{+} is $C_{11}H_{23}OI$ (r + db = 0) and m/e 269 is $(M - C_2H_5)^{+}$. The presence of an appreciable M^{+} peak indicates that the saturated oxygen functionality is an ether group (Table A-4). This should provide the strongest driving force in this molecule for radical-site reaction initiation; α-cleavages of $C_2H_5CHROCH_3$ would give the important $(M - C_2H_5)^{+}$ and $C_4H_9O^{+}$ peaks. Further decomposition of $C_2H_5CH\overset{+}{=}OCH_3$ through reaction 4-37 rationalizes the high $[m/e\ 45]/[m/e\ 59]$ ratio. The m/e 139 ion apparently arises through loss of CH_3OH from m/e 171; the m/e 141 is more surprising, as this must involve a hydrogen-rearrangement loss of CH_2O. Iodine is too weak as a reaction-initiator to expect peaks showing its location, although the lack of any other $(M - C_nH_{2n+1})^{+}$ peaks is consistent with a C_2H_5CHRI structure; the $(M - I)^{+}$ peak is also rather abundant for a 1-iodoalkane. [3-Methoxy-8-iododecane]

6.44.   Your suspicions concerning the m/e 148–150 doublet can be confirmed at masses 119–121, 105–107, 91–93, and 77–79; this is the chloroalkyl ion series. Isotopic abundances indicate the $C_nH_{2n+1}^{+}$ ion series as another important feature of the spectrum, consistent with the elemental composition $C_8H_{17}Cl$ for m/e 148 as the molecular ion. Strong peaks at $C_7H_{15}^{+}$ and $C_4H_9^{+}$ suggest cleavage at chain branching enhanced through electron withdrawal by the chlorine atom (the abundance of the $C_4H_9^{+}$ can be viewed as arising through ionization of the most labile bond, with the charge going to the least electronegative fragment). $(M - C_2H_5)^{+}$ is the prominent ion in the chloroalkyl series. The abundant ions discussed are consistent with the structure $ClCH_2CH(C_2H_5)(CH_2)_3CH_3$. [3-(Chloromethyl)heptane]

6.45.   The isotopic clusters indicate a chlorine atom in masses 166, 147, 116, 109, 97, 85, 66, and 47. Carbon contents are low: a maximum of C_3 in 166, 147, 131, and 93; C_1 in 69 and 31, and so on. Mass 166 is indicated as the molecular ion; the ion series fit those expected for chlorofluorocarbons, suggesting C_3ClF_5 as the molecular formula. Random rearrangements are common in such compounds, making assignments less secure unless reference spectra of similar compounds are available. Thus though the abundance relationship $(M - CClF_2)^{+} > (M - CF_3)^{+}$ indicates a terminal $CClF_2$ group, the less indicative methyl ions show $CF_3^{+} > CClF_2^{+}$ in abundance. Experience shows that the large $(M - Cl)^{+}/M^{+}$ ratio is indicative of allylic chlorine; in the 2-chloroperfluoropropene this abundance ratio is 0.5. [3-Chloroperfluoropropene]

6.46.   The abundant m/e 98 may be the molecular ion; isotope ratios indicate $C_6H_{10}O$ for it, consistent with the carbonyl band in the infrared spectrum. Rings-plus-double-bonds value = 2, or 1 in addition to the carbonyl group. Isotope ratios definitely indicate that m/e 43 is *not* $C_3H_7^+$, so that the alkyl ion series is limited to C_2 at most. The 27, 41, 55 (69—missing), 83 ion series suggests alkenes or cycloalkanes, consistent with the rings-plus-double-bonds calculation, *and (or)* alkenyl- or cycloalkylcarbonyl, consistent with the rings-plus-double-bonds calculation and the infrared spectrum. The abundance of m/e 43 strongly suggests the acetyl group, which would also account for the abundant $(M - CH_3)^+$. The other group attached to the carbonyl must have the formula C_4H_7. The comparable abundances of $C_4H_7^+$ and CH_3CO^+ indicate equivalent capabilities for stabilizing the positive charge. [4-Methyl-3-penten-2-one]

6.47. The ion of m/e 103 appears to be C_5; this is confirmed by the C_4 composition of m/e 88. The abundant 30, 44, 58, 72 ion series is indicative of a saturated amine; the m/e 103 composition thus should be $C_5H_{13}NO$, and it passes the $M^{\ddagger}$ tests. Alpha cleavages initiated by the amine should be dominant reactions; the $(M - CH_3)^+$ and $(M - CH_3O)^+$ peaks thus indicate the moieties $N-C-CH_3$ and $N-C-CH_2OH$, respectively, given that a hydroxyl is present. The possible molecules are (*a*) $HOCH_2CH(CH_3)NHC_2H_5$, (*b*) $HOCH_2CH(CH_3)N(CH_3)_2$, (*c*) $HOCH_2C(CH_3)_2NHCH_3$, (*d*) $HOCH_2CH_2-NHCH(CH_3)_2$, and (*e*) $HOCH_2CH_2N(CH_3)C_2H_5$; no other α-loss, except $(M - H)^+$, is possible from any of these. The base m/e 30 peak should arise by the further decomposition of one of the α-cleavage products (m/e 88 or 72) through hydrogen rearrangement (reaction 4-38); this would not be possible with the tertiary amines *b* and *e*. Reaction sequences for the remainder should be:

$$a \xrightarrow{\alpha} HOCH_2CH(CH_3)\overset{+}{N}H=CH_2 \xrightarrow{rH} H_2\overset{+}{N}=CH_2 \quad (m/e\ 30)$$

$$\xrightarrow{\alpha} HOCH_2CH=\overset{+}{N}HC_2H_5 \xrightarrow{rH} HOCH_2CH=\overset{+}{N}H_2 \quad (m/e\ 60)$$

$$\xrightarrow{\alpha} CH_3CH=\overset{+}{N}HC_2H_5 \xrightarrow{rH} CH_3CH=\overset{+}{N}H_2 \quad (m/e\ 44)$$

$$c \xrightarrow{\alpha} HOCH_2C(CH_3)=NHCH_3 \xrightarrow{\times}$$

$$\xrightarrow{\alpha} (CH_3)_2C=\overset{+}{N}HCH_3 \xrightarrow{\times}$$

$$d \xrightarrow{\alpha} HOCH_2CH_2\overset{+}{N}H{=}CHCH_3 \xrightarrow{rH} H_2\overset{+}{N}{=}CHCH_3 \quad (m/e\ 44)$$

$$\xrightarrow{\alpha} H_2C{=}\overset{+}{N}HCH(CH_3)_2 \xrightarrow{rH} H_2C{=}\overset{+}{N}H_2 \quad (m/e\ 30)$$

Thus c should give weaker m/e 30 and 44 peaks. The m/e 88 ion of a should arise mainly by loss of CH_3 from the more highly branched α-carbon, so that there should be a significant m/e 60 ion. Structure d correctly predicts the abundant m/e 30 and 44 peaks; note that the significant m/e 70 ion is consistent with the stable structure $CH_2{=}CH{-}NH{=}CHCH_3$. [N-(2-Hydroxyethyl)-N-isopropylamine]

6.48. The m/e 150 ion appears to have C_7 and O_3 components; this is supported by apparent C_8 and O_3 components in m/e 165. The mass 104 peak has maxima of seven carbon and one oxygen atoms. The m/e 43 ion isotope ratios point to the composition C_2H_3O. None of the tests eliminates m/e 165 as the molecular ion; it must then contain an odd number of nitrogen atoms. Masses 104 and 76 *may* be significant odd-electron ions. The molecule appears to be generally stable, giving a few abundant ions. The low aromatic series suggests electronegative substituents. The abundant $(M-15)^+$ indicates facile loss of CH_3, and the m/e 43 and $(M-43)^+$ make the acetyl group, $-COCH_3$, a possible source of this loss. If the acetyl group is attached to the phenyl, this offers an explanation for the abundant m/e 104:

$$Y{-}C_6H_4{-}CO{-}CH_3^{+\cdot} \xrightarrow{\alpha} Y{-}C_6H_4{-}CO^+ \xrightarrow{i} Y{\cdot} + C_6H_4CO^{+\cdot}$$

This decomposition of an even-electron ion to yield an abundant odd-electron ion is unusual, and requires Y to be strongly electron-attracting. Additional evidence comes from m/e 76; this is commonly formed from disubstituted aromatic compounds (5.2). If so, this second functional group contains $165 - (76 + 43) = 46$ amu, and is probably NO_2, $C_7H_4NO_3$ (m/e 150) $- C_7H_4O$ (m/e 104). Loss of NO is typical of nitroaromatics (Table A-5); m/e 120 may be $(M-CH_3-NO)^+$, and m/e 92 may be $(M-CH_3CO-NO)^+$. [p-Nitroacetophenone]

6.49 through 6.53. The molecular formula is $C_4H_8O_2$ in each case. Again it might be instructive to enumerate the possible compounds of this composition containing a carbonyl group, and classify them according to the expected C–O stretching frequency. The rings-plus-double-bonds value = 1, so that the molecules must be acyclic and saturated except for the carbonyl group. The possibilities include esters (1730 to 1750 cm^{-1}) $HCOOC_3H_7$, $HCOOCH(CH_3)_2$, $C_2H_5COOCH_3$, and $CH_3COOC_2H_5$; alkoxy- or hydroxyaldehydes (1715 to 1740 cm^{-1} *when not hydrogen-bonded*); $CH_3OCH_2COCH_3$ or hydroxy methyl ethyl ketones (1700 to 1720 cm^{-1} *when not hydrogen-bonded*); and acids (1685 to 1710 cm^{-1}), C_3H_7COOH and $(CH_3)_2CHCOOH$.

Unknown 6.49 should be an ester; the $(M - 27)^+$ is the double hydrogen rearrangement peak typical of ethyl esters, and the other peaks (except m/e 70) are consistent with this structure.

For Unknown 6.52 the propyl formates are eliminated as they should yield m/e 47 ions by the same double hydrogen rearrangement. The metastable at m/e 37.1 corresponds to formation of the second largest ion by $88^+ \rightarrow 57^+ +$ 31. Of the remaining possible aldehydes and ester, only $C_2H_5COOCH_3$, $CH_3OCH_2CH_2CHO$, and $CH_3OCH(CH_3)CHO$ could give plausible reactions corresponding to these masses. The last should give a sizable $(M - CH_3)^+$ and a very abundant $CH_3\overset{+}{O}=CHCH_3$ ion; for $CH_3OCH_2CH_2CHO$ the $(M-1)^+$ and m/e 45 should be more abundant. The high abundances of m/e 57 $(C_2H_5CO^+)$ and m/e 29 $(C_2H_5^+)$ strongly favor the ester.

The infrared spectrum suggests that the carbonyl group in Unknown 6.51 must be hydrogen-bonded; the base peak at m/e 29 and the $(M - 18)^+$ indicate the compound to be a hydroxyaldehyde. A β-OH is favored over α- or γ-OH by the abundance of m/e 45 as compared to m/e 31 or 59. This is borne out by the second largest peak in the spectrum, the odd-electron m/e 44 ion.

Unknown 6.53 has m/e 45 as its base peak; this most probably is CH_3CHOH—because of the low mass 31 abundance ($COOH^+$ would not be this abundant in comparison to $C_3H_7^+$ by comparative ion stabilities). The structure $CH_3CHOHCOCH_3$ is the only possibility remaining that contains this moiety, and the rest of the spectrum is consistent with this.

The remaining Unknown, 6.50, has its base peak at m/e 43. The remaining methyl ketone, $HOCH_2CH_2COCH_3$, is improbable because of the low abundance of m/e 58 and 31. The alternative assignment of m/e 43 as $C_3H_7^+$ is consistent with a butyric acid, the only possibility among the remaining structures. The large $(M - CH_3)^+$ and small m/e 60 (from a hydrogen abstraction rearrangement) support an iso structure. (In the spectrum of n-butyric acid m/e 60 represents 40% of the total ion abundance.) [6.49, Ethyl acetate; 6.50, isobutyric acid; 6.51, β-hydroxybutyraldehyde; 6.52, methyl propionate; 6.53, 3-hydroxybutan-2-one]

6.54.   The presence of at least two oxygen atoms and one nitrogen atom is required by the fact that this is the ethyl ester of an amino acid. The m/e 177/179 ratio suggests an isotopic cluster, and the abundances are consistent with one sulfur and around eight carbon atoms for m/e 177. There is probably a sulfur atom in the peaks at m/e 148, 131, 104, and 61. To calculate the elemental composition, mass $177 - 32 (S_1) - 32 (O_2) - 14 (N) = 99$, which would be C_8H_3 (impossible for an ethyl ester) or, more probably, C_7H_{15}. None of the tests eliminates m/e 177 as the molecular ion, $C_7H_{15}NO_2S$.

Other odd-electron ions are difficult to identify because of the presence of the nitrogen atom.

The large number of functional groups present makes it more difficult to judge the significance of the low mass ion series. In the alkyl amine series m/e 30 appears to be the only ion of importance; this fact plus an appreciable $(M - 17)^+$ indicate a free amine group. Of the ion series of Table A-6 containing sulfur, the alkylthiol or sulfide series m/e 47, 61, 75 offer a structure assignment for the sulfur atom in the molecule. The $(M - 15)^+$, $(M - 29)^+$, and $(M - 46)^{\ddagger}$ are roughly as expected for an ethyl ester. From Table A-5 the $(M - 48)^{\ddagger}$ ion could be due to a methyl sulfide, and this supports the assignment of $CH_3SCH_2^+$ as the structure of the base peak at m/e 61 and for the group lost in m/e 116. The $(M - 73)^+$ is expected for

$$R-\overset{\overset{\displaystyle +\cdot}{NH_2}}{\underset{|}{CH}}-COOC_2H_5 \quad \overset{\alpha}{\longrightarrow} \quad R-CH=\overset{+}{N}H_2 + \cdot COOC_2H_5$$

$R-COOC_2H_5$ when R^+ is stabilized, such as occurs for α-amino acids (Table A-5). The stable R^+ also accounts for the lack of the expected $(M - C_2H_4)^{\ddagger}$ and $(M - C_2H_3)^+$. $R-CHNH_2COOC_2H_5$ must have a mass of $177 - 102 = 75$, and must contain CH_3SCH_2-, so that the molecular structure $CH_3-SCH_2CH_2CHNH_2COOC_2H_5$ is indicated. The formation of m/e 56 is rationalized in equation 4-44. [Methionine ethyl ester]

6.55.   The maximum values for elemental compositions are not particularly meaningful. The m/e 75 peak cannot be $M^{\ddagger}$; m/e 61 would then be $(M - 14)^+$. The scarcity of even-mass peaks indicates that the true $M^{\ddagger}$ is at an even mass number. A saturated oxygen functionality is indicated by the 31, 45, (59, 73) ion series; a second one is indicated by m/e 75 and 61 ($C_2H_5O_2^+$; $C_3H_9O^+$ should not occur in this abundance without ion-molecule reactions; also the m/e 62 cannot be $C_3H_{10}O^{\ddagger}$). The metastable at m/e 30.4 indicates that m/e 61 can lose H_2O ($30.4 = 43^2/61$); the most logical structures for it are $-CH_2OCH_2OH$ and $-CH(OH)CH_2OH$. There are significant $OE^{\ddagger}$ ions at m/e 74, 62, and 44 (and 32? Did you mark these?). The most likely process for m/e 74 formation is the loss of H_2O (or ROH), so that m/e 92 (74 + 18), $C_3H_8O_3$, or a higher homolog, is a possible candidate for the $M^{\ddagger}$. Compounds such as $HOCH_2CH_2OCH_2OH$ and $CH_3OCH_2OCH_2OH$ (if stable) should give significant m/e 45 and $(M - 17)^+$, $RCH_2\overset{+}{O}=CH_2$. Glycerol, $HOCH_2CH(OH)CH_2OH$, is a logical alternative; hydrogen rearrangement can explain the m/e 62 and 44 peaks. [Glycerol]

$$m/e\ 62 \qquad\qquad m/e\ 44$$

6.56.   Elemental compositions are a key to this unknown; you should have postulated m/e 91 as $C_4H_8Cl^+$ (don't forget to subtract the ^{37}Cl contribution of m/e 90 from the m/e 92 abundance); m/e 77 as $C_3H_6Cl^+$; and m/e 71 as $C_5H_{11}^+$. All the m/e 92 and 94 peak abundances are due to isotopic contributions; thus there is no $M^{\ddagger}$. This fact (Table A-4) and the relatively low abundance of $C_4H_8Cl^+$ (reaction 4-29) show that this is not a 1-chloro-alkane. The $C_nH_{2n+1}^+$ ion series ends abruptly with the abundant $C_5H_{11}^+$ ion, suggesting that $M^{\ddagger}$ is $C_5H_{11}Cl^{\ddagger}$, as $(M - Cl)^+$ is abundant for secondary and tertiary chlorides. The $OE^{\ddagger}$ $C_5H_{10}^+$ ion is significant, and logical as the $(M - HCl)^{\ddagger}$ peak. The alkyl loss peaks, $(M - C_2H_5)^+ > (M - CH_3)^+ > (M - C_3H_7)^+$, indicate that ethyl and methyl groups are attached to the carbon bearing the chlorine; $(CH_3)_2CClC_2H_5$ is thus the most logical structure. [2-Chloro-2-methylbutane]

6.57.   The m/e 93 peak appears to be $C_6H_7N^{\ddagger}$ and passes the molecular ion tests. Its abundance and the low mass ion series indicate an aromatic compound. Aniline and methylpyridine are the most probable assignments; the latter is preferable because of the significant $(M - CH_3)^+$. [2-Methyl-pyridine]

6.58.   The m/e 141 could be $M^{\ddagger}$ if it contains an odd number of nitrogen atoms; it appears to contain C_4NO (or C_3N_3O), and m/e 126 corresponds to C_3NO. The presence of "A" elements (F and/or P) appears to be required. Calculated maxima for the carbon number of other ions are: m/e 114, 97, and 78, C_2; and m/e 72, C_3. The latter $(M - 69)^+$ peak has thus lost only C_1; a logical assignment is $(M - CF_3)^+$, which also accounts for the abundant m/e 69 as CF_3^+. Thus $M^{\ddagger}$ must be $C_4H_6NOF_3$, r + db = 1. The unusual $(M - 27)^+$ ion must be due to the loss of $C_2H_3\cdot$, not HCN, as a cyanide would require r + db > 1; Table A-5 suggests that an ethyl amide could account for $(M - C_2H_3)^+$, or a molecular structure $CF_3CONHC_2H_5$. This should show an abundant $(M - CH_3)^+$ and m/e 72 by cleavages alpha to the nitrogen function, and at m/e 97 and 72 (again) by cleavages alpha to the carbonyl function. Note that hydrogen rearrangement decomposition of m/e 72 by reaction 4-36 yields m/e 44: $H-CH_2CH_2-\overset{+}{N}H=C=O \rightarrow C_2H_4 + H_2N=C=O$. [Ethyl tri-fluoroacetamide]

6.59-6.63.   Structures d and e should show substantial $(M - CO_2)^{\ddagger}$ peaks (Table A-5); this suggests that these are 6.61 and 6.63. Reasoning from the spectral data, the base $C_4H_8^{\ddagger}$ peaks of 6.61 and 6.63 should originate from molecules in which the hydrogen-bearing carbon atoms are contiguous; only d and e fulfill this requirement. Of these, d should show the larger $(M - CH_3)^+$ peak through cleavage alpha to the saturated oxygen, indicating that d is 6.63.

Prediction of the spectra of a, b, and d without reference spectra is difficult; the behavior described above for cyclic ketones (reaction 6-28) and cyclic ethers (reaction 6-42) does not predict any of the large peaks of the remaining unknowns. These unknowns were actually chosen to give emphasis to this possible pitfall. Thus typical alicyclic ketone cleavages would give m/e 55 (and for c, m/e 69) peaks; these are weak in 6.59, 6.60, and 6.62. The ether moiety should be a more powerful reaction-directing group than the carbonyl, yet neither b nor c shows appreciable $(M - CH_3)^+$ peaks from α-cleavage.

Rationalizations of the differences in the unknown spectra can, however, lead to the correct answers. (The following mechanisms are only *postulations*, however.) In c both directing groups should induce fragmentation of the same bond, providing a rationale for the m/e 43 and 72 peaks, consistent with spectrum 6.59. An initial inductive cleavage of the ether bond to the branched carbon could rationalize the significant m/e 70 of spectrum 6.62; charge migration is more favored here than in a or c as it leads to a stabilized site for both the charge and the unpaired electron. Ether site α-cleavage for b can also rationalize the formation of m/e 57 and 58. Charge migration in the latter reaction would give m/e 42. This could also arise through charge site initiation through further decomposition of m/e 70. Similar mechanisms rationalize (*not* establish) that the peaks of spectrum 6.60 arise from a; the $(M - C_2H_3)^+$ apparently arises through a double hydrogen rearrangement which could be depicted similarly to reaction 4-39. The m/e 45 of c might arise in this fashion also. [6.59, c; 6.60, a; 6.61, e; 6.62, b; 6.63, d]

7.1.   Metastable peak assignments are m/e 8.0, 45 → 19; 16.2, 59 → 31 or 45 → 27; 18.7 (flat-topped) 45 → 29; 24.1, 28 → 26; 28.5, 59 → 41; 37.1, 41 → 39; 39.1, 43 → 41; 40.1, 44 → 42; and 42.1, 44 → 43.

7.2.   Acetic acid could possibly give the major ions of Figure 7-1; m/e 60, 59, 45, and 43 could correspond to M^+, $(M - 1)^+$, $COOH^+$, and CH_3CO^+, respectively. However, the metastable peaks corresponding to the transitions $28^+ \rightarrow 26^+ +2$ and $41^+ \rightarrow 39^+ + 2$ eliminate the possibility of acetic acid. Additionally the following decomposition reactions which are indicated by metastables would be unlikely for CH_3COOH: $60^+ \rightarrow 44^+ + 16$, $59^+ \rightarrow 41^+ + 18$, and $45^+ \rightarrow 29^+ + 16$. Such data can be misleading, however, as unusual rearrangements are much more common in unimolecular metastable decompositions. The corresponding collision-induced dissociations give much better evidence on this point; for example, isopropanol shows a substantial $45^+ \rightarrow 43^+$ transition from collisional activation, which of course could not correspond to $COOH^+ \rightarrow CH_3CO^+$.

7.3. (A) $R_1 = R_2 = R_3 = H$, $Y = H_2$;
         (B) $R_1 = H$, $R_2 = CH_3O$, $R_3 = CH_3$, $Y = H_2$;
         (C) $R_1 = CH_3O$, $R_2 = H$, $R_3 = CH_3$, $Y = O$; see ref. *1.2*, p. 309.
The peaks at $(M - 28)^+$ in A and B, and $(M - 42)^+$ in C can be explained by:

REFERENCES

1.1 J. H. Beynon, *Mass Spectrometry and Its Applications to Organic Chemistry* (Elsevier, Amsterdam, 1960).

1.2 Klaus Biemann, *Mass Spectrometry: Organic Chemical Applications* (McGraw-Hill, New York, 1962).

1.3 H. Budzikiewicz, C. Djerassi, and D. H. Williams, *Mass Spectrometry of Organic Compounds* (Holden-Day, San Francisco, 1967).

1.4 H. Budzikiewicz, C. Djerassi, and D. H. Williams, *Structure Elucidation of Natural Products by Mass Spectrometry*: Vol. I, *Alkaloids*; Vol. II, *Steroids, Terpenoids, Sugars, and Miscellaneous Natural Products* (Holden-Day, San Francisco, 1964).

1.5 R. W. Kiser, *Introduction to Mass Spectrometry and Its Applications* (Prentice-Hall, Englewood Cliffs, New Jersey, 1965).

1.6 H. C. Hill, *Introduction to Mass Spectrometry* (Heyden, London, 1966).

1.7 G. Spiteller, *Massenspektrometrische Strukturanalyse Organischer Verbindungen* (Verlag Chemie, Weinheim, 1966).

1.8 J. Seibl, *Massenspektrometrie* (Akademische Verlagsgesellschaft, Frankfurt/Main, 1970).

1.9 S. R. Shrader, *Introductory Mass Spectrometry* (Allyn & Bacon, Boston, 1971).

1.10 I. Howe and D. H. Williams, *Organic Mass Spectrometry* (McGraw-Hill, New York, 1973).

1.11 F. W. McLafferty (ed.), *Mass Spectrometry of Organic Ions* (Academic Press, New York, 1963).

1.12 C. A. McDowell (ed.), *Mass Spectrometry* (McGraw-Hill, New York, 1963).

1.13 A. L. Burlingame (ed.), *Topics in Organic Mass Spectrometry* (Wiley-Interscience, New York, 1970).

1.14 G. W. A. Milne (ed.), *Mass Spectrometry: Techniques and Applications* (Wiley-Interscience, New York, 1971).

1.15 D. H. Williams (ed.), *Mass Spectrometry*, Vol. 1 (The Chemical Society, London, 1971).

1.16 G. R. Waller (ed.), *Biochemical Applications of Mass Spectrometry* (Wiley-Interscience, New York, 1972).

1.17 Q. N. Porter and J. Baldas, *Mass Spectrometry of Heterocyclic Compounds* (Wiley-Interscience, New York, 1971).

1.18 *Mass Spectrometry Bulletin* (Mass Spectrometry Data Centre, AWRE, Aldermaston, Berkshire, England).

1.19 J. Capellen, H. J. Svec, and C. R. Sage, *Bibliography of Mass Spectroscopy Literature* (U.S. Atomic Energy Commission, Federal Scientific and Technical Information, Springfield, Virginia).

1.20   D. C. DeJongh, *Anal. Chem.*, **42**, 169R (1970).

1.21   A. L. Burlingame and G. A. Johanson, *Anal. Chem.*, **44**, 337R (1972).

2.1   A. H. Wapstra and N. B. Gove, *J. Nuclear Data*, **9**, 267 (1971).

3.1   Lewis Friedman and F. A. Long, *J. Amer. Chem. Soc.*, **75**, 2832 (1953).

3.2   F. W. McLafferty, *Anal. Chem.*, **28**, 306 (1956).

3.3   J. S. Shannon, *Proc. Roy. Australian Chem. Inst.*, 328 (1964).

3.4   F. W. McLafferty in ref. *1.11*, p. 309.

3.5   A. N. H. Yeo and D. H. Williams, *J. Chem. Soc. (C)*, 266 (1968).

3.6   F. W. McLafferty, *Anal. Chem.*, **29**, 1782 (1957).

3.7   F. H. Field, *Accounts Chem. Res.*, 1, 42 (1968).

3.8   H. M. Fales in ref. *1.14*, p. 179; G. P. Arsenault in ref. *1.16*, p. 817.

3.9   H. D. Beckey, in ref. *1.16*, p. 795.

3.10   L. A. Shaddoff, *Anal. Chem.*, **39**, 1902 (1967).

4.1   Many such studies have appeared in two specialized journals: *Org. Mass Spectrom.* (Heyden, London) and *Int. J. Mass Spectrom. Ion Phys.* (Elsevier, Amsterdam).

4.2   F. W. McLafferty, in ref. *1.13*, p. 223; F. W. McLafferty, *Chem. Commun.*, 78 (1966).

4.3   M. M. Bursey, in ref. *1.14*, p. 373.

4.4   G. Remberg and G. Spiteller, *Chem. Ber.*, **103**, 3640 (1970).

4.5   J. S. Smith and F. W. McLafferty, *Org. Mass Spectrom.*, **5**, 483 (1971).

4.6   N. Dinh-Nguyen, R. Ryhage, S. Ställberg-Stenhagen, and E. Stenhagen, *Ark. Kemi*, **18**, 393 (1961); **28**, 289 (1968); M. Kraft and G. Spiteller, *Org. Mass Spectrom.*, **2**, 541 (1969).

4.7   J. K. McLeod and C. Djerassi, *J. Org. Chem.*, **32**, 3485 (1967).

4.8   M. M. Green, R. J. Cook, J. M. Schwab, and R. B. Roy, *J. Amer. Chem. Soc.*, **92**, 3076 (1970).

4.9   R. H. Shapiro and T. F. Jenkins, *Org. Mass Spectrom.*, **2**, 771 (1969); W. J. Richter and W. Vetter, *ibid.*, **2**, 781 (1969).

4.10   F. W. McLafferty, D. J. McAdoo, and J. S. Smith, *J. Amer. Chem. Soc.*, **91**, 5400 (1969).

4.11   V. I. Kadentsev, B. M. Zolotarev, O. S. Chizov, Ch. Shachidayatov, L. A. Yanovskaya, and V. F. Kucherov, *Org. Mass Spectrom.*, **1**, 899 (1968); H. F. Grutzmacher and H. Kuschel, to be published.

4.12   K. Seiler and M. Hesse, *Helv. Chim. Acta*, **51**, 1817 (1968).

4.13   Reference *1.3*, p. 154.

4.14   M. Kraft and G. Spiteller, *Chem. Commun.*, 943 (1967).

4.15   C. W. Tsang and A. G. Harrison, *Org. Mass Spectrom.*, **3**, 647 (1970); **5**, 877 (1971).

4.16   F. W. McLafferty and I. Sakai, *Org. Mass Spectrom.*, **7**, 971 (1973).

4.17   N. A. Uccella, I. Howe, and D. H. Williams, *J. Chem. Soc. (B)*, 1933 (1971).

4.18   T. H. Kinstle, P. J. Ihrig, and E. J. Goettert, *J. Amer. Chem. Soc.*, **92**, 1780 (1970).

5.1   Eight Peak Index of Mass Spectra (Mass Spectrometry Data Centre, AWRE, Aldermaston, Berkshire, England, 1970).

5.2   F. W. McLafferty, *Mass Spectral Correlations* (*Advances in Chemistry Series* No. 40, American Chemical Society, Washington, D.C., 1963).

5.3   S. Abrahamsson, E. Stenhagen, and F. W. McLafferty, *Atlas of Mass Spectral Data* (Wiley, New York, 1969).

5.4   S. Abrahamsson, E. Stenhagen, and F. W. McLafferty, *Registry of Mass Spectral Data* (Wiley, New York, 1974).

6.1   H. K. Schnoes and A. L. Burlingame, ref. *1.13*, p. 393.

6.2   D. Henneberg and G. Schomburg, *Adv. Mass Spectrom.*, **4**, 333 (1968).

6.3   B. J. Millard and D. F. Shaw, *J. Chem. Soc. (B)*, 664 (1966).

6.4a P. D. Woodgate, K. K. Mayer, and C. Djerassi, *J. Amer. Chem. Soc.*, **94**, 3115 (1972).

6.4b L. Tokes, G. Jones, and C. Djerassi, *J. Amer. Chem. Soc.*, **90**, 5465 (1968).

6.5   W. K. Seifert, E. J. Gallegos, and R. M. Teeter, *J. Amer. Chem. Soc.*, **94**, 5880 (1972).

6.6   H. M. Grubb and S. Meyerson, in ref. *1.11*, p. 453; I. Howe and F. W. McLafferty, *J. Amer. Chem. Soc.*, **93**, 99 (1971).

6.7   A. Siegel and K. L. Rinehart Jr., in ref. *1.14*, p. 263.

6.8   L. E. Gunnarsson, D. Kimland, A. J. Aasen and C. R. Enzell, *Arch. Mass Spectr. Data*, **3**, 36 (1972).

6.9   J. R. Dias, Y. M. Sheikh, and C. Djerassi, *J. Amer. Chem. Soc.*, **94**, 473 (1972).

6.10 A. F. Thomas and B. Willhalm, *Tetrahedron Letters*, 5129 (1967).

6.11 F. W. McLafferty, T. Wachs, C. Lifshitz, G. Innorta, and P. Irving, *J. Amer. Chem. Soc.*, **92**, 6867 (1970).

6.12 We are indebted to Dr. J. R. Plimmer, U.S. Department of Agriculture, Beltsville, Maryland, for supplying these data; J. R. Plimmer and U. I. Klingbiel, *Chem. Commun.*, 648 (1969).

6.13 J. B. Wallace and M. S. Blum, *Ann. Ent. Soc. Amer.*, **62**, 503 (1968).

6.14 E. Stenhagen in ref. *1.16*, p. 11.

6.15 G. Odham and E. Stenhagen, in ref. *1.16*, p. 211.

6.16 S. Meyerson and L. C. Leitch, *J. Amer. Chem. Soc.*, **88**, 56 (1966).

6.17 R. E. Wolff, M. Greff, and J. A. McCloskey, *Adv. Mass Spectrom.*, **4**, 193 (1968); R. E. Wolff, to be published.

6.18 G. Odham, *Ark. Kemi*, **22**, 427 (1964).

6.19 H. M. Fales, G. W. A. Milne, and N. C. Law, *Arch. Mass Spectr. Data*, **2**, 655 (1971).

6.20 C. Djerassi and C. Fenselau, *J. Amer. Chem. Soc.*, **87**, 5747 (1965).

6.21 Reference *1.8*, p. 126.

6.22 S. D. Sample and C. Djerassi, *J. Amer. Chem. Soc.*, **88**, 1937 (1966).

6.23 M. Hesse and F. Lenzinger, *Adv. Mass Spectrom.*, **4**, 163 (1968).

6.24 C. Djerassi and C. Fenselau, *J. Amer. Chem. Soc.*, **87**, 5752 (1965).

6.25 Reference *1.6*, p. 68.

6.26 Reference *1.3*, p. 304.

6.27 S. M. Alam, K. A. H. Adams, and B. B. MacLean, *Can. J. Chem.*, **42**, 2456 (1964).

6.28 J. H. Bowie, R. Grigg, S.-O. Lawesson, P. Madsen, G. Schroll, and D. H. Williams, *J. Amer. Chem. Soc.*, **88**, 1699 (1966).

6.29 N. C. Rol, *Rec. Trav. Chim*, **87**, 321 (1968).

6.30 J. A. Nicholson, C. H. Jarboe, W. F. Haddon, and F. W. McLafferty, *Experientia*, **24**, 251 (1968).

7.1   K. R. Jennings, in ref. *1.14*, p. 419.

7.2   Reference *1.3*, p. 369.

7.3   F. W. McLafferty, R. Venkataraghavan, and P. Irving, *Biochem. Biophys. Res. Commun.*, **39**, 274 (1970); H.-K. Wipf, P. Irving, M. McCamish, R. Venkataraghavan, and F. W. McLafferty, *J. Amer. Chem. Soc.*, **95**, 3369 (1973).

7.4   F. W. McLafferty and T. A. Bryce, *Chem. Commun.*, 1215 (1967).

7.5   J. H. Beynon, J. E. Corn, W. E. Baitinger, J. W. Amy, and R. A. Benkeser, *Org. Mass Spectrom.*, **3**, 191 (1970).

7.6   F. W. McLafferty and R. B. Fairweather, *J. Amer. Chem. Soc.*, **90**, 5915 (1968).

7.7   W. F. Haddon and F. W. McLafferty, *J. Amer. Chem. Soc.*, **90**, 4745 (1968); *Anal. Chem.*, **41**, 31 (1969).

7.8   F. W. McLafferty, P. F. Bente III, R. Kornfeld, S.-C. Tsai, and I. Howe, *J. Amer. Chem. Soc.*, **95**, 2120 (1973); F. W. McLafferty, R. Kornfeld, W. F. Haddon, K. Levsen, I. Sakai, P. F. Bente, III, S.-C. Tsai, and H. D. R. Schuddemage, *ibid.*, **95**, 3886 (1973); I. Howe in ref. *1.15*, p. 50.

7.9   T. W. Shannon and F. W. McLafferty, *J. Amer. Chem. Soc.*, **88**, 5021 (1966).

7.10   J. L. Occolowitz, *J. Amer. Chem. Soc.*, **91**, 5202 (1969).

7.11   Reference *1.2*, p. 305.

7.12   M. Barber, P. Jolles, E. Vilkas, and E. Lederer, *Biochem. Biophys. Res. Commun.*, **18**, 469 (1965).

7.13   M. Senn, R. Venkataraghavan, and F. W. McLafferty, *J. Amer. Chem. Soc.*, **88**, 5593 (1966).

7.14   M. Fetizon, International Mass Spectrometry Meeting, Edinburgh, 1973, *Adv. Mass Spectrom.*, **6**; ref. *1.9*, pp. 179–201; refs. *1.14-1.16*.

7.15   G. Spiteller and M. Spiteller-Friedmann, *Ann. Chem.*, **690**, 1 (1965).

7.16   H. D. Beckey and F. J. Comes in ref. *1.13*, p. 1; H. M. Fales in ref. *1.14*, p. 179; J. M. Wilson in ref. *1.15*, p. 1.

7.17   C. E. Melton in ref. *1.16*, p. 777.

7.18   J. H. Bowie and P. Y. White, *Org. Mass Spectrom.*, **6**, 75 (1972) and references cited therein.

7.19   J. D. Baldeschwieler and S. S. Woodgate, *Accounts Chem. Res.*, **4**, 114 (1971); D. J. McAdoo, F W. McLafferty, and P. F. Bente III, *J. Amer. Chem. Soc.*, **94**, 2027 (1972).

7.20   S. A. Benezra and M. M. Bursey, *J. Amer. Chem. Soc.*, **94**, 1024 (1972); M. L. Gross, *ibid.*, **94**, 3744 (1972).

7.21   K. Biemann in ref. *1.13*, p. 185.

7.22   R. Venkataraghavan, R. J. Klimowski, and F. W. McLafferty, *Accounts Chem. Res.*, **3**, 158 (1970).

7.23   R. Venkataraghavan and F. W. McLafferty, *Chem. Tech.*, 364 (1972).

7.24   S. Abrahamsson, *Sci. Tools*, **14**, 29 (1967); R. G. Ridley in ref. *1.16*, p. 177.

7.25   P. V. Fennessey in ref. *1.14*, p. 77.

7.26   K.-S. Kwok, R. Venkataraghavan, and F. W. McLafferty, *J. Amer. Chem. Soc.*, **95**, 4185 (1973).

7.27   R. Venkataraghavan, F. W. McLafferty, and G. E. Van Lear, *Org. Mass Spectrom.*, **2**, 1 (1969); L. R. Crawford and J. D. Morrison, *Anal. Chem.*, **43**, 1790 (1971).

7.28   J. Lederberg in ref. *1.16*, p. 193; B. G. Buchanan, A. M. Duffield, and A. V. Robertson in ref. *1.14*, p. 121.

7.29   T. L. Isenhour and P. C. Jurs, *Anal. Chem.*, **43** (10), 20A (1971).

8.1   H. M. Rosenstock, M. B. Wallenstein, A. L. Wahrhaftig, and H. Eyring. *Proc. Nat. Acad. Sci.*, **38**, 667 (1952); M. L. Vestal in *Fundamental Processes in Radiation Chemistry* (P. Ausloos, ed.) (Wiley-Interscience, New York, 1968).

8.2   F. W. McLafferty, T. Wachs, C. Lifshitz, G. Innorta, and P. Irving, *J. Amer. Chem. Soc.*, **92**, 6867 (1970).

8.3   D. W. Turner, C. Baker, A. D. Baker, and C. R. Brundle, *Molecular Photoelectron Spectroscopy* (Wiley-Interscience, New York, 1970).

8.4   D. J. McAdoo, P. F. Bente III, F. W. McLafferty, M. L. Gross, and C. Lifshitz, *Org. Mass Spectrom.*, submitted.

8.5 L. D. Spicer and B. S. Rabinovitch, *Ann. Rev. Phys. Chem.*, **21**, 349 (1970); P. J. Robinson and K. A. Holbrook, *Unimolecular Reactions* (Wiley-Interscience, London, 1972).

8.6 J. L. Franklin, J. G. Dillard, H. M. Rosenstock, J. T. Herron, K. Draxl, and F. H. Field, *Ionization Potentials, Appearance Potentials, and Heats of Formation of Gaseous Positive Ions* (NSRDS-NBS 26, U.S. Government Printing Office, 1969).

8.7 A. G. Harrison, P. Kebarle, and F. P. Lossing, *J. Amer. Chem. Soc.*, **83**, 777 (1961).

8.8 G. G. Meisels, C. T. Chen, B. G. Giessner, and R. H. Emmel, *J. Chem. Phys.*, **56**, 793 (1972).

APPENDIX

TABLE A-1   *Standard Interpretation Procedure*

1. Study all available information (spectroscopic, chemical, sample history). Give explicit directions for obtaining spectrum.
2. Verify masses; determine elemental compositions, rings plus double bonds.
3. Test molecular ion identity: must be highest mass peak in spectrum, odd-electron ion, and give logical neutral losses.
4. Mark "important" odd-electron ions.
5. Study general appearance of spectrum; molecular stability, labile bonds.
6. Identify all low mass ion series.
7. Identify the neutral fragments accompanying high mass ion formation (including metastables).
8. Check for characteristic ions; postulate structures for "important" ions.
9. Postulate molecular structures; test against reference spectrum, against spectra of similar compounds, or against spectra predicted from mechanisms of ion decompositions.

TABLE A-2   *Natural Abundances of Combinations of Chlorine, Bromine, Silicon, and Sulfur*
(Other isotopic abundance data are given in Tables 2-1, 2-2, and Figure 2-1)

Number of chlorine atoms	Mass	Number of bromine atoms				
		0	1	2	3	4
0	A		100.0	51.0	34.0	17.4
	A + 2		98.0	100.0	100.0	68.0
	A + 4			49.0	98.0	100.0
	A + 6				32.0	65.3
	A + 8					16.0
1	A	100.0	76.6	43.8	26.1	14.2
	A + 2	32.5	100.0	100.0	85.1	60.3
	A + 4		24.4	69.9	100.0	100.0
	A + 6			13.7	48.9	80.1
	A + 8				8.0	30.5
	A + 10					4.3

TABLE A-2 (continued)

Number of chlorine atoms	Mass	Number of bromine atoms				
		0	1	2	3	4
	A	100.0	61.4	38.3	20.4	11.9
	A + 2	65.0	100.0	100.0	73.3	54.3
	A + 4	10.6	45.6	89.7	100.0	100.0
2	A + 6		6.6	31.9	63.8	94.2
	A + 8			3.9	18.7	47.3
	A + 10				2.0	11.8
	A + 12					1.2
	A	100.0	51.2	31.3	16.4	
	A + 2	97.5	100.0	92.0	64.5	
	A + 4	31.7	65.0	100.0	100.0	
3	A + 6	3.4	17.6	49.9	77.7	
	A + 8		1.7	11.6	31.8	
	A + 10			1.0	6.5	
	A + 12				0.5	
	A + 14					
	A	76.9	43.8	24.1	13.6	
	A + 2	100.0	100.0	78.7	57.7	
	A + 4	48.7	83.6	100.0	100.0	
4	A + 6	10.5	33.2	63.4	91.1	
	A + 8	0.9	6.3	21.4	47.2	
	A + 10		0.5	3.7	13.9	
	A + 12			0.3	2.2	
	A + 14				0.1	
	A	61.5	37.7	19.2		
	A + 2	100.0	98.3	68.9		
	A + 4	65.0	100.0	100.0		
5	A + 6	21.1	52.0	76.4		
	A + 8	3.4	14.8	33.5		
	A + 10	.2	2.2	8.5		
	A + 12		.1	1.1		
	A + 14			0.1		

	Mass	Number of chlorine atoms				
		6	7	8	9	10
	A	51.2	43.9	33.8	26.3	21.0
	A + 2	100.0	100.0	87.9	76.9	68.3
	A + 4	81.2	97.5	100.0	100.0	100.0
	A + 6	35.2	52.8	65.0	75.8	86.6
	A + 8	8.5	17.1	26.4	36.9	49.2
	A + 10	1.1	3.3	6.8	12.0	19.2
	A + 12	0.06	0.36	1.1	2.6	5.2
	A + 14		0.02	0.10	0.36	0.97
	A + 16				0.03	0.12
	A + 18					0.01

TABLE A-2 (continued)

Mass	Number of silicon atoms				
	1	2	3	4	5
A	100.0	100.0	100.00	100.00	100.00
A + 1	5.1	10.20	15.30	20.40	25.50
A + 2	3.4	7.1	11.00	15.16	19.60
A + 3		0.35	1.05	2.13	3.60
A + 4		0.12	0.37	0.80	1.42
A + 5			0.02	0.07	0.19
A + 6				0.02	0.05

Mass	Number of sulfur atoms				
	1	2	3	4	5
A	100.0	100.0	100.0	100.0	100.0
A + 1	0.80	1.6	2.4	3.2	4.0
A + 2	4.4	8.8	13.2	17.6	22.0
A + 3		0.07	0.21	0.42	0.70
A + 4		0.19	0.58	1.2	1.9
A + 5				0.02	0.05
A + 6				0.03	0.09

TABLE A-3   *Typical Ionization Potential Values (8.6)*

Compound	eV	Compound	eV	Compound	eV
CH_4	12.7				
C_2H_6	11.5	C_2H_4	10.5	C_2H_2	11.4
C_3H_8	11.1	$CH_3CH=CH_2$	9.8	$CH_3C\equiv CH$	10.4
$n\text{-}C_4H_{10}$	10.6	$C_2H_5CH=CH_2$	9.6	$CH_2=C=CH_2$	10.2
$i\text{-}C_4H_{10}$	10.5	$(CH_3)_2C=CH_2$	9.2	$CH_3C\equiv CCH_3$	9.9
$n\text{-}C_6H_{14}$	10.2	$CH_3CH=CHCH_3$	9.1	$CH_2=CHCH=CH_2$	9.1
$i\text{-}C_6H_{14}$	10.1	Cyclohexane	9.9	Cyclohexene	8.9
Benzene	9.2	C_6H_5COOH	9.7	Biphenyl	8.3
$C_6H_5CH_3$	8.8	C_6H_5Cl	9.1	Naphthalene	8.1
$C_6H_5NO_2$	9.9	C_6H_5Br	9.0	Anthracene	7.6
$C_6H_5COCH_3$	9.3	C_6F_6	10.0	Coronene	7.6
C_6H_5OH	8.5	Pyridine	9.2	$(C_6H_5)_3N$	6.9
$C_6H_5NH_2$	7.7	Thiophene	8.9		
$n\text{-}C_3H_7CN$	11.7	$n\text{-}C_4H_9OH$	10.0	$n\text{-}C_4H_9NH_2$	8.7
$n\text{-}C_3H_7NO_2$	10.8	$C_2H_5OC_2H_5$	9.5	$C_2H_5NHC_2H_5$	8.0
		$CH_3CH(OCH_3)_2$	9.7		
$n\text{-}C_3H_7COOH$	10.2	$n\text{-}C_3H_7CHO$	9.9	$CH_3CON(CH_3)_2$	8.8
$C_2H_5COOCH_3$	10.2	$C_2H_5COCH_3$	9.5		
$n\text{-}C_4H_9Cl$	10.7	$n\text{-}C_4H_9SH$	9.1	$(CH_3)_4Si$	9.8
$n\text{-}C_4H_9Br$	10.1	$C_2H_5SC_2H_5$	8.4	$(CH_3)_3P$	ca. 8.9
$n\text{-}C_4H_9I$	9.2	$(CH_3)_4Sn$	8.2	$C_2H_5HgC_2H_5$	8.5

TABLE A-4   Molecular Ion Abundances vs. Compound Type (C_n indicates a n-alkyl chain of n carbon atoms)

Compound type	Intensity of molecular ion relative to most intense ion			M.W. for [M⁺] < 0.1%
	M.W. ~75	M.W. ~130	M.W. ~185	
Aromatic	(benzene) 100	(naphthalene) 100	(anthracene) 100	> 500
Heterocyclic	(pyridine) 100	(quinoline) 100	(acridine) 100	> 500
	(thiophene) 100	(benzothiophene) 100	(dibenzothiophene) 100	> 500
Cycloalkane	(cyclohexane H) 70	(decalin H H) 88	(H H / H H) 90	> 500
Mercaptan	C_3SH 100	C_7SH 39	$C_{10}SH$ 46	≫ 200
Sulfide	C_1SC_2 65	C_1SC_6 46	C_5SC_5 13	≫ 200
Conjugated olefin	Hexatriene 54	allo-Ocimene 41	— —	> 500
Olefin	$C_2C=CC_2$ 36	$C_3C=CC_4$ 20 / $C_6C=CC$ 7.3	$C_{11}C=C$ 3.3	> 500
Amide	C_2CONH_2 56 / $HCON(C_1)_2$ 100	C_6CONH_2 0.9 / $C_1CON(C_2)_2$ 4.0	$C_{11}CONH_2$ 0.9 / $C_1CON(C_4)_2$ 5.1	—
Acid	C_2COOH 78	C_6COOH 0.6	C_9COOH 9.4	—[b]

Group							
Ketone[a]	C₁COC₂	24	C₂COC₅	8.0	C₆COC₅	8.3	> 500
			C₁COC₆	3.0	C₁COC₉	9.6	
Aldehyde[a]	C₃CHO	46	C₇CHO	2.1	C₁₂CHO	4.6	> 500
Alkane	C₅	8.8	C₉	6.4	C₁₃	4.6	—[b]
Amine[a]	C₄NH₂	10	C₈NH₂	0.6	C₁₂NH₂	2.3	—
	(C₂)₂NH	31	(C₄)₂NH	11	(C₇)₂NH	4.1	—
			(C₂)₃N	20	(C₄)₃N	6.7	
Ether[a]	C₂OC₂	30	C₄OC₄	2	C₆OC₆	0.05	180
Ester[a]	C₁COOC	19	C₁COOC₅	0.1	C₁COOC₈	0.1	—[b]
			C₅COOC₁	0.3	C₇COOC₁	2.6	—[b]
Halide	C₄F	0.07	C₇F	0.1	C₁₁Cl	0.3	RF > 120
	C₃Cl	4.3	C₇Cl	0.1	C₇Br	2.4	RCl > 300[a]
			C₃Br	45	C₄I	5.5	RBr 300
			C₁I	100	(C₄)₃CH	1.0	RI ~400
Branched alkane	C-C-C-C / C / C-C-C-C / C	6.3	(C₂)₂CC₄	1.2			
	C-C-C-C / C / C-C-C-C / C	0.01	C-C-C-C-C / C / C-C-C-C / C	0.02	C-C-C-C-C-C / C / C-C-C-C-C / C	0.03	70
Nitrile[a]	C₄CN	0.3	C₈CN	0.4	C₁₁CN	0.8	—[b]
Alcohol[a]	C₄	1.1	C₈	0.1	C₁₂	0.0	90
Acetal[a]	C(OC)₂	0.00	C₂(OC₃)₂	0.0	C₇(OC₂)₂	0.0	All

[a] (M + 1)⁺ possible (see Section 3.6).
[b] [M⁺] increases with increasing molecular weight at higher molecular weights.

TABLE A-5   *Common Neutral Fragments*

m/e	Formula	Example[a,b]
39 53 67	C_nH_{2n-3}	Allyl esters—specific rearrangement loss of (C_nH_{2n-1} − 2H)
26 40 54 68	C_nH_{2n-2}	Aromatics; $M^{\ddag}$ − 69 − $(68)_n$ in polyisoprenes[a]
26 40	$C_nH_{2n}CN$	R⊹CN, R⊹CH$_2$CN (stable R$^+$ only)
27 41 55 69, etc.	C_nH_{2n-1}	RCOOR′—specific rearrangement loss of (R′ − 2H) or (R′ − 2H) + (R − H), also from carbonates, amides, ketones, etc.; loss of activated C_nH_{2n-1} groups[a]
27	HCN	Nitrogen heterocyclic compounds, cyanides, aryl-NH$_2$
28 42 56	C_nH_{2n}	RCH$_2$COCH$_2$R—specific rearrangement loss of (R − H) or (R − H)$_2$, also from many unsaturated functional groups; retro-Diels-Alder[a]
28	N$_2$	Aryl—N=N—Aryl, $>$C=N$_2$
28	CO	Aromatic oxygen compounds (carbonyls, phenols), cyclic ketones, R⊹C≡O$^{+ a}$
42 56 70	$C_nH_{2n}CO$	Unsaturated acetates, acetamides, some diketones and cyclic ketones
43 57 71	HNCO	Loss of —NR—CO— from carbamates, cyclic amides
1	H	Labile H; alkyl cyanides, lower fluorides and aldehydes (stable RCO$^+$), cyclopropyl compounds
15 29 43 57 71, etc.	C_nH_{2n+1}	Alkyl loss (α-cleavage or branched site favored); elimination from cyclo-alkyl group with hydrogen rearrangement[a]
29 43 57	$C_nH_{2n+1}CO$	C_nH_{2n+1}CO⊹R (stable R$^+$ only); aromatic oxygen compounds[a]
2 16 30 44 58 72, etc.	C_nH_{2n+2}	Loss of RH from branched site; loss of H$_2$ or CH$_4$ mainly from even-electron ion
16	NH$_2$	Aromatic amines; uncommon to be abundant
30 (46)	NO, (NO$_2$)	Nitroaromatics, nitroesters, N-nitroso compounds
44	CONH$_2$	R⊹CONH$_2$ (stable R$^+$ only)·
16	O	Sulfoxides, N-oxides; smaller for epoxides, nitro compounds, quinones
30	CH$_2$O	ROCH$_2$OR, cyclic ethers, methoxy aromatics[a]

TABLE A5   (continued)

m/e	Formula	Example[a,b]
44 58 72, etc.	$C_nH_{2n+2}CO$	$RCOCH_2R'$—specific hydrogen rearrangement → $(R'-H)^{+\cdot}$ (stable ion only)[a]
44	CO_2	Carbonates, cyclic anhydrides,[a] lactones
44	CS	Thiophenols, aryl-S-aryl
17	NH_3	Amines: uncommon unless other group to stabilize charge
17	OH	Acids, oximes; rearrangement (e.g., $o\text{-}NO_2C_6H_4CH_3$)
31 45 59	$C_nH_{2n+1}O$	$R\div OR'$ (stable R^+ only); $RCO\div OR'$
59 73	$C_nH_{2n+1}CO_2$	$R\div OCOR'$, $R\div COOR'$ (stable R^+, small R' only)[a]
18 32 46 60	H_2O, $H_2O + C_nH_{2n}$	Alcohols (primary favored); higher aldehydes, ketones, ethers,[a] some esters; loss of ROH from esters with labile hydrogen; $o\text{-}CH_3$-aryl-COOH
46	CH_2O_2	Aliphatic dicarboxylic acids; methylenedioxy group
60 74	$C_nH_{2n+1}COOH$	$R'COO-R-H$ (stable $R^{+\cdot}$, small R')
60	COS	Thiocarbonates
32	S	Sulfides, polysulfides,[a] aryl thiols
33	$CH_3 + H_2O$	Some alcohols
19 33 47	$C_nH_{2n}F$	Fluoroalkanes
33 47 61	$C_nH_{2n+1}S$	$R\div SR'$, R^+ more stable than R'^+; $(M-33)^+$ in aryl thiols, isothiocyanates
20	HF	$R\div HF$ (primary favored)
34 48 62 76	H_2S, $H_2S + C_nH_{2n}$	Thiols (primary favored); methyl sulfides
35 49 63	$C_nH_{2n}Cl$	Chlorides (labile bond cleaved)
36	HCl	$R\div HCl$ (distinctive ^{37}Cl, primary favored)
64	SO_2	RSO_2R, Aryl—SO_2OR
38		Some polycarboxylic acids
79	Br	$R\div Br$ (distinctive ^{81}Br)
127	I	$R\div I$

[a] Also see elimination rearrangement in Table 4-1.

[b] Specific cleavages giving a major peak are usually indicative of a particular structural moiety; these are summarized in Section 4.7. Lower mass even-electron ions which are formed through secondary decompositions involving randomizing rearrangements are often of significant abundance, so that such ions are generally useful to indicate compound *types*, not specific structural moieties.

TABLE A-6   *Series of Common Fragment Ions (Mainly Even-Electron)*[a]

m/e	Formula	Compound type[b]
60 74 88 102	$C_nH_{2n+2}NO$	RCONHR′, RCONR′$_2$—specific rearrangement loss of (R′ − 2H) or (R′ − 2H) + (R − H) or (R′ − 2H) + (R′ − H)
60 74 88 102	$C_nH_{2n}NO_2$	R $\div$ CR$_2$—ONO (specific)
46	NO$_2$	Nitrates
19 33 47 61 75 89 103 117	$C_nH_{2n+3}O$	Alcohols, polyols, ROR′ → ROH$_2^+$ (R′ > n-C$_5$)
47 61 75 89 103 117	$C_nH_{2n+1}O_2$	RCOOR′—specific rearrangement loss of (R′ − 2H) or (R′ − 2H) + (R − H); also higher esters, etc.; ROR′OH, HOROH, ROR′OR″ (some specific)
33 (34,35,45) 47 61 75 89 103	$C_nH_{2n+1}S$	Alkyl thiols, sulfides (some specific)
77 91 105 119 133	$C_6H_5C_nH_{2n}$	Phenylalkyl (specific cleavage, also rearrangement)
105 119 133	$C_nH_{2n+1}C_6H_4CO$	Benzoyl (specific); 119 and above, unsaturated or cyclic phenoxy
63 77 91	$C_nH_{2n+1}O_3$	ROCOOR—specific rearrangement loss of (R − 2H) or (R − 2H) + (R − H)
78 92 106 120 134	$C_5H_4NC_nH_{2n}$	Pyridyl, aminoaromatic (specific cleavage, also rearrangement)
79 93 107 121	C_nH_{2n-5}	Terpenes and derivatives (rearrangement; other m/e also common)
107 121 135	$C_nH_{2n+1}C_6H_4O$	HOC$_6$H$_4$CHR $\div$ Y, RC$_6$H$_4$OCH$_2$ $\div$ Y, etc.
38 (39,50,51,63,64,75,76)	Aromatic series—low	More abundant for aromatic compounds with electronegative substituents
39 (40,51,52,65,66,77,78,79)	Aromatic series—high	More abundant with electron-donating substituents, heterocyclic compounds
39 53 67 81 95 109	C_nH_{2n-3}	Dienes, alkynes, cycloalkenes[c]
81 95 109	$C_nH_{2n-1}O$	Furylalkyl (specific); polyunsaturated or cyclic alcohols and ethers
54 68 82 96 110 124 138	$C_nH_{2n}CN$	Alkyl cyanides; cycloalkenyl, bicycloamines
83 97 111 125	$C_4H_3SC_nH_{2n}$	Thiophenes (specific)
(45, 57, 58, 59, 69, 70, 71, 85)	Endo-sulfur aromatic series	Thiophenes
69, 81–84, 95–97, 107–110	Exo-sulfur aromatic series	Sulfur attached to an aromatic ring
27 41 55 69 83 97 111	C_nH_{2n-1}	Alkenes, cycloalkanes[c]

TABLE A-6 (continued)

m/e	Formula	Compound type[b]
55 69 83 97	$C_nH_{2n-1}CO$	Alkenyl-, cycloalkyl carbonyl (specific); diunsaturated, cyclic alcohols, ethers[c]
56 70 84 98	$C_nH_{2n}N$	Alkenyl-, cycloalkylamines; cyclic amines[c]
56 70 84 98 112 126	$C_nH_{2n}NCO$	Alkyl isocyanates
15 29 43 57 71 85 99 113	C_nH_{2n+1}	Alkyl
29 43 57 71 85 99	$C_nH_{2n+1}CO$	Saturated carbonyl (specific); $> m/e$ 43: cyclic ethers, cycloalkanols[c]
30 44 58 72 86 100 114 128	$C_nH_{2n+2}N$	Alkyl amines (specific; also secondary rearrangement reactions)
44 58 72 86 100	$C_nH_{2n+2}NCO$	Amides, ureas, carbamates (some specific)
72 86 100 114	$C_nH_{2n}NCS$	Alkyl isothiocyanates
31 45 59 73 87 101	$C_nH_{2n+1}O$	Aliphatic alcohols, ethers (some specific)
59 73 87 101	$C_nH_{2n-1}O_2$	Acids, esters; cyclic acetals, ketals (some specific)
31 45 59 73 87 101	$C_nH_{2n+3}Si$	Alkyl silanes (rearrangement common); m/e 73 in Me_3SiOR
45 59 73 87 101	$C_nH_{2n-1}S$	Thiacycloalkanes; unsaturated, substituted sulfur compounds
31 (50,69,100,119,131,169,181,193)	C_nF_m	Perfluoroalkanes

[a] Chlorine and bromine have been omitted as they are usually recognizable by their distinctive natural isotopic abundances.

[b] See footnote b, Table A-5.

[c] Might also be formed by H_2 or CH_4 loss from abundant series 2 mass units higher.

TABLE A-7   *Common Odd-Electron Fragment Ions[a]*

Mass number	Formula	Compound type
94 108 122	$C_nH_{2n+1}C_6H_4OH$	R-phenyl$-O\dot{+}Z\dot{+}H$, HO-phenyl(R)$\dot{+}$ $Z\dot{+}H$
66 80 94	$C_nH_{2n+2}S_2$	RSS$\dot{+}Z\dot{+}H$, H$\dot{+}Z\dot{+}$SS$\dot{+}Z\dot{+}H$
66 80 94	C_nH_{2n-4}	Cycloalkene$\not\Rightarrow YY'$, $C_nH_{2n-4}\not\Rightarrow YY'$
68 82 96 110	C_nH_{2n-2}	Cycloalkyl$\not\Rightarrow HY$, cycloalkyl$\not\Rightarrow YY'$, $C_nH_{2n-2}\not\Rightarrow YY'$
41 55 69 83 97 111 125, etc.	$C_nH_{2n-1}N$	Alkyl cyanides (not specific)
126, etc.	C_nH_{2n-14}	R-naphthyl$\not\Rightarrow HY^*$, R-naphthyl$\not\Rightarrow YY'$, R-naphthyl$\dot{+}C_nH_{2n-1}\not\Rightarrow HY^*$
42 56 70 84 98 112 126	C_nH_{2n}	CHR=CR$'$CHR$''\dot{+}Z\dot{+}H$, cycloalkanes, $C_nH_{2n}\not\Rightarrow RY$, H$\dot{+}C_nH_{2n}\dot{+}Y^*$
98 112 126, etc.	$C_nH_{2n-4}S$	R-thienyl$\dot{+}$CHR$'\dot{+}Z\dot{+}H$
85 99 113	$C_nH_{2n-1}NO$	Alkyl isocyanates (not specific)
44 58 72 86 100	$C_nH_{2n}O$	RCOCHR$'\dot{+}Z\dot{+}H$, O=C(CHR$\dot{+}Z\dot{+}H)_2$, CHR=CR$'$O$\dot{+}Z\dot{+}H$, $C_nH_{2n}O\not\Rightarrow HY$, cycloalkanols
59 101 115	$C_nH_{2n-1}NS$	Alkyl isothiocyanates
59 73 87 101 115	$C_nH_{2n+1}NO$	RR$'$NCOCHR$''\dot{+}Z\dot{+}H$, HON=CRCHR$'\dot{+}Z\dot{+}H$
46 60 74	$C_nH_{2n}S$	Cyclic sulfides, $C_nH_{2n}S\not\Rightarrow HY$
60 74 88 102	$C_nH_{2n}O_2$	ROCOCHR$'\dot{+}Z\dot{+}H$, H$\dot{+}Z\dot{+}$OCOCHR$\dot{+}$ $Z'\dot{+}H$, $C_nH_{2n}O_2\not\Rightarrow RY$
76 90 104 118 132, etc.	C_nH_{2n-8}	R-phenyl$\not\Rightarrow HY^*$, R-phenyl$\not\Rightarrow YY'$, R-phenyl$\dot{+}C_nH_{2n-1}\not\Rightarrow HY^*$
77 91 105 119 133, etc.	$C_nH_{2n-7}N$	R-pyridyl$\not\Rightarrow HY^*$, R-phenyl$\dot{+}$N(R$'$)$\not\Rightarrow$ YY$'$, etc. (see 76, 90, . . .)
92 106 120	C_nH_{2n-6}	R-phenyl$-$CR$'$R$''\dot{+}Z\dot{+}H$
92 106 120 134, etc.	$C_nH_{2n-8}O$	$(-O-$phenyl$-R)\not\Rightarrow HY^*$, $(-O-$phenyl$-R)\not\Rightarrow YY'$, R-phenyl$-$COCHR$'\dot{+}Z\dot{+}H$

[a] Abbreviations: R, H or alkyl group; X, any halogen atom; Y, a functional group; Y^*, an electron-withdrawing functional group—for example, $-X$, $-NO_2$, $-COOR$, $-CN$; Z, a group from which a hydrogen atom is rearranged—for example, RCOCH$_2\dot{+}Z\dot{+}H$ could be RCOCH$_2$CH$_2$CH$_3^+ \rightarrow$ RC(OH)CH$_2^+$ + C$_2$H$_4$. Common Z groups are $-CH_2CH_2-$, $-CH_2O-$, $-OCH_2-$, $-COCH_2-$, $-COOR$, and analogs which are substituted or contain other heteroatoms.

TABLE A-8   *Metastable Ion Nomograph*

m/e 30–150 (3–15)

m_1	m_2	m^*
30	30	30
40	40	40
50	50	50
60	60	60
70	70	70
80	80	80
90	90	90
100	100	100
110	110	110
120	120	120
130	130	130
140	140	140
150	150	150

TABLE A-8 (continued)

m/e 100–500 (10–50)

m_1	m_2	m^*
100	100	100
110	110	110
120	120	120
130	130	130
140	140	140
150	150	150
160	160	160
170	170	170
180	180	180
190	190	190
200	200	200
250	250	250
300	300	300
350	350	350
400	400	400
450	450	450
500	500	500

Sigma Electron Ionization (σ):

			See equations
Alkanes: $R\overset{+}{\cdot}CR_3$	$\overset{\sigma}{\longrightarrow}$	$R\cdot + \overset{+}{C}R_3$	4-1
S, Si, etc.: $R\overset{+}{\cdot}YR$	$\overset{\sigma}{\longrightarrow}$	$R\cdot + \overset{+}{Y}R$	4-2

Charge site initiation (inductive effect, i): Halogens $> O, S \gg N, C$. Attracts electron pair, cleaves bond, moves + site; formation of most stable R^+ favored; less important than radical site initiation.

OE^{+}: $R\overset{\frown}{-}\overset{+\cdot}{Y}-R$	$\overset{i}{\longrightarrow}$	$R^+ + \cdot YR$	4-9
EE^+: $R\overset{\frown}{-}\overset{+}{Y}H_2$	$\overset{i}{\longrightarrow}$	$R^+ + YH_2$	4-12, 4-25–4-27
$R\overset{\frown}{-}\overset{+}{Y}=CH_2$	$\overset{i}{\longrightarrow}$	$R^+ + Y=CH_2$	4-13, 4-15

Radical site initiation (alpha cleavage, α): $N > S, O, \pi, R\cdot > Cl > Br > I$. Donates an electron, forms a new bond to an adjacent atom concomitant with cleavage of a bond to that atom, moves radical site; loss of largest R group favored.

Saturated group:	$R\overset{\frown}{-}CR_2\overset{\curvearrowleft}{-}\overset{+\cdot}{Y}R$	$\overset{\alpha}{\longrightarrow}$ $R\cdot + CR_2=\overset{+}{Y}R$	4-3, 4-8
	$\overset{+}{Y}R-CH_2\overset{\curvearrowleft}{-}CH_2$	$\overset{\alpha}{\longrightarrow}$ $YR^{+}_{\cdot} + CH_2=CH_2$	
Unsaturated heteroatom:	$R\overset{\frown}{-}CR=\overset{+\cdot}{Y}$	$\overset{\alpha}{\longrightarrow}$ $R\cdot + CR\equiv\overset{+}{Y}$	4-4
Alkene (allylic cleavage):	$R\overset{\frown}{-}CH_2\overset{\curvearrowleft}{-}CH\overset{+\cdot}{-}CH_2$	$\overset{\alpha}{\longrightarrow}$ $R\cdot + CH_2=CH-\overset{+}{C}H_2$	4-5
Retro-Diels-Alder (double α-cleavage):	$\bigcirc \overset{-e}{\longrightarrow}$	$\overset{\alpha 2}{\longrightarrow}$ $\begin{matrix} H_2C \\ \| \\ H_2C \end{matrix} +$	4-7

Rearrangements (r): radical and "incipient radical" site initiation. Formation of a new bond from the radical site to another atom *through space* concomitant with cleavage of a bond to that atom; a subsequent reaction is usually required for loss of the neutral. The transition state size is influenced by the stabilities of the products and of the bonds formed and cleaved, and by steric factors; in most cases a six-membered ring is the minimum size if there is a double bond in the ring, and a four-membered ring is the minimum if there is none.